Globalization of food systems in developing countries: impact on food security and nutrition

FAO
FOOD AND
NUTRITION
PAPER

83

FOOD AND AGRICULTURE ORGANIZATION OF THE UNITED NATIONS
Rome, 2004

The designations employed and the presentation of material
in this information product do not imply the expression of any
opinion whatsoever on the part of the Food and Agriculture
Organization of the United Nations concerning the legal or
development status of any country, territory, city or area or of
its authorities, or concerning the delimitation of its frontiers or
boundaries.

ISBN 92-5-105228-X

Contents

I Overview papers

II Country case studies

Acknowledgements

Special thanks go to all of the authors whose papers appear in this publication. Additionally thanks are due to the following persons for their assistance in reviewing one or more of the papers in this volume; Ruth Charrondiere, Margarita Flores, Stuart Gillespie, Lawrence Haddad, Yasmeen Khwaja, Tim Lang, Christian Romer Lovendal, Philip McMichael, Carlos Monteiro, Mark Montgomery, Barry Popkin and Ricardo Uauy. Special note goes to Nicolas Lemery-Nantel for the cover design which was also used as the workshop logo.

Foreword

The workshop "Globalization of food systems: impact on food security and nutrition" was held at the headquarters of the Food and Agriculture Organization of the United Nations (FAO) in Rome, Italy from 8 to 10 October 2003. The workshop was convened to gain a better understanding of the influence of globalization and urbanization on food systems (food supply, marketing and distribution) in developing countries and to analyse the effects of these changes on smallholders and small firms, on food consumption patterns and on nutrition and health outcomes. The event was jointly organized by two divisions within FAO, representing two sectors: the Agricultural and Development Economics Division, examining key economic issues, and the Food and Nutrition Division, addressing health and nutrition outcomes. Thus, two parallel themes were explored: i) the transformation of food systems and its effect on small farmers in developing countries and ii) the impact of globalization, largely influenced by urbanization, on dietary patterns and the nutritional status of urban populations. The workshop was partially funded through the FAO-Netherlands Partnership Programme.

This publication examines in detail the second theme, related to features of globalization, changes in dietary patterns and shifts in the burden of malnutrition and diet-related chronic diseases. It comprises a synthesis paper bringing together the salient features of the impact of the globalization process on nutrition and reflecting some of the discussions at the workshop, three overview papers and 11 country case studies that were presented at the workshop. The overview papers describe shifts in food availability, food consumption and food and nutrition security in the urban environment. The topics are further explored through a series of 11 country case studies from Africa (Nigeria, the United Republic of Tanzania and South Africa), Asia (Bangladesh, China, India, and the Philippines) and the Pacific (Fiji) and Latin America (Brazil, Chile and Colombia). Each case study presents unique insights on different aspects of globalization, including urbanization, access to services and technologies, evolution of the workforce and impact of government decentralization on dietary changes and alterations in population health and nutritional status.

The compilation of the 11 case studies represents each individual author's perspective using the best available national data to highlight those features thought to be most important to changes in food systems, nutrition and health in each country covered. Some case studies explore the issues from an economic perspective (India, Nigeria) while others are more focused on nutrition and health outcomes (Bangladesh, Chile). The purpose of this collection of papers is not to provide a value judgment of the differing forces related to globalization, but to contribute to the body of knowledge by documenting the pace and spread of change.

The overview papers appearing in the first part of this publication will also be published in the electronic *Journal of Agriculture and Development Economics*, which can be found at www.fao.org/es/ESA/en/ejade.htm/.

Dr Kraisid Tontisirin
Director
Food and Nutrition Division

Acronyms

AIDS	acquired immunodeficiency syndrome
APIN	AIDS Prevention Initiatives in Nigeria
ARMM	Administrative Region of Muslim Mindanao
ASFs	animal source foods
BMI	body mass index
CBN	Central Bank of Nigeria
CHD	coronary heart disease
CHNS	China Health and Nutrition Survey
CHS	community health worker
CREN	Centro de Recuperação e Educação Nutritional (Centre for Nutritional Recovery and Education) (Brazil)
DALYs	disability-adjusted life years
DES	dietary energy supply
DHS	Demographic and Health Survey
EBF	exclusive breastfeeding
FAO	Food and Agriculture Organization of the United Nations
FGN	Federal Government of Nigeria
FMoH	Federal Ministry of Health (Nigeria)
FOS	Federal Office of Statistics (Nigeria)
GDP	gross domestic product
GNP	gross national product
HIES	Household Income and Expenditure Survey (Fiji)
HIV	human immunodeficiency virus
HKI	Helen Keller International

HTN   hypertension

ICMR   Indian Council of Medical Research

ICT   information and communication technologies

IDA   iron deficiency anaemia

IDD   iodine deficiency disorder

IMR   infant mortality rate

IOTF   International Obesity Task Force

IPHN   Institute of Public Health Nutrition (Bangladesh)

LSMS   Living Standards Measurement Study

MDGs   Millennium Development Goals

NAFDAC   National Agency for Food and Drug Administration and Control

NCDs   non-communicable diseases

NCFN   National Committee on Food and Nutrition (Nigeria)

NGO   non-governmental organization

NPC   National Planning Commission (Nigeria)

NSP   Nutrition Surveillance Project (Bangladesh)

NSS   National Sample Surveys (India)

OECD   Organisation for Economic Co-operation and Development

OFW   overseas Filipino workers

RDA   recommended daily allowance (China)/recommended dietary allowance
            (Philippines and South Africa)

SAP   Structural Adjustment Programme

SES   socio-economic status

STDs   sexually transmitted diseases

STIs   sexually transmitted infections

TTD	type-2 diabetes
UNDP	United Nations Development Programme
UNICEF	United Nations Children's Fund
UWC	University of the Western Cape (South Africa)
VAD	vitamin A deficiency
VAT	value-added tax
WHO	World Health Organization
WTO	World Trade Organization
YLL	years of life lost

Globalization of food systems in developing countries: a synthesis of country case studies

Gina Kennedy[1], Guy Nantel and Prakash Shetty

INTRODUCTION

The phenomenon of globalization is having a major impact on food systems around the world. Food systems are changing, resulting in greater availability and diversity of food, although access to this food is by no means universal. Many of these changes are closely associated with urbanization, increasing incomes, market liberalization and foreign direct investment. Competition for a market share of food purchases tends to intensify with entry into the system of powerful new players such as large multinational fast food and supermarket chains. The losers tend to be the small local agents and traditional food markets and, to some extent, merchants selling "street foods" as well as other food items. The supermarkets bring with them significant improvements in standards of food quality and safety at competitive prices and convenience, factors which are highly attractive to an increasingly sophisticated consumer. Thus these changes in food systems affect availability and access to food through changes to the food production, procurement and distribution systems and the food trade environment. In turn this is bringing about a gradual shift in food culture (towards a more universal one), with consequent changes in dietary consumption patterns and nutritional status that vary with the socio-economic strata. Indeed, the lower socio-economic population groups drift towards poor-quality, energy-dense but cheap and affordable foods.

The main drivers to changes in food systems and dietary patterns, such as urbanization, increased income, capital flow and market liberalization, have been discussed by others (de Haan *et al.*, 2003; Haddad, 2003; Popkin, 2003; Reardon *et al.*, 2003; Lang and Heasman, in press). This paper looks at the impact of globalization and increasing urbanization on dietary and physical activity patterns and their effect on nutritional status and health.

First a conceptual framework of the determinants of these profound changes to food systems in the societies of developing countries is provided. The remainder of the paper draws upon and summarizes observed dietary changes and their resulting impact on nutritional status from 11 case studies in Latin America (Brazil, Chile and Colombia), Asia (Bangladesh, China, India and the Philippines), Africa (Nigeria, the United Republic of Tanzania and South Africa) and the Pacific (Fiji).

---

[1] Gina Kennedy, Guy Nantel and Prakash Shetty
Nutrition Planning, Assessment and Evaluation Service
Food and Nutrition Division
Food and Agriculture Organization of the United Nations
Viale delle Terme di Caracalla
Rome, Italy
E-mail: gina.kennedy@fao.org

CONCEPTUAL FRAMEWORK

The conceptual framework shown in Figure 1 was elaborated in an attempt to illustrate the major driving forces behind the observed changes in food systems.

FIGURE 1
Changes in food systems

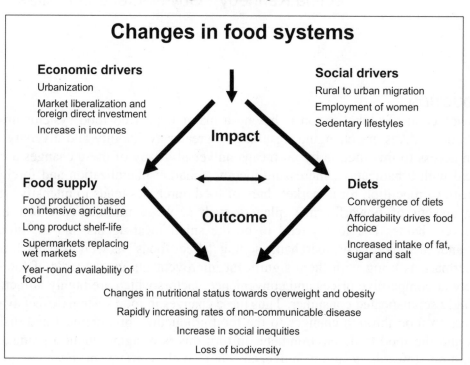

Figure 1 highlights urbanization, increasing incomes and foreign direct investment in markets of developing countries as the main economic drivers influencing changes in food supply and diet. In addition to the economic forces, concomitant social changes are taking place, such as more women entering the workforce and increasingly sedentary lifestyles. Accompanying these trends are changes in nutritional status and disease burden. The relationships between environment, diet and disease are complex and influenced by several external factors. Urbanization and the connection to dietary changes, health and nutritional status (the lower right and bottom areas of Figure 1) will be the primary focus of this paper. However, a brief summary[2] of the changes in the food supply chain (left side of Figure 1) may be instructive.

Lang (2003) describes changes to agricultural and food systems. These include massive use of agrochemicals and hybrid plants and, more recently, genetically modified plants; changes in food processing designed to produce uniform quality, size and shape, particularly suited for brand name products; and changes in distribution and marketing systems supported by computer systems for ordering, delivery and improved corporate control over markets. These food system features are already well in place in developed countries, and are now rapidly moving into developing country markets, impacting agriculture systems, squeezing small farmers out of business and contributing to increasing urbanization.

---

[2] *Development Policy Review*, vol. 21, No 5-6, 2003 provides a comprehensive review of these changes.

GLOBALIZATION OF FOOD SYSTEMS IN CONTEXT

In order to embark upon a discussion of the globalization of food systems it is first necessary to define what globalization means in this context. For the purposes of this paper, globalization refers to reduction in barriers to the cross-border movement of goods, services and capital; an increased flow of commodities, technologies, information, financial capital, modes of distribution and marketing; and, to a certain extent, migration of peoples and labour (Shetty, 2003a). A common feature of this process of globalization is a convergence, although at differing speeds, of many institutional, legal, economic, social and cultural practices and processes across different countries. In terms of food systems, changes are occurring all along the food chain from production and processing to retail and marketing. An attempt is made to refrain from assigning any value judgement to this process, but rather to isolate the common features of the phenomenon, citing examples of changes taking place in 11 country case studies from developing countries.

The pace and depth of change in food systems are occurring at different rates across regions and countries, although all countries appear to be moving in the same direction. Country-specific examples are useful in identifying factors that may contribute to the rapidity with which these changes are taking place and their impact on the nutritional status of the populations. For some case study countries such as Colombia, South Africa, the United Republic of Tanzania and India, a definite period of recent economic reform and market liberalization marks the opening of the national market to wider international trade.

> In Colombia the government undertook a series of reforms in the early 1990s which removed tariffs on imported food and created a more competitive market environment. In turn this led to increased importation of goods, in particular cheap feedgrains which spurred massive increases in livestock production (Fajardo, Colombia case study).

Reardon *et al.* (2003) also cite the 1990s as an influential period in terms of impact on forces of supply and demand, which facilitated changes in food retail systems and, in particular, the growth of supermarkets. On the demand side are urbanization, women in the workforce and greater access to refrigeration – the latter two fuelling and promoting convenience foods – while the supply side is characterized by liberalization of markets, foreign direct investment and better technology to track food stocks/shipments (Reardon *et al.*, 2003).

The following section compares and contrasts, in the 11 case study countries, specific regional and national variables broadly associated with globalization, and their impact on income, health, education, infrastructure and communications.

Urbanization

Probably the greatest influencing factor in dietary change and subsequent changes in nutritional status is urbanization and the myriad lifestyle changes associated with it. In 2001, 47.7 percent of the global population lived in urban areas, including 75.5 percent of the population in more developed countries and 40.9 percent of the population in less developed countries (United Nations Population Division, 2002). Within developing regions, there is a wide disparity in terms of urbanization. In Latin America and the Caribbean 75.8 percent of the population is classified as urban while in both Asia and Africa it is only 38 percent (United Nations Population Division, 2002). It is therefore not surprising that in the latter two regions urbanization is projected to increase the most, with a forecast of 50 percent of the population living in urban areas by 2020.

Table 1 demonstrates large differences in the extent of urbanization in the case study countries, with all countries moving towards even greater levels of urbanization. In 2000, all three case study countries in Latin America were highly urbanized while just about half of the populations of Fiji, the Philippines and South Africa lived in urban areas. Attention needs to be paid not only to the current level of urbanization, but also to the pace at which urbanization is expected to occur. The greatest projected increases in urban growth rate for the period 2005-2010 are expected in Bangladesh, the United Republic of Tanzania and Nigeria (United Nations Population Division, 2002). These case study countries have among the lowest per capita gross domestic product (GDP).

TABLE 1
Increasing urban populations in case study countries

Countries	Trends in percentage of the population living in urban areas				Current urban population
	1960	1980	2000	2020	2001
Brazil	45.6	66.8	81.2	88.9	141 041 000
Chile	67.8	81.2	85.8	89.8	13 254 000
Colombia	49.1	62.6	75.0	82.8	32 319 000
Bangladesh	5.1	14.9	25.0	37.7	35 896 000
China	16.0	19.6	35.8	53.4	633 651 000
India	18.0	23.1	27.7	34.7	285 608 000
Philippines	30.3	37.5	58.6	71.4	45 812 000
Fiji	29.7	37.8	49.4	62.8	413 000
Nigeria	14.4	26.9	44.1	58.3	52 539 000
South Africa	46.6	48.1	56.9	69.6	25 260 000
United Republic of Tanzania	4.7	14.8	32.3	49.4	11 982 000

Source: United Nations Population Division, 2002.

It is beyond the scope of this paper to discuss in detail the myriad forces influencing urbanization. The answers are neither uniform nor simplistic. While cities are generally considered engines for economic growth, Nef (1995) argues that "hyperurbanization" or "overurbanization" occurs more as a result of poverty than affluence, with megacities and their surrounding sprawl becoming more associated with conditions of deprivation than prosperity. Sachs *et al.* (2004) cite abject rural poverty as fuel for rural-urban migration. Explicit and implicit evidence of the uneven global trading climate, including unfair tariffs, export dumping and agricultural subsidies to farmers in industrialized countries are cited by many as factors deepening poverty in developing countries (Murphy, 2002; Pinstrup-Andersen, 2001; Watkins, 2003).

While migration to urban areas may often occur as an act of desperation, given the destruction of agricultural-based rural livelihoods and reducing returns on domestic agriculture, caution should be employed before making generalizations about urbanization being absolutely reflective or either prosperity or poverty. Context-specific socio-economic, political, historical and ecological situations need to be considered over generalized statements regarding the nature and motives surrounding urbanization (Tacoli, no date).

Despite the impetus for migration, the urban environment appears to exert an influence on dietary habits that reaches both the rich and the poor segments of the population and can impact health and nutritional status. The positive dimensions of urbanization on diet and health include greater access to education and health care services, and greater availability of diverse foods. However, these advantages may not reach all urban residents. There are also negative or potentially negative features, including diets with greater amounts of fat and sugars or sweeteners, increasingly sedentary lifestyles, environmental pollution, unsanitary and overcrowded living conditions and crime. These features will be discussed in more detail in the following sections.

Economics, health and education

Table 2 gives indicators of economics, health and education in the 11 case study countries.

TABLE 2
Indicators of economics, health and education

Case study countries by GDP	Economics		Health		Education	
	GDP per capita (purchasing power parity [PPP] US$, 2001)	Inequality Gini index	General government expenditure on health as % of total government expenditure, 2001	Infant mortality rate (IMR)	Public expenditure on education (as % of total government expenditure)[1]	Adult literacy (% age 15 and over), 2001
United Republic of Tanzania	520	38.2	12.1	104	11.4	76.0
Nigeria	850	50.6	1.9	110	-	65.4
Bangladesh	1 610	31.8	8.7	51	15.7	40.6
India	2 840	37.8	3.1	67	12.7	58.0
Philippines	3 840	46.1	6.2	29	20.6	95.1
China	4 020	40.3	10.2	31	-	85.8
Fiji	4 850	-	6.9	18	17.0	93.2
Colombia	7 040	57.1	10.8	19	-	91.9
Brazil	7 360	60.7	8.8	31	12.9	87.3
Chile	9 190	57.5	12.7	10	17.5	95.9
South Africa	11 290	59.3	10.9	56	25.8	85.6

[1] Some data are preliminary or United Nations Children's Fund (UNESCO) estimates where there is no national estimate.
Source: UNDP, 2003; WHO, 2003.

Those countries with the greatest proportion of population living in urban areas also tend to have the highest GDP per capita. Figure 2 shows the relationship between GDP, infant mortality rate and urbanization. Benefits are not necessarily evenly distributed and averages can mask inequalities. Those countries with a higher GDP have the most pronounced social and economic inequalities. (Table 2).

> The infant mortality rate in Brazil is estimated to be 31 deaths per 1 000 live births. The Brazil case study points out that in certain pockets of the population the infant mortality rate exceeds 100 (Sawaya, Martins and Martins, Brazil case study).

Among the case study countries, Chile has one of the highest government expenditures on health and education, combined with low infant mortality rates and high adult literacy rates. In contrast, Nigeria has the lowest government expenditure on health and the highest infant mortality rate. Figure 2 compares GDP, urbanization and infant mortality rate. There is a relatively consistent relationship with GDP and urbanization, with notable exceptions in South Africa, the Philippines, Nigeria and the United Republic of Tanzania. The peak in urbanization seen in the Philippines, Nigeria and the United Republic of Tanzania, given lower GDP, may be a result of hyperurbanization patterns driven by poverty, as described by Nef (1995). Infant mortality also appears roughly inverse to urbanization, except in South Africa.

FIGURE 2
Relationship between gross domestic product (GDP), infant mortality rate (IMR) and urbanization

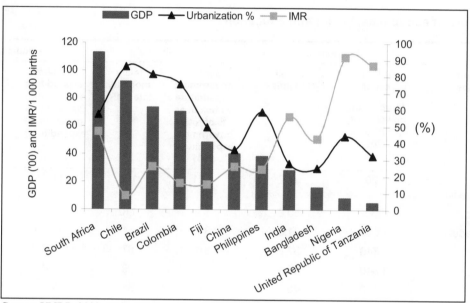

Source: UNDP, 2003; United Nations Population Division, 2002.

Employment

The case studies converged on three urban employment trends: i) increasing number of women entering the workforce; ii) expansion of the informal employment sector; and iii) rising unemployment. The trends are associated with migration from rural areas to cities and in some case study countries massive inflation and cuts in the number of salaried government employees.

Women are entering the workforce in larger numbers through necessity and greater opportunities and availability of jobs traditionally filled by women, such as house cleaners and child carers.

In São Paulo, Brazil 70 percent of new jobs created were filled by women (Sawaya, Martins and Martins, Brazil case study).

In the Philippines, the situation is slightly different. Large numbers of women are seeking work as domestic helpers overseas (Pedro, Barba and Candelaria, Philippines case study).

Nearly all the case studies report a growth in unemployment alongside the simultaneous increase in informal sector jobs; the two would seem to go hand in hand.

In South Africa, unemployment increased from 33 to 41 percent over the period 1996 to 2001, with the ethnic African population experiencing the largest increase up to 50 percent (Chopra, South Africa case study).

In Nigeria, the government has reduced jobs and unemployment is high. The informal sector is estimated to account for 75 percent of employment (Olayiwola, Soyibo and Atinmo, Nigeria case study).

Much of the growth in the informal sector involves food preparation and retailing. Families engage in food preparation or the sale of street foods since entry into the system is largely unregulated, requires skills that most families already possess and does not require much upfront investment. Complementary to this trend is an increasing demand for meals away from home as commuting distances between residence and employment increase, and working hours are long and often unpredictable.

Technology and facilitating mechanisms
Availability of and access to modern technologies also exert significant influences that change food systems. It is useful to look at these factors, although data are sparse and not always in a form that lends itself to comparisons. For example, a convenient starting-point would be to look at infrastructure and access to services and technology. It would be helpful to have an estimate of the percentage of the population with access to electricity, the proportion of well-maintained and/or paved roads, statistics on car ownership and number of households with refrigerators. Unfortunately, most of this information is not available in a standardized form that allows cross-country comparisons. Despite these limitations, some trends are visible.

The most complete and current set of comparable information relates to Millennium Development Goal (MDG) indicators, such as access to safe water and sanitation, to telephones, computers and the Internet. For purposes of cross-country comparison, indicators of MDGs from the UN Statistics Division (2000) are presented in Table 3. Access to water, sanitation and paved roads are taken as indicators of infrastructure. Telephone, computer and Internet user rates are used to describe access to communications.

TABLE 3
Indicators of infrastructure and communications

Countries	Economy	Infrastructure			Communications		
	GDP per capita (PPP US$, 2001)	Access to improved water source,[1] 2000	Access to improved sanitation,[2] 2000	Paved roads (as % of total)	Telephones and mobile subscribers/ 100 population, 2000	Internet users/100 population, 2000 (ITU)[3]	Computer users/100 population, 2000 (ITU)
United Republic of Tanzania	520	68	90[4]	5	1.08	0.12	0.31
Nigeria	850	62	54	31	0.46	0.07	0.66
Bangladesh	1 610	97[5]	48	9	0.58	0.08	0.15
India	2 840	84	28	46	3.56	0.54	0.45
Philippines	3 840	86	83	20	12.44	2.01	1.93
China	4 020	75	40	19	17.76	1.74	1.59
Fiji	4 850	47	43	49	17.51	1.49	4.46
Colombia	7 040	91	86	24	22.33	2.07	3.54
Brazil	7 360	87	76	9	31.87	2.94	5.01
Chile	9 190	93	96	14	44.63	16.68	9.34
South Africa	11 290	86	87	17	30.45	5.49	6.64
Sources		UNDP, 2003			CIA, 2003		United Nations Statistics Division, 2000

[1] Improved water sources are defined as household connection, public standpipe, borehole, protected dug well, protected spring and rainwater collection. *Reasonable access* is defined as availability of 20 litres/person/day within 1 km of the user's dwelling.

[2] Adequate sanitation facilities are defined as connection to a sewer or septic tank, a pour flush latrine, simple pit latrine or ventilated improved pit latrine. The facility should effectively prevent human, animal and insect contact with excreta. The facility is considered adequate if it is private or shared (but not public).

[3] International Telecommunication Union.

[4] This figure was cross-referenced with the 1999 the United Republic of Tanzania Reproductive and Child Health Survey in which it was reported that 86 percent of households had access to a pit latrine (12 percent had no kind of toilet facility).

[5] A recent estimate by UNICEF (www.unicef.org/infobycountry/bangladesh.html) has decreased this figure to 70 percent because of arsenic contamination in groundwater.

Source: United Nations Statistics Division, 2000.

The first three indicators of basic infrastructure present a somewhat inconsistent picture within and across countries. The figures should be considered best estimates, their reliability having been questioned elsewhere (Satterthwaite, 2003). It is also important to note that, given the great inequalities in many of the countries, there will be sections of the population, particularly those in poorer areas, with little or no access to services despite high national averages.

When considering population access to water and sanitation, the more urbanized countries – Brazil, Chile, Colombia and the Philippines – appear to be slightly better off. However, access to improved water and sanitation does not correlate strongly with GDP. For example, Fiji ranks lowest in terms of water and sanitation access yet has the fourth highest GDP. The geography of small island countries, which limits the availability of fresh drinking-water, is the most likely explanation for this discrepancy between GDP and access to a safe water supply. The United Republic of Tanzania also presents an exception, with relatively high population access to improved water and sanitation services and the lowest GDP among the 11 case study countries.

Roads, particularly paved roads that are not subject to seasonal deterioration, are an imprecise indicator of ease of interstate movement of goods and market access. It is difficult to use this indicator as a comparison across countries, largely because of the variations in country sizes. Brazil, for example, has 1.98 million km of road, 9 percent of which are paved. Fiji, on the other hand, has 3 440 km of road, with half paved.

The three indicators of communications seem to follow urbanization closely, with Chile, Brazil and Colombia having the greatest number of telecommunications users, followed by South Africa and the Philippines.

Refrigeration and freezer technology is a primary spark for the transformation of food systems. Extension of cold storage from food processing centres to large or small food outlets and eventually to private homes creates vast potential for changing the patterns of food procurement. A large variety of foods can be stored in a way that maintains quality, and consumers can choose between fresh or frozen (often ready to eat) products. Lack of access to a reliable source of electricity is undoubtedly the greatest barrier to access to refrigeration in many developing countries. According to the International Energy Agency (2002), 56 percent of people in developing countries lack access to electricity. Electrification rates by region show Latin America with 87 percent access, South Asia with 41 percent and sub-Saharan Africa with 23 percent. Thus, a prerequisite for expansion of the frozen food market is household ownership of refrigerators/freezers, which in turn requires access to electricity. Large supermarket chains are still able to establish markets in countries with limited electricity; however, it would be interesting to research any differences in the products sold in areas with different access levels to electricity.

The case study from Brazil indicates that refrigeration capacity is currently reaching individual homes, with over 80 percent of households owning refrigerators and 20 percent owning freezers (Sawaya, Martins and Martins, Brazil case study).

CHANGES IN DIETARY PATTERNS

Details of the dynamics of change in diet are provided in the paper in this volume by Mendez and Popkin. Overall, the changes can be described by two distinct phenomena: dietary convergence and dietary adaptation. Dietary convergence is occurring as a result of increased reliance on a narrow base of staple grains, increased consumption of meat and meat products, dairy products, edible oil, salt and sugar, and a lower intake of dietary fibre. Dietary adaptation is characterized by an increased consumption of brand name processed and store-bought foods, an increased number of meals eaten outside the home and consumer behaviours driven by the appeal of new foods available.

Dietary convergence

Income and price are the two most influential factors leading to dietary convergence. These in turn are affected by supply and availability. On the price side, low prices for the three dominant global staples – rice, wheat and maize – are largely maintained by subsidies to farmers in producing countries, particularly for wheat and maize. The rice trade has increased dramatically, fuelled by increasing demand in Africa and parts of Asia. World trade in rice reached a historic high of 28 million tonnes in 2002 (FAO, 2003). Dramatic production increases that have driven down cost were made possible as a result of yield improvements and intensive agricultural practices.

Increased consumption of fat, particularly from vegetable oils, is another phenomenon of dietary convergence. Higher fat intakes are now possible at a lower gross national product (GNP). Using GNP values standardized to 1993 US$, Popkin (2003) found that in 1962 an average GNP of $1 475 was necessary to derive 20 percent of energy from fat, while by 1990 the GNP needed for a diet with 20 percent of energy derived from fat was only half that at $750.

Similar price reductions have been seen for animal source foods (ASFs). Delgado *et al.* (1999) show dramatic declines in the price of milk and beef and more modest declines in the price of pork and poultry.

TABLE 4
Twenty-year trends in dietary energy supply (DES) and percentage of DES from fat, oil and animal source foods (ASFs)

Countries	Total DES		% DES from fat		% DES from vegetable oil		% DES from ASFs	
	(kcals/per capita/day)							
	1980	2000	1980	2000	1980	2000	1980	2000
Brazil	2 677	3 002	22	26	11	11	15	20
China	2 328	2 974	13	25	3	6	7	20
South Africa	2 819	2 894	21	23	6	11	15	12
Chile	2 665	2 851	20	27	8	9	16	22
Fiji	2 501	2 782	32	33	10	11	20	19
Nigeria	2 030	2 768	25	21	15	12	6	3
Colombia	2 293	2 572	18	23	7	11	14	16
India	2 083	2 492	14	19	6	10	6	8
Philippines	2 221	2 374	15	18	5	6	11	15
Bangladesh	1 976	2 156	7	11	3	7	3	3
United Republic of Tanzania	2 191	1 970	13	13	4	5	6	6

Source: FAO, 2004. FAOSTAT (three-year averages – 1980 (1979-1980), 2000 (1999-2001).

The data in Table 4 do not distinguish between urban and rural availability. Nevertheless, they provide an overall view of the direction and pace of change related to dietary convergence. In all case study countries except the United Republic of Tanzania, the per capita availability of dietary energy has increased. The percentage of dietary energy obtained from fat has consistently risen over time in all but two countries. An increased percentage of dietary energy from vegetable oil is seen in nine of the case study countries, while an increased percentage of dietary energy from ASFs is noted in six countries.

Many of the case studies provide supporting evidence for the trends observed in Table 4.

In China, animal food intake (meat, poultry, fish and eggs) increased on average by 26 g/day from 1991 to 1997. The most dramatic increases were noticed in "less urbanized" urban areas and "more urbanized" rural areas (Mendez, Du and Popkin, China case study).

Significant gains were achieved in poultry production from 1990 to 2001 in Colombia, where increases of 55 percent for chicken meat and 36 percent for egg production were noted. These dramatic increases in poultry production were achieved through importation of cheaper animal feed (Fajardo, Colombia case study).

For urban India as a whole, from 1987-1988 to 1999-2000, consumption of rice and wheat declined marginally. The consumption of milk and eggs records an increase. A substantial increase over the three time periods is seen in the consumption of eggs, tea, biscuits, salted refreshments, prepared sweets, edible oils, sugar and country sugar (jaggary) (Vepa, India case study).

Dietary adaptation

Adaptation of diets to include more processed, refined and brand name foods is influenced by dramatic changes in lifestyle which are driven by, among others, demands on time, increased exposure to advertising, availability of new foods and emergence of new food retail outlets. Urban residents are the first to undergo lifestyle and environmental changes, but these eventually filter down into less urbanized areas as well.

Lifestyle changes and adaptation of meal patterns

In urban areas, men and women are driven into the workforce by the overriding need for an increase in income to pay for food, shelter, clothing and other household expenses. Working hours and commuting times are often long and, with growing numbers of family members entering the workforce, there is less time available to prepare food and hence there is a greater desire and necessity to consume meals outside the home.

> In Chile the average working day is ten hours, with an additional one to three hours commuting time (Vio and Albala, Chile case study).

These factors have fuelled demand and led to massive market expansion of convenience and fast food options. Traditional meals and meal times are replaced by spontaneous often unplanned food purchases on street corners or in small kiosks. The traditional model of one family member taking responsibility for meal planning and food preparation for the household has fractured in most urban environments. Increasingly it is street food vendors, cafeterias at work or school and child care facilities that provide family members with at least one and often several meals per day. Thus, attention to dietary balance and dietary quality, which was traditionally "intuitive" at the household level, is now subject to wider cultural changes and external influence.

Street foods

In the context of rapid urbanization, street foods are becoming increasingly important as both a cheap and quick meal option and as an income-generating strategy. The meals and snacks served on the streets cater for a wide variety of customer tastes and range from traditional recipes of rice or maize with vegetables and beans, to more modern items including various types of fried or grilled meats, potatoes and bread. Many countries do not regulate street vendors and it is therefore possible to enter into street food vending with a relatively low start-up cost, making this activity attractive to many low-income urban residents.

> In the United Republic of Tanzania, street foods account for 70 percent of total caloric intake of low- and middle- income groups (Kinabo, the United Republic of Tanzania case study).

Quality and safety are two common concerns cited with regard to street foods, yet there are very few concrete data on pathogen levels of street foods compared to home-prepared or restaurant food. The WHO Regional Office for Africa has conducted research on bacterial contamination of street food in Ghana. In this study, the microbial quality of most of the 511 food samples was within acceptable limits. Of the 26 types of foods (each food was sampled from multiple vendors) included in the study, four items – salad and macaroni dishes, red pepper and *fufu* – had total bacterial counts above acceptable limits (Mensah *et al.*, 2002). Lack of knowledge about sanitary practices, vehicle pollution, absence of structural insect barriers and scarcity of water for preparation and cleaning up all contribute to the likelihood of street foods being unhygienic.

Street food vending is not limited just to meals but also includes beverages, fruit juices and yoghurt drinks, and various snack foods: a practice that is little discussed in the nutrition community. In contrast to street vending of beverages made from fresh fruit is the continuously growing sale of carbonated beverages such as Coca-Cola and Fanta. Vendors are trained and promoted by multinational beverage companies that also employ and equip them. China, India and Nigeria are listed among the top emerging markets in the Coca-Cola Company's Annual Report (Coca-Cola Company, 2002) and mobile street vending is one effective promotional technique.

Supermarkets

Reardon and colleagues have documented a phenomenal increase in supermarkets[3] in developing countries (Reardon *et al.*, 2003). They may be independently owned, but increasingly are part of larger commercial conglomerates, such as Ahold, Carrefor and Walmart. Supermarkets began to spread through Latin America in the early 1990s followed five to seven years later in Asia, and most recently in Africa. Their share in national retail reached 75 percent in Brazil in 2000 and 50 percent in Chile while in urban China and the Philippines the share in sales of packaged and processed foods reached 48 and 57 percent, respectively (Reardon, Timmer and Berdegue, 2003). An important aspect related to dietary adaptation is the range of products sold. The general pattern of supermarket entry into retail is first to specialize in the sale of packaged and processed foods, followed by fresh or frozen meat and lastly fresh produce. The initial entry into the market using packaged and processed foods exposes consumers to "exotic" food items or those with a long shelf-life such as powdered milk, ramen noodles and many varieties of sweet and savoury snack foods. Many processed foods contain added sodium and sweeteners and are also high in fat.

Fast food industry

The past decade has seen a dramatic increase in convenience food markets in developing countries. In 1985, the McDonald's restaurant chain operated 9 000 restaurants worldwide; by 2001 this number had expanded to 30 000 restaurants in 121 countries (Ghezan, Mateos and Viteri, 2002). In China, the first foreign fast food company, Kentucky Fried Chicken, opened a restaurant in Beijing in 1987 and, after nine years, the business had expanded to 100 restaurants. Today, 15 years after the opening of the first restaurant, there are 600 Kentucky Fried Chicken outlets in China, the majority in urban centres (Agriculture and Agri-food Canada, 2002). Similarly, in Latin America 15 years ago there were 100 McDonald's outlets, whereas today there are 1 581, with one-third located in the urban areas of Brazil (Ghezan, Mateos and Viteri, 2002).

Role of advertising

Secondary factors such as marketing, advertising, the appeal of new products, new retail outlets including supermarkets and multinational fast food chains contribute to dietary adaptation and convergence. Aside from the driving force of time constraints, part of the rapid adoption of new foods in the diet stems from successful advertising. The advertising budget of the largest food companies can exceed national expenditures on health promotion and health education by massive proportions (Lang, 2003). For example, British

---

[3] A supermarket outlet is defined as a food retail market of 350-400 m^2 in size with three to four or more cash registers.

government expenditure on healthy eating advice is about £5 million per year while the Coca-Cola company spends £27 million per year in the United Kingdom of Great Britain and Northern Ireland alone, and total advertising expenditures by the food industry is just under £0.5 billion (Lang, 2003).

> The global marketing of products and lifestyles via television in small island countries such as Fiji has become common. Subtle as well as aggressive advertising by transnational tobacco and alcohol companies in particular, both in print and electronically, appears to be aimed at younger receptive age groups. Generally, these advertisements portray lifestyles that are economically unachievable in local circumstances, generating expectations and a sense of envy and frustration that is deemed to be socially disruptive for individuals and groups (Schultz, Fiji case study).

Increasingly in developing countries television is becoming a good medium for advertising to large audiences and, with the spread of mobile phones and text messages, new channels for reaching consumers are emerging. In Brazil and Chile individuals watch four to five hours of television per day, while in the Philippines children spend on average more than one and a half hours per day in front of the television. Advertisements for food are becoming increasingly predominant and are expected to have greater impact as television audiences grow.

> A review of food-related television advertisements in Brazil reported 58 percent of commercials promoting high fat and high sugar products, 9 percent featuring meat, beans or eggs and no advertisements for fresh fruit and vegetables (Sawaya, Martins and Martins, Brazil case study).

Changing attitudes

> Value judgements in response to the appeal "to be modern" also influence food purchases and food preparation. In the urban areas of Johannesburg, residents consider fried food to be a sign of modern living and wealth, while food that is boiled is considered inferior and demonstrates outdated customs (Chopra, South Africa case study).

In the Cape Town region of South Africa the notion of farming characterized by physical effort and hardship in general remains an issue for recent migrants to urban slums (South Africa case study). Dwellers of Khayelitsha, an informal settlement of about 750 000 people, are willing to engage in communal gardening only to the extent that they need to do it for survival and have no alternative. They prefer to earn an income and to purchase food instead. Of those who work in the community gardens, the majority leave as soon as they have found a source of revenue. The result is that what were created as "community gardens" to meet the food needs of the Khayelitsha communities are now being transformed into businesses of market gardening and produce is sold to local markets where community dwellers do their food purchasing. Those individuals remaining active in the community gardens now consider themselves as "employees" in some sort of a cooperative arrangement from which they draw revenue.

DIET-RELATED HEALTH AND NUTRITION CHALLENGES

It is important to study changing food systems and dietary patterns in order to understand how these alterations affect the health and nutrition of populations. Diet-related factors such as cholesterol; low fruit and vegetable intake; and iron, zinc and vitamin A deficiency rank among the major risk factors for decreased disability-adjusted life years (DALYs) (WHO, 2002). Health problems related to diet may be caused by a limited intake of dietary energy or micronutrients, an excessive intake of dietary energy, or poorly balanced intakes. There are direct health consequences from nutritional deficiencies such as blindness from severe vitamin A deficiency or mental incapacity as a result of iodine deficiency. Likewise, diet plays a critical albeit more covert role in the development of many other diseases including type-2 diabetes, cardiovascular disease, cancer, dental disease and osteoporosis (WHO/FAO, 2003).

High levels of undernutrition in adults and children in developing countries remain a grave concern and a top priority for public health action in many of the case study countries, as do deaths from communicable diseases such as malaria, diarrhoea, tuberculosis and other respiratory infections. However, the increasing prevalence of obesity and non-communicable diseases (NCDs) in developing countries is rapidly becoming a concern necessitating more attention. The most recent global estimates indicate that as many as 1.7 billion persons could be overweight or obese (IOTF, 2004). The majority of these people live in developed countries; however, overweight and obesity have been increasing exponentially in several regions of the developing world, particularly Latin America and the Caribbean and North Africa (Martorell, 2001). The term "double burden" has been used to describe countries experiencing continuing high prevalence rates of infectious and communicable diseases while at the same time NCDs are on the increase.

Popkin (2003) has defined a set of three stages which he terms the "nutrition transition". In brief, the stages are: i) receding famine as incomes rise; ii) changes in diet and activity patterns, which increase the incidence of diet-related chronic disease; and iii) a stage of behavioural change where intake and activity are regulated such that health ageing is prolonged as diet-related chronic diseases are better prevented or controlled. The stages are closely linked to demographic and epidemiological shifts.

Burden of disease

Figure 3 shows the relative percentage of mortality from communicable and non-communicable diseases and injuries based on the WHO mortality classification. The data presented do not correspond to individual countries, but to the WHO region and mortality stratum in which each case study country is located. WHO uses a quintile distribution to classify countries by different levels of child and adult mortality. The WHO mortality stratum classification can be found in the Annex. For further details on the methodology used to derive the mortality strata, the *World Health Report 2002* can be consulted (WHO, 2002).

Figure 3 illustrates the largest dual burden of mortality for countries in the WHO Southeast Asia Region, which includes Bangladesh and India. In this regional stratum, deaths caused by communicable and non-communicable diseases are nearly equal. In the America and Pacific regional strata, NCDs account for the majority of mortalities, while the opposite pattern is observed in both WHO Africa mortality strata. Clearly public health strategies will need to be adapted accordingly in the different regions presented.

FIGURE 3

Deaths from communicable diseases, non-communicable diseases and injuries by WHO region and mortality stratum (MS)

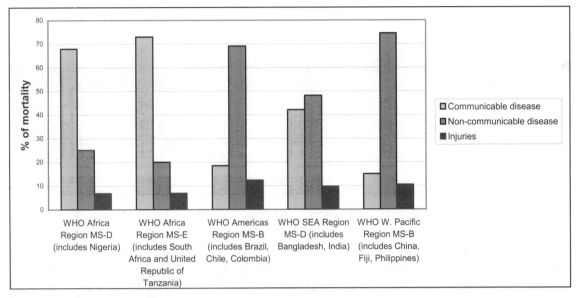

Source: WHO, 2003.

FIGURE 4

Estimated past, current and predicted prevalence of diabetes

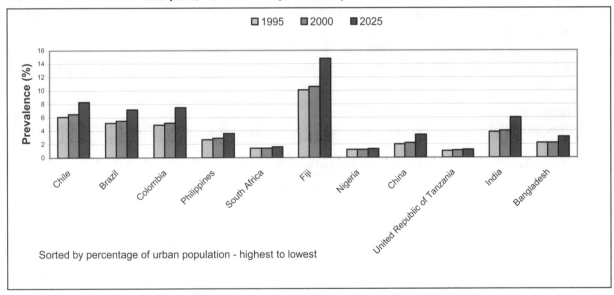

Note: Many extrapolations were necessary because of a lack of suitable survey data. All estimates for sub-Saharan Africa come from data from the United Republic of Tanzania. For a full description of the methodology used, refer to the article by King, Aubert and Herman (1998).
Source: King, Aubert and Herman, 1998.

WHO and FAO have signalled concern about the increasing prevalence of chronic NCDs linked to diet including diabetes mellitus, cardiovascular disease, hypertension and strokes and some types of cancer (WHO/FAO, 2003). Estimates for 2000 indicate 171 million persons had diabetes with a projected increase to 366 million by 2030 (Wild *el al.*, 2004). Diabetes is a condition closely linked to diet and exercise. Figure 4 provides an estimate of the prevalence of diabetes along three time points. The highest prevalence of diabetes by 2025 among the case study countries is predicted in Fiji, followed by Chile,

Colombia and Brazil. In terms of the absolute number of persons with diabetes, India and China are predicted by 2025 to have the highest global burden at 57.2 and 37.6 million cases, respectively (King, Aubert and Herman, 1998).

Malnutrition

The term malnutrition is often used as a synonym for undernutrition. In the context of the changing burden of nutritional disorders, more clarity of terminology is needed. Malnutrition is any state of nutritional imbalance and includes under- and overnutrition and inadequacies in micronutrients. Undernutrition is the preferred term for describing nutrition disorders related to lack of adequate dietary energy, while overnutrition is used to describe excess dietary energy intake, most often also associated with low energy expenditure or reduced levels of physical activity (Shetty, 2003b). Micronutrient deficiencies occur when intake of micronutrients is inadequate or when disease processes prevent adequate absorption of micronutrients available in the diet. Lack of adequate dietary diversity tends to lead to micronutrient deficiency.

The burden of malnutrition in the case study countries is shown in Table 5. Bangladesh, India, the Philippines, Nigeria and the United Republic of Tanzania have levels of undernutrition in children that are still considered high by WHO standards. In Chile, stunting and underweight have nearly disappeared, yet 8 percent of the children are malnourished at the other end of the spectrum because they are overweight.

WHO has classified stunting above 30 percent and underweight above 20 percent as problems of high public health concern (WHO, 1995). The highlighted cells in Table 5 indicate prevalence levels of undernutrition which are of a magnitude to cause public health concern. Ideally, criteria for signalling concern over the magnitude of overweight and obese individuals in populations will also become available, making it possible to isolate more clearly the most immediate priorities. Currently, no such criteria have been established. The picture for adults reveals more of a problem with overweight in those countries with data. Even in some countries where chronic malnutrition is prevalent in children (Philippines, Nigeria), the prevalence of overweight and obese adults is of concern.

TABLE 5
Prevalence of malnutrition (sorted by underweight in children)

Countries	Children under five years of age			Adults[3]					
	Underweight[1]	Stunted[2]	Overweight[2]	Underweight M	Underweight F	Overweight M	Overweight F	Obese M	Obese F
Bangladesh	48	45	1.1				3.7		0.7
India	47	46	1.6				4.7		1
United Republic of Tanzania	29	44	2.5						
Nigeria	27	46	3.3		16.2		15.8		7.1
Philippines	28	30	1.0	11.1	15.4	14.9	18.9	2.1	4.4
South Africa	12	25	6.7	12.2	5.6			9.1	29.4
China	10	17	2.6	9.1	9.9	14.6	11.9		
Fiji	8	3	1.2	10.7	9.6	25.2	29.9	7.4	20.6
Colombia	7	14	2.6		3.1	32		21	
Brazil	6	11	4.9		6.2	31	36.8	26.5	10.2
Chile	1	2	7.9					15.7	23

Note: Years for data range from 1992 to 1999.
[1] *Source*: UNDP, 2003.
[2] *Source*: de Onis and Blossner, 2003.
[3] *Source*: IOTF, 2004; Demographic and Health Surveys (www.measuredhs.com); FAO Nutrition Country Profiles.

Figure 5 shows the prevalence of underweight and overweight children by GDP. Child overweight increases relatively consistently with GDP. The prevalence of underweight in children is less consistent with economic ranking.

FIGURE 5

Relationship between GDP, underweight and overweight children (under five years of age)

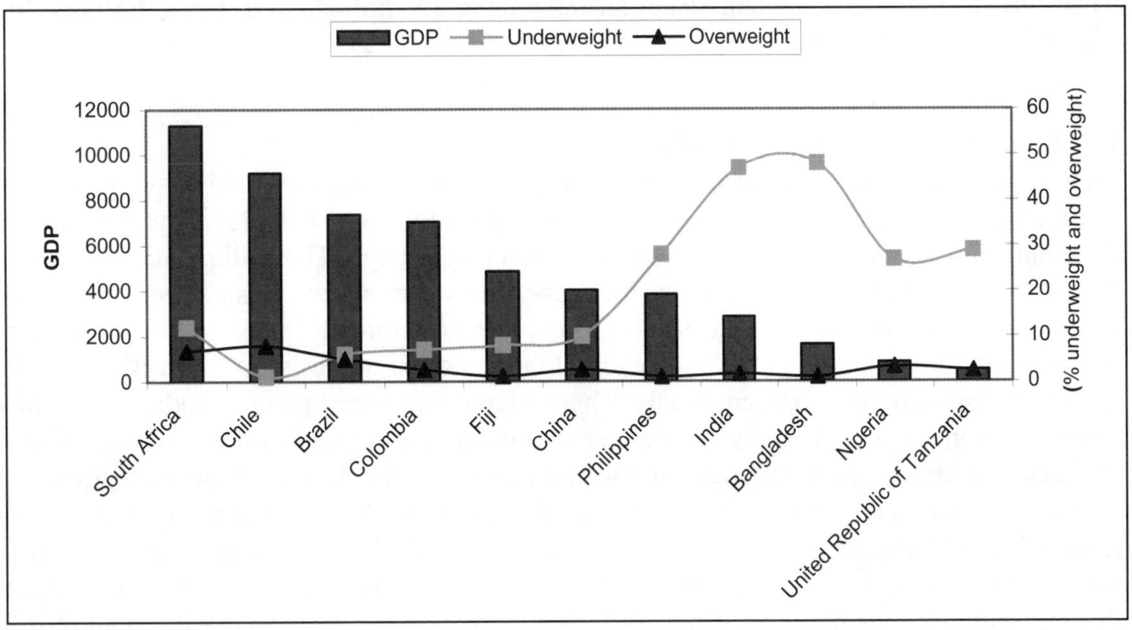

Source: UNDP, 2003; de Onis and Blossner, 2003.

BROAD CONCERNS

Cities are engines of national economic growth and can provide citizens with diverse income-earning opportunities. At the same time there are negative factors associated with urban life such as crime, pollution, increased cigarette and alcohol consumption and decreased physical activity. The rapid pace of urbanization in many cities outstrips the capability of municipalities to provide basic services such as water, sanitation and housing. In this respect, the forces of globalization appear to drive the phenomenon of urbanization to a pace that is beyond the accommodative capacity of municipalities.

The changing food systems brought about by the forces of globalization and characterized by increasing urbanization have led to new challenges and opportunities. Many countries in the developing world are faced with the continuing burden of undernutrition and food insecurity. At the same time, changes in diet and physical activity patterns are increasing the incidence of diet-related NCDs, principally obesity, coronary heart disease, diabetes and hypertension. In addition, for most countries, regardless of the stage of transition, micronutrient deficiencies are of concern.

Broader issues related more specifically to food systems were also raised in the case study reports and during the discussions. There is concern about the impact (both positive and negative) on dietary change exerted as a result of the greater influence and control of national food systems by multinational and transnational corporations. There is alarm that local culture and food traditions are disappearing. Environmental concerns included the effects of changed production and distribution systems, which could lead to environmental degradation as a result of intensification of inputs into the agricultural system, the overall sustainability of the system and loss of biodiversity through narrowing of the crop base.

There is policy debate about the supermarket and shopping mall phenomenon that attracts consumers away from the traditional small community stores and erodes traditional community life, yet can increase the range and cross-seasonal availability of foods, albeit at a cost to local food supplies. Supermarket suppliers tend to be large producers who can provide guarantees of quality (nutritional and safety) and reliability, thus gradually eliminating smaller farmers who are less able to meet these standards or production quotas. This further undermines small-scale farming as a livelihood, and these farmers find themselves with little choice other than to migrate to the cities.

POTENTIAL SOLUTIONS AND STRATEGIES

This paper has presented evidence of the way in which changing food systems have an impact on the health and nutritional status of populations and has drawn on background data and analyses to depict the determinants of dietary change. These illustrate some of the forces of globalization at work in the case study countries. Basic needs including education, access to health services and critical infrastructure still need to be met in many of the case study countries. The fundamental targets to be achieved are clearly delineated in the Millennium Development Goals. These include a commitment to reduce childhood undernutrition, increase literacy and deliver improved access to safe water and sanitation.

Reaching these goals requires, at the very least, collaboration between agriculture, health, nutrition and education to address the problems of malnutrition in a holistic manner. The Millennium Development Goals are a reminder of the absolute necessity of cross-sectoral cooperation. Achieving the targets will be possible only if different disciplines work together. Opportunities for collaboration towards decreasing malnutrition are presented below.

General education

Education is a proven strategy at both ends of the nutrition spectrum. In countries where undernutrition is prevalent, it is lower among the better educated; likewise for countries where overnutrition problems predominate, the better educated have less prevalence of overweight (most of the latter examples come from industrialized nations). Even though in this example, the spectrum of educational achievement is vastly different, it would still seem that one of the best policies for optimal nutritional status is general education. In a recent review of best practices in poverty eradication, education – both formal and informal – was highlighted as essential (UN Sub-Committee for the Eradication of Poverty, 2003).

The importance of education is amplified by a quote from a representative of the Carmen Papa University in Bolivia:

> *"Education is key in the search for more justice in the world. The untapped excellence of the poor is being wasted in the need to survive."* (UN Sub-Committee for the Eradication of Poverty, 2003, p. 29).

Healthy food culture

Many of the case studies highlighted changing patterns of meal provision and a large influence of advertising on shaping food habits. For many urban families, one to two meals per day are eaten outside the home. For many children this means the majority of meals are consumed at school or day care centres. Coordination between agriculture, education, health and nutrition is essential in this arena to provide favourable environments and appropriate messages for maintaining or recreating healthy food cultures.

As a direction towards a solution, the United Republic of Tanzania case study suggests that there should be a healthy relationship between the rural and urban communities, pointing out that it is in the interest of both urban and rural areas to maintain linkages. In Dar es Salaam, newly arrived residents from rural areas tend to maintain links with their rural place of origin as insurance in obtaining supplies of fresh produce. This is a frequently occurring pattern with new migrants to cities but, over time, these connections tend to fade. A challenge might be to search for ways of maintaining and nurturing these links. There is a definite need to develop a vision of cities and the rural world as different ends of a sociogeographic spectrum, rather than as individual worlds on their own.

Increased consumption of fruit and vegetables

One of the most obvious unions between agriculture, health, nutrition and education is via the promotion of fresh fruit and vegetables. Most national and international dietary guidelines are in agreement that consumption of fresh fruit and vegetables is a healthy food choice and generally needs to be increased. The benefits of fruit and vegetable consumption span the spectrum of nutritional disorders. Fruit and vegetables are rich sources of micronutrients, needed by children for optimal growth and development. Consumption of fruit and vegetables also decreases risks of obesity, cardiovascular disease and some cancers (WHO/FAO, 2003), perhaps in part through their contribution of bioactive substances.

Schools and child care facilities are an ideal place to promote fresh fruit and vegetables. Here children can be taught the health benefits of consuming them in adequate amounts. Appreciation of local produce can also be cultivated through exposing children to indigenous crops and teaching them about their nutritional properties.

Street food vendors can easily and usefully be involved in projects to promote traditional fruit and vegetables. Vendors selling near schools and workplaces can be provided with incentives to include more fruit and vegetables in the meals they prepare. Mobile vendors selling fruit and natural fruit juices can be encouraged.

Regulatory measures

Case study evidence of the use of regulatory measures to limit the negative or accentuate the positive impacts of food systems on health and nutrition outcomes was limited. China initiated a policy to provide subsidies and price adjustments to promote vegetable production and consumption; the impact thus far is thought to be positive, although there is little in the way of supportive data (Mendez, Du and Popkin, China case study). Fiji passed a bill in 1999 banning the importation of mutton flaps (a fatty cut of mutton). This regulation is now being bypassed by importation of the entire mutton carcass and sale of the same cut under a different name (Schultz, Fiji case study).

Additional regulatory measures that could be considered include tax on certain foods; better, more widespread and appropriate food labelling; advertising restrictions; rewards for good practices; and incorporation of nutritional and health concerns into currently existing food legislation. In a recent review (Haddad, 2003), the most successful strategy for curbing dietary fat intake was the use of food labelling descriptors, for example, low fat and dietary information for consumers such as food guide pyramids. More research on the potential impact of similar strategies is needed.

TABLE 6
Activity options for improving nutritional status

Primary health and nutrition problems	Focus of activity for improving nutritional status	
Undernutrition, micronutrient deficiencies and communicable diseases	Monitoring and surveillance	Undernourished preschool and school-age children; micronutrient deficiencies (children and adults, particularly women of child-bearing age); low birth weight; chronic energy deficiency in adults
	Thematic	Food and nutrition security; rural development; market access
	Educational	Nutritional value of foods; emphasis on increasing dietary intake of foods rich in iron, vitamin A, iodine and zinc. Appropriate weaning foods. Dietary variety and diversity. Educational media – radio, community/religious leaders, church groups
	Operational	Home, school and community gardens. Targeted feeding programmes. Focus on incorporating nutrition education into curriculum for teachers and nurses
	Legislative	Social programmes and safety nets
Double burden of disease and malnutrition	Monitoring and surveillance	Monitoring double burden of nutritional disorders and diseases (infectious and diet-related). Inequalities in health and nutritional status
	Thematic	Diet and chronic disease; urban planning
	Educational	Healthy food choices, reading nutritional information on food labels; appropriate portion sizes. Greater emphasis on nutritionally appropriate food choices available from restaurant and fast food chains. Internet, television, mobile phones as more prominent educational media
	Operational	Home, school and community gardens for promotion of fruit and vegetable consumption. Promotion of increased physical activity during leisure time. Civil society and community action groups
	Legislative	International trade; food labelling. Urban planning (particularly for physical activity)
Overweight and obesity, NCDs	Monitoring and surveillance	Monitoring of health and nutritional status of children and adults, with particular attention to the health and nutritional status of older population groups
	Thematic	Ageing, diet and chronic disease
	Educational	Nutrition advice for healthy ageing; physical activity. Strengthening and promotion of urban connections with agriculture
	Operational	School field trips to farms. Programmes to promote greater awareness of food systems including school and community gardens. Civil society groups. Integration of local farmers into urban communities via ties to school meal programmes and farmers' markets
	Legislative	Food standards; health claims

Regulations in public (state) schools

Lessons on how not to proceed can be learned from observations of schools in developed countries. For example, state school systems in the United States of America and the United Kingdom of Great Britain and Northern Ireland have engaged in partnerships with private food industry, leading to promotion and sales of certain food products on the school campus. This policy of sales of foods and beverages of little nutritional value and often with high saturated fat, added sugars and salt has been implicated in the burgeoning overweight population and obese schoolchildren in these countries (American Academy of Pediatrics, 2003; Dalmeny, Hanna and Lobstein, 2003). This issue as a whole has been thoroughly documented recently in an important British parliamentary report (House of Commons, 2004). Governments or school districts that have not yet had to make policy decisions on this issue should formulate guidelines and a position on which types of foods are to be promoted and sold in the schools.

In a national context, the key nutrition strategies to be pursued should be developed based on a thorough assessment of the most pressing national nutritional concerns. A combination of activities listed in the categories in Table 6 could provide useful guidance. The list given is not exhaustive, but rather illustrative of a mixture of interventions that could be used based on the predominant nutritional problems being experienced in the country.

CONCLUSION

This paper has attempted to synthesize the main issues raised during the workshop and presented in the individual country papers in this publication. For the sake of completion it has also included some points raised during discussions in the course of the workshop. It is the hope of the authors that the paper has been able to provide an adequate overview of the forces of globalization responsible for bringing about important changes in food systems and lifestyles, and how these are having a major impact on the health and nutritional status of populations of developing countries.

In studying the main drivers of globalization, one is drawn to the observation that the overall political and policy environment is clearly important in making the necessary commitment to strive for adequate health and nutrition of entire populations, both rural and urban, in any country. The provision of infrastructure, including roads and electricity, and education and health care systems, is a basic prerequisite to allow citizens to avail themselves of greater economic opportunities created through market liberalization and increased foreign investment. Greater individual economic prosperity fuels several household-level changes in lifestyles, including greater access to communications technologies, labour-saving devices and entertainment options. The synthesis demonstrates that access to these new technologies varies markedly from country to country and within countries, and certainly also between urban areas. In many instances the forces at work are overloading the capacity of cities to accommodate the large and ever increasing influx of people who are leaving the rural areas to migrate to the cities. A significant part of the reality underlying this phenomenon is that rural areas are no longer able to provide adequate livelihoods for the majority of populations. People move to cities because they are perceived to offer better "survival" opportunities.

The forces of globalization affect economic development and lifestyles in developing countries in a variety of ways. From a health and nutrition point of view, the most obvious changes are those resulting in sedentary lifestyles and adoption of dietary patterns that can lead to high rates of obesity and NCDs. Despite some improvement, undernutrition and micronutrient deficiencies are generally still present. In other words, for the majority of cases, the issue of food and nutrition security has not been resolved, yet another level of complexity is being added to the problem as the incidence of diet-related NCDs increases.

The emergence of supermarkets and fast food chains, while catering to the changing demands of the consumer in terms of convenience, quality and safety, engenders new problems. These include erosion of food culture and reduction in biodiversity as a result of newly created demand for standardized, uniform produce. Additionally there has been a loss of livelihood opportunities at various stages of the food sector, including agricultural production.

Creating more equitable access to the new opportunities provided through globalization seems unlikely, at least in the short term, without very generous development assistance and a large dose of international good will, including fair access to world markets for agricultural products. A concerted effort to diminish inequalities and focus on delivering positive gains is needed to stem the tide of the increasing double burden of undernutrition and overnutrition coupled with excessive urbanization rates and growing poverty. The challenge for the global community to move smoothly towards a truly sustainable and inclusive "global village" has never been as great as it is at present.

Bibliography

Agriculture & Agri-Food Canada. 2002. *Do you want a Big Mac or rice?* Report on the fast food industry in China. Agri-Food Trade Service (atn-riae.agr.ca/asia/e3292.htm).

American Academy of Pediatrics. 2003. Prevention of pediatric overweight and obesity. *Pediatrics,* 112(2): 424-430.

CIA. 2004. *The World Factbook 2003* (www.odci.gov/cia/publications/factbook). Accessed October 2003.

Coca-Cola Company. 2002. *The Coca-Cola Company Annual Report* (www2.coca-cola.com/investors/annualreport/2002/financial.htm). Accessed February 2004.

Dalmeny, K., Hanna, E. & Lobstein, T. 2003. *Broadcasting bad health. Why food marketing to children needs to be controlled.* International Association of Consumer Food Organizations (IACFO). July.

de Haan, H., Stamoulis, K., Shetty, P. & Pingali, P. 2003. The world food economy in the twenty-first century: challenges for international cooperation. *Development Policy Rev.,* 21(5-6): 683-696.

Delgado, C., Rosegrant, M., Steinfeld, H., Ehui, S. & Courbois, C. 1999. *Livestock to 2020 – the next food revolution.* Food Agriculture and Environment Discussion Paper No. 28. International Food Policy Research Institute (IFPRI).

de Onis, M. & Blossner, M. 2003. The World Health Organization global database on child growth and malnutrition: methodology and applications. *International J. Epidemiology,* 32: 518-526.

FAO. 2003. FAO Rice Market Monitor, May. Commodities and Trade Division (www.fao.org/es/esc/common/ecg/23001_en_RMM_May03.pdf). Accessed October 2003.

FAO. 2004. FAOSTAT. Last updated February 2004 (apps.fao.org/default.jsp).

Ghezan, G., Mateos, M. & Viteri, L. 2002. Impact of the rise of supermarkets and fast-food chains on horticulture in Argentina. *Development Policy Rev.,* 20(4): 389-408.

Haddad, L. 2003. Redirecting the diet transition: what can food policy do? *Development Policy Rev.,* 21(5-6): 599-614.

House of Commons. 2004. *Obesity.* Third Report of Session 2003-4. House of Commons Health Committee. London, The Stationery Office Limited. Printed 10 May 2004.

International Energy Agency. 2002. *World Energy Outlook 2002* (www.worldenergyoutlook.org/pubs/weo2002/EnergyPoverty.pdf). Accessed May 2004.

International Obesity Task Force (IOTF). 2004. *Call for obesity review as overweight numbers reach 1.7 billion.* International Association for the Study of Obesity (IASO) press release, 17 March 2003 (www.iotf.org/).

King, H., Aubert, R. & Herman, W. 1998. Global burden of diabetes, 1995-2025. *Diabetes Care*, 21(9): 1414-1428.

Lang, T. 2003. Food industrialization and food power: implications for food governance. *Development Policy Rev.,* 21(5-6): 555-568.

Lang, T. & Heasman, M. 2004 *Food wars*. London, Earthscan.

Martorell, R. 2001. Obesity. An emerging health and nutrition issue in developing countries. *In* P. Pinstrup-Andersen & R. Pandya-Lorch, eds. *The unfinished agenda. Perspectives on overcoming hunger, poverty and environmental degradation.* Washington, DC, IFPRI.

Mensah, P., Yeboah-Manu, D., Owusu-Darko, K. & Ablordey, A. 2002. Street foods in Accra, Ghana: how safe are they? *Bulletin of the World Health Organization,* 80(7): 546-554.

Murphy, S. 2002. WTO Agreement on Agriculture: suitable model for a global food system? *Foreign Policy in Focus,* 7(8).

Nef, J. 1995. *Human security and mutual vulnerability. An exploration into the global political economy of development and underdevelopment.* First ed. International Development Research Centre (IDRC). 110 pp.

Pinstrup-Andersen, P. 2001. *Achieving sustainable food security for all: required policy action.* Paper prepared for Mansholt Lecture, Wageningen University, the Netherlands, 14 November.

Popkin, B. 2003. The nutrition transition in the developing world. *Development Policy Rev.,* 21(5-6): 581-597.

Reardon, T., Timmer, P., Barrett, C. & Berdegue, J. 2003. The rise of supermarkets in Africa, Asia and Latin America. *American Journal of Agricultural Economics* 85(5): 1140-46.

Reardon, T., Timmer, P. & Berdegue, J. 2003. The rise of supermarkets in Latin America and Asia: implications for international markets for fruits and vegetables. *In* A. Regmi & M. Gehlar, eds. *Global markets for high value food products.* Agriculture Information Bulletin. US Department of Agriculture Economic Research Service (USDA-ERS).

Sachs, J., McArthur, J., Schmidt-Traub, G., Kruk, M., Chandrika Bahadur, C., Faye, M. & McCord, G. 2004. *Ending Africa's poverty trap* (www.med.harvard.edu/chge/course/solutions/globalization/EndingAfricasPovertyTrap.pdf).

Satterthwaite, D. 2003. The Millennium Development Goals and urban poverty reduction: great expectations and nonsense statistics. *Environment and Urbanization,* 15(2): 181-190.

Shetty, P. 2003a. Impact of globalization on food and agriculture from the farm to the plate. Presented at *Impacts of Globalization on Agricultural Production and Marketing with Focus on Food Quality*, 22-24 January, Tokyo.

Shetty, P. 2003b. Measures of nutritional status from anthropometric survey data. In *International Scientific Symposium on Measurement and Assessment of Food Deprivation and Undernutrition*, 26-28 June. Rome, FAO.

Tacoli, C. n.d. *Urban governance, partnership and poverty.* International Development Department Working Papers (www.idd.bham.ac.uk/research/working_papers/urbangov_wp.htm).

United Nations Development Programme (UNDP). 2003. *Human Development Report 2003* (www.undp.org/hdr2003/). Accessed February 2004.

United Nations Population Division. 2002. *World Urbanization Prospects*: *The 2001 Revision.*

United Nations Statistics Division. 2000. **(**unstats.un.org/unsd/demographic/social/inc-eco.htm).

United Nations Sub-Committee for the Eradication of Poverty. 2003. *Best practices in poverty eradication.* NGO Committee for Social Development.

Watkins, K. 2003. Farm fallacies that hurt the poor. *Development Outreach,* July. World Bank Institute.

WHO. 1995. *Physical status: the use and interpretation of anthropometry.* Report of a WHO Expert Committee. WHO Technical Report Series No. 854. Geneva, World Health Organization.

WHO. 2002. *World Health Report 2002. Reducing risks, promoting healthy life* (www.who.int/whr/2002/en/whr_overview_eng.pdf).

WHO. 2003. *World Health Report 2003. Shaping the future* (www.who.int/whr/2003/en/Annex5-en.pdf). Accessed February 2004.

WHO/FAO. 2003. Diet, *nutrition and the prevention of chronic diseases.* Report of a Joint WHO/FAO Expert Consultation. WHO Technical Report Series No. 916. Geneva.

Wild, S., Roglic, G., Green, A., Sicree, R. & King, H. 2004. Global prevalence of diabetes. Estimates for the year 2000 and projections for 2030. *Diabetes Care,* 27(5):1047-1053.

Annex

WHO Mortality Stratum

Countries	WHO mortality stratum*
Brazil	Low child, low adult
Chile	Low child, low adult
China	Low child, low adult
Colombia	Low child, low adult
Fiji	Low child, low adult
Philippines	Low child, low adult
Bangladesh	High child, high adult
India	High child, high adult
Nigeria	High child, high adult
South Africa	High child, very high adult
United Republic of Tanzania	High child, very high adult

* Further information on the mortality stratum can be found in WHO, 2002.

Features of urban food and nutrition security and considerations for successful urban programming

Marie T. Ruel[1] and James L. Garrett [2]

INTRODUCTION

This paper updates our earlier reviews of urban food and nutrition security (Ruel, Haddad and Garrett, 1999; Ruel *et al.*, 1998). These earlier pieces reviewed existing knowledge from published literature concerning the unique characteristics of urban food and nutrition security and their determinants, and experience of successful programme and policy responses to alleviate urban food insecurity and malnutrition. The reviews also identified key research gaps.

The present review focuses more on what we have learned on these issues from five years of empirical research and through our collaboration with partners directly involved in the design and implementation of urban programmes in the field. CARE International and some of their country offices have been our main partners to date, and we have also collaborated with the Government of Guatemala in the evaluation of a community day care programme. Our research programme combined primary data collection in a number of countries and secondary analysis of data from the Demographic and Health Surveys (DHS) and the World Bank Living Standards Measurement Surveys (LSMS).

The paper is structured as follows. First we present new information from our empirical research on urban/rural differences in food security and child nutritional status, and on socio-economic differentials within area. Then some of the unique features of urban food security and its determinants are highlighted. The paper concludes with a discussion of lessons learned and implications for urban programming.

URBAN/RURAL DIFFERENCES IN FOOD SECURITY AND CHILD NUTRITIONAL STATUS

This section updates the empirical evidence concerning urban/rural differences in food security and child nutritional status, using newly available data sets from several developing countries.

Urban/rural differences in food security

Quantitative data on urban food security are scarce, but a recent analysis of nationally representative consumption/expenditure surveys from ten African countries provides useful

[1] Marie T. Ruel
    International Food Policy Research Institute
    2033 K Street, N.W. Washington, DC 20006
    E-mail: m.ruel@cgiar.org
[2] James L. Garrett
    International Food Policy Research Institute
    2033 K Street, N.W. Washington, DC 20006
    E-mail:j.garrett@cgiar.org

insight (Smith and Aduayom, 2003). Figure 1 presents an estimate of the percentage of the population who are energy deficient by urban/rural area (see also the Annex for more information about methods used and results). Contrary to expectations, the percentage of the population found to be energy deficient is higher in urban areas in six of the ten countries studied. In all countries except Kenya and Uganda, at least 40 percent of the urban population is energy deficient; with percentages reaching 90 percent in urban Ethiopia and 76 and 72 percent in urban Malawi and Zambia, respectively. However, because Africa is not yet as highly urbanized as other regions, the absolute numbers of energy deficient people in rural areas still exceed the numbers in urban areas. Nevertheless, the urban population is currently contributing a significant proportion to the total number of energy deficient individuals – more than a third in four of the ten countries studied (Zambia, Ghana, Guinea and the United Republic of Tanzania, by descending order). Similar analyses are currently ongoing for several Latin American and Asian countries. We expect that the findings will differ substantially between regions and countries depending on their stage of urbanization.

FIGURE 1
Urban/rural differences in food insecurity (percentage energy deficient individuals) in sub-Saharan Africa

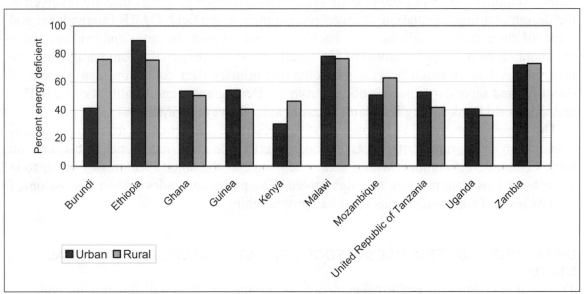

Source: Smith and Aduayom, 2003.

It is important to note, however, that the methodology used to derive the statistics presented here on the numbers and percentages of energy deficient individuals does not take into account potential differences in energy expenditures (and therefore requirements) between individuals living in urban and rural areas. Typically, individuals living in rural areas have higher energy requirements because they tend to have more physically demanding employment such as farming, and they may need to walk long distances to and from their place of work. Household chores may also require greater energy expenditure, especially to fetch water and/or do the laundry. Although there is clearly a good proportion of urban dwellers who may also have high energy expenditures, from physically demanding employment and travel, on average it is believed that urban dwellers tend to live a more sedentary life, especially in countries experiencing rapid economic growth (Popkin, 1994; Popkin and Doak, 1998). Therefore, failure to account for differences in energy expenditure/requirements in the urban/rural comparisons presented here is likely to underestimate the true prevalence of energy deficient individuals in rural areas. These findings should thus be interpreted with caution.

Considering the caveat described above, a potentially more useful comparison is to look at the magnitude of socio-economic differentials in food security within urban and within rural areas. The differences (in percentage points) in the percentage of energy deficient individuals between the lowest and the highest income quintile within each area are presented in Figure 2. If we take the example of the first country, Burundi, the first bar shows for the urban sample the percentage point difference in the proportion of food insecure individuals between the lowest income quintile compared to the highest income quintile. The next bar (still for Burundi) gives the same information, but for the rural sample. So, in the case of Burundi, the socio-economic differentials in food insecurity are larger in urban compared to rural areas, but this is not the case for all countries. In fact there are no clear patterns emerging in the magnitude of the socio-economic differentials between urban and rural areas; in some countries differences are wider in urban areas, whereas in other countries they are wider in rural areas and yet in others, the differences are very small and insignificant. Overall, socio-economic differentials are very large – often larger than 60 percentage points – both in urban and rural areas.

FIGURE 2
**Socio-economic differentials in food insecurity by area of residence
(sub-Saharan Africa)**

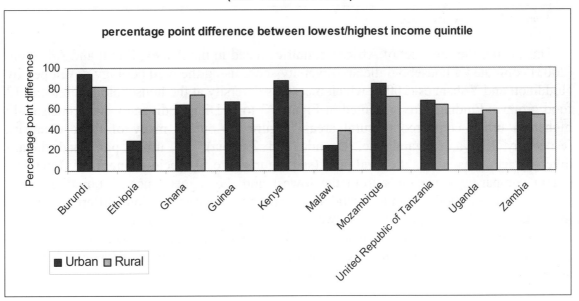

Source: **Smith and Aduayom, 2003.**

Household dietary diversity, defined as the number of foods or food groups consumed by households over a reference period, has been recently shown to be strongly associated with household consumption/expenditure and food security in a multicountry analysis (Hoddinott and Yohannes, 2002). This research was based on the premise that as income increases people tend to diversify their diet, largely because greater variety makes diets generally more palatable and more pleasant. Diversity also significantly improves dietary quality and the likelihood that individuals will meet their daily nutrient requirements, especially with regard to essential micronutrients. Therefore greater dietary diversity is highly desirable, both from a quality of life and a dietary quality point of view, and appears to be a good proxy for household income/expenditure and food security.

FIGURE 3
**Urban/rural differences in household dietary diversity
(sub-Saharan Africa)**

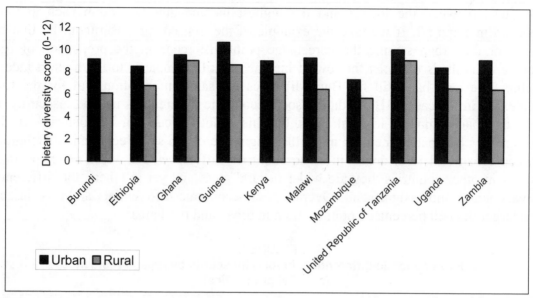

Source: Smith and Aduayom, 2003.

Thus, using the same set of African countries listed in the Annex, Smith and Aduayom (2003) computed a household dietary diversity score using the methodology developed by Hoddinott and Yohannes (2002), which measures diversity at the household level, using 12 food groups[3]. Findings are presented in Figures 3 to 5. Dietary diversity was consistently higher in urban compared to rural areas (Figure 3), but in many of these countries (especially Kenya, Mozambique, Uganda and Zambia), the urban poor had dietary diversity scores as low as the rural poor (see Figures 4 to 5). Socio-economic differentials (again comparing households from the lowest and the highest income quintiles) were generally large in both urban and rural areas, but there were no obvious differences in the magnitude of these differentials between urban and rural areas. Consistent with the findings from Hoddinott and Yohannes (2002), dietary diversity seemed to be strongly associated with income, and in the set of countries from sub-Saharan Africa used here, the association was generally linear (not shown).

---

[3] This study adopted the 12 food groups used by the Food and Agriculture Organization of the United Nations (FAO) food balance sheets.

FIGURE 4
Socio-economic differentials in household dietary diversity (sub-Saharan Africa)

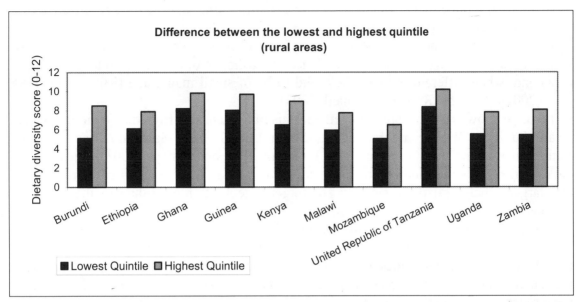

Source: Smith and Aduayom, 2003.

FIGURE 5
Socio-economic differentials in household dietary diversity (sub-Saharan Africa)

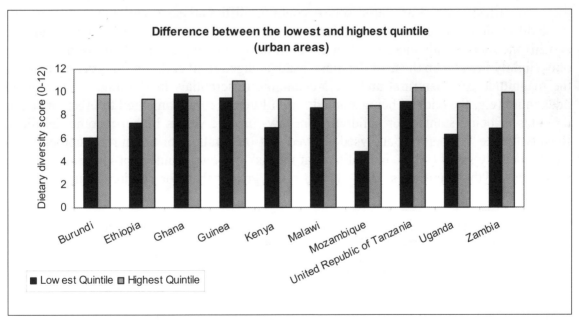

Source: Smith and Aduayom, 2003.

Urban/rural differences in child nutritional status

Global statistics on child nutritional status could not be more consistent in showing that urban children are better nourished than rural children. No matter which country or sets of countries are analysed, the prevalence of undernutrition among urban children is consistently lower than among rural children (Ruel *et al.*, 1998; Ruel, 2000; Ruel, 2001b; Smith, Ruel and Ndiaye, 2003; National Research Council, 2003; Menon, Ruel and Morris,

2000; Garrett and Ruel, 1999b). This is particularly true for stunting (low height-for-age)[4] and for underweight (low weight-for-age). Urban/rural differences in stunting are generally of smaller magnitude in Africa and Asia compared to Latin America, where differences of up to twofold are observed (Ruel *et al.*, 1998; Ruel, 2001b).

Urban/rural differences in wasting (low weight-for-height) are less consistent. Although generally lower in urban areas, the prevalence of wasting is often similar in urban and rural areas and, when differences exist, they tend to be of small magnitude (Ruel *et al.*, 1998; Ruel, 2001b; National Research Council, 2003).

Figure 6 shows results from a pooled analysis of 36 data sets from the Demographic and Health Surveys (DHS) from three regions: South Asia (SA), sub-Saharan Africa (SSA) and Latin America and the Caribbean (LAC)[5] (Smith, Ruel and Ndiaye, 2003). These pooled data confirm previous findings of lower stunting rates in urban compared to rural areas, and larger urban/rural differences in stunting in the LAC region than in the other two regions.

Yet global comparisons can be misleading ...

Clearly, global comparisons such as the ones presented above are misleading because they hide the wide disparities that exist within areas. Socio-economic differentials are particularly large in urban areas, and therefore central statistics reporting overall rates of undernutrition may be deceiving.

Research by the International Food Policy Research Institute (IFPRI), using DHS surveys from 11 countries from three regions, specifically tested the hypothesis that socio-economic, intra-urban differentials in child stunting were greater than intra-rural differentials[6] (Menon, Ruel and Morris, 2000). The analysis clearly showed that across these countries: i) there are large socio-economic differentials in childhood stunting; ii) these differentials are commonly greater in urban than in rural areas (see Figures 7 and 8); and iii) the most disadvantaged urban children have rates of stunting that are on average only slightly lower than those of the most disadvantaged rural children. In order to quantify the magnitude of urban/rural and socio-economic differentials in stunting, we computed odds ratio[7] (e.g. the odds of being stunted for children in rural compared to urban areas; or the odds of being stunted for children from low- income versus higher-income families). Results for the 11 countries analysed showed that odds ratios for urban/rural comparisons were relatively small (<3.3), indicating that the risk of being stunted for children living in rural areas of the countries studied is <3.3 times greater than for children living in urban

---

[4] Stunting, or linear growth retardation, is an indicator of long-term chronic undernutrition. Stunting is defined as height-for-age lower than -2SD from the median of the CDC/WHO reference population (WHO, 1979). Wasting, an indicator of short-term, acute undernutrition, is defined as weight-for-height lower than -2SD from the median of the reference population. Underweight, a global indicator of undernutrition, which does not differentiate between stunting and wasting, is defined as weight-for-age lower than -2SD from the median of the reference population.

[5] This analysis uses data from 36 of the most recent DHS conducted between 1990 and 1998 in three regions: South Asia (SA), sub-Saharan Africa (SSA) and Latin America and the Caribbean (LAC). Eighty percent of all SA countries, 58 percent of SSA countries and 36 percent of LAC countries are included. The sample included 129 351 children under three years of age and 117 007 women, usually their mothers.

[6] In this study, a socio-economic status (SES) index was derived from data on household assets, housing quality and availability of services. The index was created separately for urban and rural areas of each country, using principal components analysis (11).

[7] Odds ratio were used to assess the magnitude of urban/rural differentials in childhood stunting, as well as within-urban and within-rural socio-economic differentials. The latter were computed by comparing the lowest SES quintile group with the highest quintile group. Odds ratio were computed using the following formula: [p/(1-p)]/[q/(1-q)] where, for the urban/rural comparison p is the proportion of stunted children in rural areas and q is the proportion of stunted children in urban areas. For more information, see (11).

areas. The gap between the lowest and highest socio-economic status (SES) quintile in urban areas, however, was much larger (ranging from 2.8 to 10.2) than between the lowest and highest SES quintile in rural areas (all <3.3 except Brazil). The risk of being stunted among poor children was up to ten times higher than for the wealthiest group in two urban areas of Latin America (Peru and the Dominican Republic). The fact that such strong socio-economic gradients are consistently found in urban areas of developing countries implies that reliance on global average statistics to allocate resources between urban and rural areas could be dangerously misleading, a point originally made in the late 1970s (Basta, 1977).

FIGURE 6
Stunting prevalence across urban and rural areas, by region

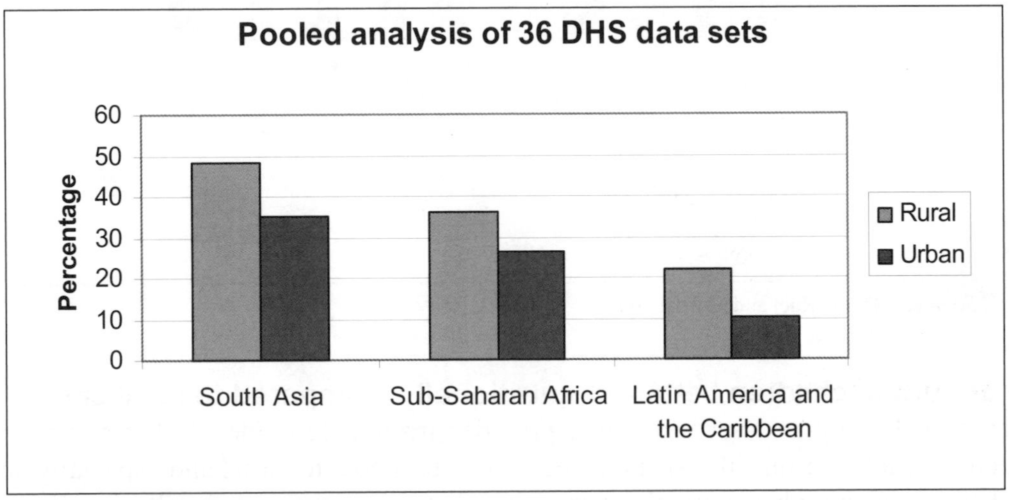

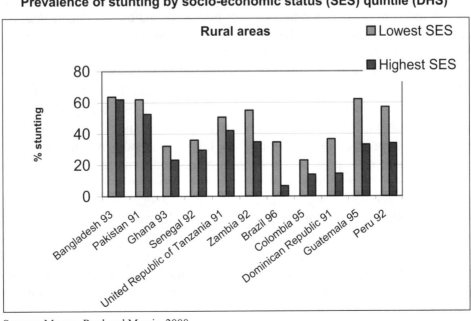

Source: Smith, Ruel and Ndiaye, 2003.

An additional concern for countries undergoing rapid economic and nutritional transitions is the rising prevalence of overweight and obesity among children. This topic, however, is addressed in this publication by Popkin and collaborators.

FIGURE 7
Prevalence of stunting by socio-economic status (SES) quintile (DHS)

Source: Menon, Ruel and Morris, 2000.

FIGURE 8

Prevalence of stunting by socio-economic status (SES) quintile (DHS)

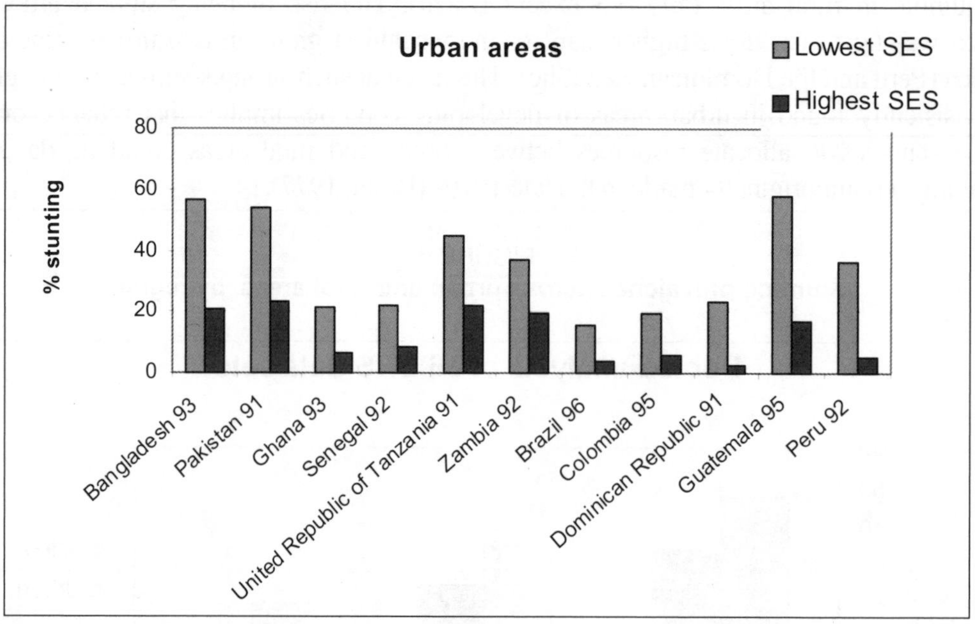

Source: Menon, Ruel and Morris, 2000.

Why are urban children better off nutritionally, compared to rural children?

The empirical analysis described above provides irrefutable evidence that overall, urban children have a better nutritional status than their rural counterparts, and especially so with regard to linear growth (stunting). A question that arises then, especially in view of the evidence concerning the high rates of urban poverty and food insecurity, is why are urban children better off than rural children? We examined this issue, first with a nationally representative sample from Mozambique and then through a multicountry pooled analysis of DHS data sets from 36 developing countries (Garrett and Ruel, 1999a; Smith, Ruel and Ndiaye, 2003). The main question that was addressed in both studies was whether the socio-economic determinants of child nutritional status differed across urban and rural areas. The socio-economic determinants examined were maternal education and maternal status (only in the multicountry analysis); household access to services such as safe water and sanitation; and household socio-economic status.

The findings showed little evidence of differences in the nature of the socio-economic determinants or in the strength of their association with child nutritional status between urban and rural areas. Marked differences in the levels of these determinants in favour of urban areas were found, however. Urban mothers were consistently more educated (by a difference of approximately twofold) and had higher decision-making power. Maternal education is known to have profound beneficial effects on a range of child feeding, health seeking and care giving practices, and thus may be an important driver of urban/rural differences in child nutrition (Engle *et al.*, 1997; Engle, Menon and Haddad, 1997; Armar-Klemesu *et al.*, 2000). Urban women were also more likely to have access to electricity, water and sanitation services (Smith, Ruel and Ndiaye, 2003). Similar findings regarding the availability of electricity and sanitation services have been documented recently, using a different set of DHS data (National Research Council, 2003). The authors show that, compared to rural dwellers, the urban poor have better access to electricity and flush toilets, but they are at a clear disadvantage when compared to other wealthier urban dwellers.

In our pooled analysis, large gaps in favour of urban areas were also found in the levels of key proximate determinants of child nutritional status in all three regions (see Table 1). This was true especially for access and use of preventive maternal and child health care (e.g. maternal prenatal and birthing care and child immunization), and the timing and quality of complementary feeding. The only exceptions were practices related to breastfeeding, which were more likely to be optimal among rural compared to urban women (i.e. exclusive for the first six months and continued for up to 24 months).

Other evidence supporting the advantage of urban children over their rural counterparts is provided by country-level analyses. The findings are consistent with the pooled analyses; they show that: i) urban children tend to have better access to health services, which in turn is reflected by higher immunization rates (Ruel *et al.*, 1998); ii) urban households are also more likely to have access to water and sanitation facilities, although they may come at high cost, especially for the poor (World Resource Institute, 1996); and iii) except for breastfeeding practices, which are more likely to be optimal among rural mothers, children's diets in urban areas are generally more diverse and more likely to include nutrient-rich foods such as meat, dairy products and fresh fruit and vegetables (Ruel, 2000; Arimond and Ruel, 2002). Examples from IFPRI's analysis of 11 most recent DHS surveys show the consistently higher intake of milk and meat products by toddlers in urban compared to rural areas (Arimond and Ruel, 2004) (see Figures 9 to 10). Foods of animal origin are of critical importance in young children's diets because they provide essential micronutrients such as iron, zinc and vitamin A, which promote health, growth and motor and cognitive development.

Thus, the better nutritional status of urban children appears to be the result of the cumulative effect of a series of more favourable socio-economic conditions, which in turn seem to lead to better caring practices for children and their mothers. As cautioned previously, however, global comparisons between urban and rural areas can be misleading because they do not take into account the large heterogeneity within area.

Finally, it is also important to recognize that although urbanization seems to bring about positive improvements in young children's diets, it also brings a number of unhealthy diet changes such as increased consumption of saturated and trans fats, sugars, salt and processed foods that contain excessive amounts of these components. This, combined with more sedentary lifestyles is causing dramatic increases in the prevalence of overweight/obesity and risk factors for a number of chronic diseases such as diabetes, cardiovascular diseases and certain forms of cancer (WHO/FAO, 2003). Although these dietary changes affect mostly adults at first, they rapidly trickle down to other age groups such as schoolchildren and adolescents and eventually reach young children as well. This topic is addressed by Popkin and collaborators in this publication.

TABLE 1
Comparison of proximate determinants of child nutritional status across urban and rural areas, by region (pooled analysis of 36 DHS data sets) (Smith, Ruel and Ndiaye, 2003)

Proximate determinants	South Asia		Sub-Saharan Africa		Latin America and the Caribbean	
	Rural	Urban	Rural	Urban	Rural	Urban
Mother's nutritional status[1]						
Woman's body mass index (BMI)	19.1	20.5***	21.4	22.8***	23.6	24.3***
Percentage of women underweight	44.3	32.0***	11.6	8.8***	6.2	5.1***
Prenatal and birthing care for mother						
Percentage of women receiving any prenatal care	57.3	83.9***	75.4	93.4***	72.8	92.5***
Percentage of women with any prenatal care $\geq$3 visits	58.5	80.1***	78.8	87.9***	86.3	94.4***
Mean number of months before birth of first prenatal visit	4.9	5.6***	4.1	4.4***	5.7	6.4***
Percentage of women giving birth in a medical facility	22.5	60.9***	32.5	72.0***	66.7	90.6***
Child feeding practices						
Percentage of children breastfeeding within one day of birth	39.6	50.6***	68.6	73.3***	69.6	75.1***
Percentage of children 0-4 months exclusively breastfed	54.2	38.3***	20.0	17.7***	34.2	35.9***
Mean number of months of breastfeeding	14.8	12.1***	17.7	15.8***	8.6	7.2***
Percentage of children 6-12 months having received foods	42.3	54.6***	80.3	84.0***	79.7	84.6***
Mean number of times child >6 months eats per day	3.1	3.1	2.9	3.2***	4.5	5.0***
Percentage of children >6 months receiving high-quality food[2]	42.3	54.6***	80.3	84.0	69.5	80.3***
Health seeking behaviours for children						
Percentage of children with diarrhoea who are treated	82.7	91.4***	81.2	90.2***	78.8	89.2***
Percentage of children receiving any vaccinations	80.0	90.5***	74.2	90.2***	90.2	96.6***
Percentage of children receiving recommended vaccinations	38.6	56.7***	41.8	62.7***	53.1	66.9***
Quality of substitute child caretakers						
Percentage of children with adult caretaker as women work[3]	82.8	91.0***	79.2	87.7***	73.8	91.2***

Notes: Stars indicate significant differences across rural and urban areas at the 1 percent (***), 5 percent (**) and 10 percent (*) levels.

Country level means and percentages are calculated using sample weights provided with the DHS data sets. Regional means and percentages are calculated using a population-weighted average of the country level numbers.

[1] Data not available for Pakistan, Nigeria, Rwanda and Paraguay.

[2] Nepal only. Data not available for Bangladesh, India, Pakistan, Burkina Faso, Côte d'Ivoire, Malawi, Namibia, Nigeria, Rwanda, Senegal, the Dominican Republic, Haiti, and Paraguay.

[3] Data not available for the United Republic of Tanzania.

FIGURE 9

Percentage of children (12-24 months) who consumed milk products in the previous 24 hours (ongoing analysis of 11 DHS data sets)

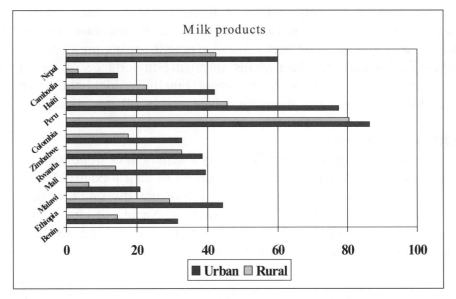

Source: Arimond and Ruel, 2004.

FIGURE 10

Percentage of children (12-24 months) who consumed meat products in the previous 24 hours (ongoing analysis of 11 DHS)

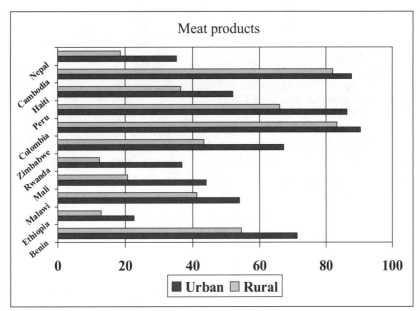

Source: Arimond and Ruel, 2004.

FEATURES AND DETERMINANTS OF URBAN FOOD SECURITY

In this section we review key aspects of urban life that shape food security, particularly for the poor.[8] We focus on the implications of urban residents' much greater reliance, in comparison with rural dwellers, on cash income and much decreased reliance on natural resources for food and other basic needs. We also note the rising presence of supermarkets on the urban food scene and the perhaps surprising importance of the formal sector, agriculture, seasonality and links with rural areas. Finally we highlight the changing roles of women and the potential implications for child care use and care giving practices.

The urban food economy

Urban residents purchase most of their food. City dwellers in metropolitan areas as diverse as Maputo, Cairo and Lima buy more than 90 percent of their food (Table 2). Even though the figures are lower for smaller urban areas, an urban-rural division is noticeable. Even in less urbanized countries such as Mozambique or Nepal, residents of smaller and intermediary cities commonly buy 75 percent or more of their food, while rural residents purchase less than half of the food they consume.

TABLE 2
Percentage of total food consumption value that is purchased

Country	Metropolitan areas	Other urban areas	Rural areas
Egypt	98	95	85
Malawi	91	90	36
Mozambique	92	73	29
Nepal	94	78	42
Peru	92	89	58

Note: Metropolitan areas are: Egypt, Cairo, Alexandria, El Suez, Malawi, Blantyre City, Lilongwe, Mozambique, Maputo, Matola, Nepal, Kathmandu and Peru: Lima, Callao.
Source: Garrett and Ersado, unpublished.

These outlays are significant, as food expenditures are by far the largest portion of total household budgets (Table 3). Even in the largest cities, where households must also spend on housing and several other services, food is commonly close to, and sometimes even more than, half of household consumption expenditure. In secondary and intermediary cities the figure is higher – around 60 percent – but is still lower than in rural areas where food budget shares in countries such as Malawi, Mozambique and Peru reach 70 percent and higher. The poorest (the lowest expenditure tercile) allocate even more to food, and this is true across urban and rural areas (see Table 3).

Housing, which is usually the second largest budget item in urban areas, varies widely between metropolitan areas, accounting for between 6 and 28 percent of total expenditures. With the exception of Egypt, the share of the total budget spent on housing is consistently lower in rural compared to urban areas.

---

[8]   For additional reviews see Ruel *et al.*, 1998; Ruel, Haddad and Garrett, 1999; Garrett and Ruel, 2000; Garrett and Ruel, 1999a.

TABLE 3
Food and housing expenditures as a percentage of total consumption expenditure (budget shares)

Country	Metropolitan areas	Other urban areas	Rural areas
Egypt			
Food budget share (all)	48	49	58
Lowest expenditure tercile	53	54	62
Housing budget share	6	8	8
Malawi			
Food budget share	43	53	75
Lowest expenditure tercile	53	64	78
Housing budget share	16	9	4
Mozambique			
Food budget share	59	65	70
Lowest expenditure tercile	63	67	70
Housing budget share	9	8	7
Nepal			
Food budget share	37	50	64
Lowest expenditure tercile	55	57	74
Housing budget share	28	14	7
Peru			
Food budget share	46	51	70
Housing budget share	21	16	8

Note: Metropolitan areas are: Egypt, Cairo, Alexandria, El Suez, Malawi, Blantyre City, Lilongwe, Mozambique, Maputo, Matola, Nepal, Kathmandu and Peru: Lima, Callao.
Source: Garrett and Ersado, unpublished.

Urban food prices and expenditures depend on a number of factors including: i) the efficiency of the food marketing system; ii) household purchasing patterns such as whether the family buys in bulk or in small quantities and where they purchase their food; iii) the household's ability to produce some of its own food through home garden or urban agriculture; iv) the household's access to public transfers, such as food subsidies or food aid programmes, or private transfers, such as an exchange relationship with rural or other relatives; and v) macroeconomic policies, including the availability of food subsidies.

Urban food marketing systems, especially those that serve the poor, are frequently inefficient, in terms of providing adequate quantities, good quality, or competitive prices (Aragrande and Argenti, 2001; Argenti, 2000). Wholesale markets, when they exist, frequently have not adapted to the dramatic rise in food quantities consumed by the cities that has accompanied urbanization. Most were built decades ago and now sit in central areas of cities, hemmed in by and creating congestion. Their storage facilities are often inadequate or badly managed. Traffic congestion, lack of storage (especially refrigeration for perishables) and atomization of retail outlets add to marketing costs.

More and more, however, supermarket chains are displacing traditional retailers in many countries of Africa, Asia and Latin America (Reardon *et al.*, 2003), perhaps presenting a way to overcome these structural inefficiencies with new store placements and large purchasing and distribution networks. In Argentina, Brazil, Chile, Colombia, Costa Rica and Mexico, for example, supermarkets now account for 45 to 75 percent of food retailing. In the remainder of Latin America, largely lower-income and less urbanized, the share is 20 to 40 percent (Reardon and Berdegué, 2002). Supermarkets have about 50 to 60 percent of food retail sales in South Africa, and have a significant presence in Kenya. Multinational supermarket chains have expanded, at least nominally, into most other countries of southern and eastern Africa as well (Weatherspoon and Reardon, 2003).

Supermarket chains will undoubtedly grow quickly to capture more of the retail share in the future. In 1994, for example, supermarkets accounted for 15 percent of national food retail in Guatemala and now, ten years later, account for 35 percent (Reardon and Berdegué, 2002). But even these statistics show that the traditional food retail sector, including public markets, street vendors and small shops, still dominates urban food marketing. In Africa, multinational chains do not yet extend into poor urban neighbourhoods and towns, and have a significantly reduced presence in the poorer countries (Weatherspoon and Reardon, 2003). In addition, evidence is mixed as to whether these large format "modern retail" outlets result in lower food prices (Reardon and Berdegué, 2002), especially for staples that make up the bulk of the diet of the poor.

Thus, the burgeoning of supermarkets in developing countries may not be of immediate relevance for the urban poor. Large chains are unlikely to establish a significant presence in slums or ghettoes any time soon. Even if they appear at the periphery of poor settlements, they may not be convenient for the poorest slum dwellers if they lack transport or cash to purchase in bulk. It is also not clear that the prices offered at supermarkets would be attractive enough for the poor to make them change their purchasing patterns in the short term. Supermarkets may also have a negative effect on employment, since many of the poor work as food vendors or transporters. It is likely that a purchasing pattern similar to that of some developed countries will emerge: upper- and lower-income consumers shop at chains, with lower prices and better quality, while the inner-city urban poor have limited options and continue to purchase food on a daily basis at small corner stores that may also offer credit. Although developing country producers and processors must pay attention to the new market opportunities that supermarkets present, policy-makers must continue to pay attention to improving the efficiency of traditional systems that will continue to serve the bulk of the urban poor.

Urban livelihoods

The importance of the market in urban areas means that urban dwellers, including the poor, need cash income and thus employment. Here we summarize recent findings concerning employment and income in urban areas.

The poor work in a variety of jobs, but working long hours in often precarious conditions for low wages is a constant. Jobs tend to be irregular and tenure insecure. The poor may work in clothes factories, run small shops, sell food or cigarettes in the street, scavenge in rubbish dumps, sweep streets and clean latrines, drive rickshaws, or seek day work in construction (Asian Development Bank, 1994; International Labour Organization, 1998; CARE Bangladesh, 1998; CARE Tanzania, 1998).

Many, though not all, work in the informal sector. In the 1990s, the informal sector represented 60 to 75 percent of urban employment in Guatemala, El Salvador and Honduras, but only one-third in Costa Rica (Funkhouser, 1996). It generated 60 percent of female employment in many West African cities (Meagher, 1995) and was one-third of the urban labour force in Nigeria (Simon, 1998). Once thought to be only a coping strategy or a dead end, numerous studies have now illustrated the dynamism and heterogeneity of the informal sector. Although workers tend to earn low wages, incomes of business owners in the informal sector can be 25 percent or more higher than those in the formal sector (Portes, Blitzer and Curtis, 1986).

Jobs in the informal sector are important, but formal sector jobs (government, private sector) are too. In fact, in most countries most urban residents, even poor ones, do not work in the informal sector (meaning here the self-employed). Comparing data in metropolitan areas in four countries in Latin America, Africa and Asia, Garrett (2004) found that at least as many, and often a large majority of paid urban dwellers work in the formal sector (Table 4). In Egypt and Malawi 70 percent or more of jobs paid wages or salaries.

The public sector also remains an important source of employment (Table 4). In Egypt, half of all urban residents in the major metropolitan areas of Cairo, Alexandria and El Suez, worked in the public sector, with two-thirds of working women having jobs there. According to the International Labour Organization, public sector employment still accounts for more than 20 percent of formal sector wage employment in a number of African countries, including Ghana, Nigeria and the United Republic of Tanzania (Garrett, 2004).

TABLE 4
**Job sector (percentage), by country, area and gender
(Living Standards Measurement Surveys [LSMS])**

Country/area	Overall	By sex	
		Male	Female
Egypt			
Metropolitan areas			
Private wage/salary	34	37	27
Public wage/salary	48	44	66
Self-employed	18	20	7
Ghana			
Accra			
Private wage	27	45	14
Public wage	11	18	6
Self-employed	60	37	77
Unpaid	2	1	3
Malawi			
Metropolitan areas			
Private	44	49	29
Public	31	28	41
Self-employed	20	18	25
Other	5	5	5
Peru			
Lima			
Private	32	37	26
Public	12	9	15
Self-employed	44	48	38
Unpaid	13	6	22

Source: Garrett, 2004.

Agriculture, forestry and fishing are still important to the incomes of urban dwellers, especially outside large metropolitan areas. Even in the largest cities, many workers earn their living indirectly from agriculturally based enterprises, such as transporting, processing or selling food. Urban businesses also provide agricultural inputs such as seeds, chemicals, tools and machinery. Garrett (2004) notes that even in large metropolitan areas, 2 or 3 percent of urban dwellers earn a living from agriculture. In Lima, almost 10 percent of workers (mostly men) earn a living from farming or fishing. Outside the largest cities, the numbers jump: agriculture is the main livelihood for almost 10 percent of urban dwellers outside major metropolitan areas in Egypt and Malawi. The differences between the importance of agriculture in the metropolitan and other areas are more dramatic in Mozambique. While in Maputo, the capital city, agriculture provides 7 percent of jobs (still not negligible), agriculture is the main occupation for *63 percent* of urban residents outside Maputo – and the main occupation for about 85 percent of women (Massingarela and Garrett, 2002). Finally, in Dar es Salaam, 90 percent of all green leafy vegetables consumed are grown inside the city limits.

Women (see below) and children are also engaged in income-generating activities in urban areas. Ersado (2003) found that 10 percent of urban children in Nepal, but only 2 percent in urban Peru, and 3 percent in urban Zimbabwe, work exclusively (that is, they do not also go to school). The study suggests, however, that although working can have a negative impact on learning and may expose children to exploitive and dangerous labour practices, working does not always come at the expense of school. Five percent of children in urban Nepal and 9 percent in urban Peru both go to school and work.

A final, largely underestimated characteristic of urban life is the threat that seasonal changes pose to the livelihoods of the urban poor. The changes are often related to rains, but not necessarily to agriculture. Threats to health arise when rains cause sewers to overflow and spread disease. Rains can bring the activities of causal labourers, such as rickshaw drivers, construction workers and street vendors, to a halt. CARE Bangladesh (1998) reports that incomes decrease among casual labourers such as rickshaw drivers and construction workers in Dhaka in the rainy season, primarily because they work outdoors and may suffer from increased likelihood of illness or reduced clientele (CARE Bangladesh, 1998). An additional factor is the increased migration of rural dwellers to cities when rains take them out of a job at home, which results in increased competition for already scarce jobs in urban areas. The rainy season may also complicate transport of food from rural to urban areas, resulting in increases in food prices, which exacerbate the effects of declines in income.

Women's changing roles, food security and child care in urban areas

With current worldwide globalization trends, employment opportunities for women have been increasing – more jobs, more variety in job types and more diverse work environments are available (Johnson-Welch *et al.*, 2000). It is estimated that about 50 percent of women are currently part of the formal labour force; and women constitute up to 75 percent of the informal and semiformal sectors (Mehra and Gammage, 1999 in Johnson-Welch *et al.*, 2000). Unfortunately, information on the urban/rural breakdown for these numbers is not available, to our knowledge.

Even with their new employment opportunities and their increasing contribution to the labour force, women continue to face the same issues they have always faced in the labour market; they are still over-represented in less secure and irregular jobs, often getting paid less than men even for the same job (de Haan, 2000), and they often work as unpaid family labour. Also, the recently documented trend of a narrowing in the wage gap between men and women, which could suggest improvements in employment conditions for women, actually reflects a drop in men's wages, rather than an increase in those of women (UN Research Institute for Social Development [UNRISD]), 2000 in Johnson-Welch *et al.*, 2000).

Furthermore, although women's participation in the labour force has grown much faster than men's in recent decades, still proportionally far fewer women work than men (de Haan, 2000). Generally, women have less access to capital, unpaid family labour and markets, social and formal networks (Ypeij, 2000; Marcucci, 2001). They also increase the resilience of the household in its ability to respond to shocks, frequently carrying the burden of having to work and devise innovative coping strategies for the household (de Haan, 2000). Pradhan and van Soest (1997) found that in Bolivia lower earnings by the husband led to more hours of work by the wife.

In some cases, religious or cultural restrictions may restrict mobility or the kinds of jobs women can have (Simon, 1998; Sutter and Perine, 1998). Other less obvious institutional discrimination also restricts women's choices. In Bangladesh, the lack of housing or hostels for single women limits their mobility and may influence rural women's decisions to migrate to the city for work. Half of the women working in the clothes factories live less than 1 km away, whereas only 20 percent of the men live so close (Asfar, 1997). Similarly, lack of good-quality child care may restrict women's choices, forcing them to do informal work at home or not work at all (see following section on women's employment and child care).

Women working outside the home challenge traditional conceptions of women's roles held by men and the women themselves. Zhang (1999) describes a process of empowerment in China as women workers, many of whom who came to the city from rural areas, discovered new freedom. They spent their wages on their own personal items and hobbies. Their circle of social contacts widened.

Women's employment and child care use

With increased employment opportunities, however, the trade-offs women face between their role as income earners and their child care and family responsibilities become even more acute. Women are largely involved in informal jobs that are not subject to labour laws and do not offer social or medical benefits. For those in the semiformal or formal sector, they often risk losing their job when they have to skip work to attend to a sick family member, and maternity benefits are largely unavailable or minimal.

The question as to whether women's employment outside the home translates into net benefits for their children and their household remains contentious. Evidence suggests that although the overall impact of maternal employment on child health and nutrition is linked to the amount of income generated (and of control over resources), other factors such as the type and conditions of work, the availability and quality of child care alternatives and the child's age are more important (Engle, Menon and Haddad, 1997).

High-quality alternative child care is obviously key to tempering the potentially negative impact of women's labour force participation on children's well-being. Little information exists, however, on the supply and use of different child care arrangements in urban areas of the developing world and on the availability of informal alternatives such as older siblings, other relatives or neighbours.

Our analysis of 11 Demographic and Health Surveys (DHS) data sets[9] from the early 1990s (Ruel, Haddad and Garrett, 1999) provides some, albeit slightly outdated, information on this issue. In this set of countries, a smaller percentage of employed urban mothers compared to rural mothers took their child to work with them, probably because they tended to work in the streets, in markets or in factories rather than in agriculture as most rural women do. In Latin America, a greater percentage of urban than rural mothers used relatives as alternative child care givers, but no consistent pattern was found in Asia and Africa. Hired help and institutional care were consistently higher in urban areas in all three regions, although institutional care use was almost non-existent in Asia and very uncommon in three of the four African countries studied. It is likely that such low reported use of institutional care is related to the lack of availability of these services in the countries studied.

A recent IFPRI comparative study of Accra (Ghana) and Guatemala City (Guatemala) indicates that in both sites, women's employment and child care choices are highly influenced by the age of their youngest child (Quisumbing, Hallman and Ruel, 2003).

---

[9] This analysis included two data sets from Asia (Bangladesh, 1993; Pakistan, 1991); four countries from Africa (Ghana, 1993; United Republic of Tanzania, 1991-92; Senegal, 1992-93; Zambia, 1992); and five countries from Latin America (Brazil, 1996; the Dominican Republic, 1991; Peru, 1992; Colombia, 1995; and Guatemala, 1995).

Mothers with children under three years of age are less likely to be working and, if they do work, they are less likely to use formal child care compared to mothers with older children. In Guatemala City, another important determinant of women's decision to work is the presence of an adult woman (a potential alternative child care giver) in the household. In Ghana, where most urban women work in the informal sector, those who have to resume work for economic reasons when their infant is still young usually take the infant along to their workplace. Depending on the work environment, this may or may not be positive for the child, but at least it is likely to help preserve breastfeeding, which should confer important nutritional benefits to the child.

These findings confirm that women do adapt their work patterns to their specific family circumstances and that the well-being of their children is the overriding force behind their decisions to work and to use child care alternatives. These "adaptive strategies" by which mothers stop working, or work fewer hours, or even take their infant to work if they have to work, may be successful in protecting their infant. They may, however, seriously jeopardize the mothers' ability to generate income and to protect their household's livelihood and food security, especially if they are the sole income earner. Effective programmes and policies are urgently needed in developing countries to support working women, especially women with young children who have limited or no access to extended family networks or other affordable, yet reliable substitute child care options.

Women's employment and care giving practices

Evidence on the effect of women's employment on care giving practices such as breastfeeding, complementary feeding, preventive and curative health seeking behaviour, and psychosocial care is mixed (Engle, Menon and Haddad, 1997). But overall, there is little evidence that maternal labour supply has a negative effect on these practices or on children's health and nutritional status (Blau, Guilkey and Popkin, 1997; Glick and Sahn, 1988). For example, studies have shown that, contrary to general belief, maternal employment was not a main determinant of breastmilk substitute use in developing countries (Hight-Laukaran *et al.*, 1996) nor was it systematically related to shorter breastfeeding duration (Winikoff, Castle and Hight-Laukaran, 1988).

Our study in Accra documented that child feeding, hygiene or health seeking behaviours were not affected by maternal employment (Amar-Klemesu *et al.*, 2000). In this context, the key factor that was consistently associated with better care giving practices was higher maternal schooling, which in Accra is not related to whether or not mothers work. In this large urban centre, the majority of women do work, irrespective of their educational level, and they work mostly in the informal sector in petty trade, street food processing and vending. As noted above, mothers of young infants in Accra are more likely to take their young infant along when they have to resume work soon after delivery, than leave the child with an alternate care giver. This is probably the main reason why maternal employment has not resulted in poorer child care practices.

Additional, indirect evidence that women's employment in urban areas may not necessarily have a negative impact on child care practices again comes from global urban/rural comparisons. We showed previously that, with the exception of breastfeeding, child feeding practices are substantially better in urban compared to rural areas, in spite of the fact that a larger proportion of women in most developing countries are engaged in income-generating activities, often away from home (see section on why urban children are better off nutritionally than rural children, p. 38).

Overall, mothers appear to be amazingly efficient at combining their income-generating activities and their child care responsibilities, and at buffering the potentially negative impacts of their employment patterns on their children's well-being. But at what cost – for themselves and for their household food and livelihood security? This question remains largely unanswered because whether the food security situation of poor working women is alleviated or aggravated by their participation in the labour force largely depends on their specific set of resources and constraints.

LESSONS LEARNED AND IMPLICATIONS FOR URBAN PROGRAMMING

What have we learned from this research and what are the implications for urban programming? This section summarizes our key findings with a focus on their implications for the design and implementation of effective urban programmes. We also draw from our collaborative work with CARE International on urban livelihoods in Bangladesh, Ethiopia and Peru (Garrett, 2002) and from our experience with the government-sponsored Community Daycare Program in Guatemala (Ruel *et al.*, 2002)[10] and suggest some approaches to addressing the challenges and opportunities of urban programming.

Lessons learned and challenges and opportunities for urban programming

Here we provide a brief overview of some of the challenges and opportunities of urban programming, based on the results of our research and our experience collaborating with CARE in the implementation of the programmes noted above.

Heterogeneity and mobility: where are the poor, food insecure and malnourished?

Urban areas are immensely diverse and our findings confirm the wide disparities that exist in childhood malnutrition and food insecurity within an area. This heterogeneity may add complexity to the design, targeting and implementation of programmes, as social mores and networks, conditions, cultural practices and livelihood strategies change from household to household and neighbourhood to neighbourhood. The fact that the poor and the rich live side by side also complicates programme targeting. Community targeting, a popular and generally effective programme targeting approach in rural areas, may not be effective in urban areas where the poor do not necessarily cluster geographically (Morris *et al.*, 2002).

Livelihood strategies are also equally diverse and programme strategies must take this heterogeneity into account. Programmes to raise employment and income, for instance, will probably be more effective if they focus on providing the context for growth (training to increase worker productivity; policies to provide firms with credit and encourage them to identify and respond to market demand; and good communications and transportation networks), rather than pursuing a sector focus, such as might be done in rural areas.

Mobility of urban residents can also add complexity to programme targeting and reduce programme impact. Evictions can erase gains due to projects, and projects may completely miss those who are most vulnerable if they are the most mobile (the homeless, for instance). But the general perception that urban residents are so mobile that projects cannot provide them with any beneficial effects seems misguided. A large proportion of the urban poor in our case study countries, for example, were not recent migrants; they were residents who sought stability and an inviting environment to establish their roots. In Peru, many of the residents interviewed in the CARE programme areas had been in the area for

---

[10] These programmes all aim to reduce urban food and nutrition insecurity, although they differ in their specific approach, components and operational aspects. They all involve some type of food aid, whether monetized or used directly as food.

15 to 20 years and had since been fighting for land and for later improvements, such as in water and sanitation. In Bangladesh, about 80 percent of residents in the two areas studied (one a suburb of Dhaka, the other, a good-size city) had been in the area for more than five years. In Ethiopia, with government ownership of land, there was very little movement in or out of the communities. In addition, the extent to which mobility matters depends mostly on the specific nature of the project. Infrastructure projects and community kitchens, for example, meet the needs of the community, regardless of how mobile the population is.

What can programmes do to reduce childhood malnutrition in urban areas?

Our data confirm that, although on average childhood malnutrition is lower in urban compared to rural areas, the rates of malnutrition among poor urban children often rival those of their rural counterparts. Moreover, we demonstrated that the factors responsible for poor child nutritional outcomes are the same in urban and rural areas. Thus, the same programme framework and sets of interventions developed for rural areas can be used to address childhood malnutrition in urban areas. As indicated above, however, it is likely that programme targeting will have to be done differently, i.e. either at the individual level or at the group level, but probably not at the community (geographic) level. Poor urban children deserve as much attention in the development agenda as rural children, because their health and development are equally key to national human capital formation and growth. Advocacy efforts should continue to highlight inequalities in urban areas and the heavy toll that poverty and food insecurity exert on urban children, so that resources can be mobilized to address the needs of this highly vulnerable group.

Urban livelihoods: employment and income, and women's work and child care

Livelihood security in urban areas depends on a complex set of interrelated factors, of which employment and income are crucial. Our empirical data also confirm that most food consumed by urban dwellers is purchased and that food expenditures account for more than half of the urban household budget. Thus, programmes aiming at reducing the cost of food for the urban poor – such as food aid, food subsidies, urban agriculture, technology and food policies to reduce the cost of food – are likely to be particularly important for urban livelihoods. Similarly, employment is essential because urban dwellers need money for most of their basic needs. For women, however, employment brings about yet another basic need to be fulfilled, i.e. the need for support with child care.

Our empirical data concerning women, employment and child care point to an apparently widespread and effective system of *maternal buffering*, by which mothers adapt their working patterns to the special needs of their children. Mothers use a variety of mechanisms to protect their child while they work: they work part-time; they take their child along; they work at home; or they work in the informal sector to have more flexible schedules. But at what cost do these coping strategies have for them (in terms of stress, time, famine, physical and mental health, and household food security) and for their young child (in terms of safety of the environment, and time and quality of care received)? Clearly, more research in this area is needed, but there is no doubt that urban mothers, and especially single income earners, need support with child care responsibilities. An example of a successful programme that specifically addresses the needs of urban working mothers is the government-sponsored Community Daycare Program in Guatemala (see Box on p. 55 for details). This type of programme, which is highly popular in Latin America, has the double advantage of providing affordable and reliable child care for extended hours, and allowing women to secure a more formal employment and receive employment benefits.

Land and housing security

Land and housing security are critical to project success. Infrastructure improvements, for example, may lead to increases in rent, thereby forcing the programme's beneficiaries to move to cheaper housing. Tenure security is also critical for a variety of social programmes. For example, in the context of the community kitchen programme in Peru, local authorities have on occasion tried to take over the kitchen, claiming it was a government organization that belonged to them. But by owning their own space and officially incorporating the kitchen as a community organization, the women used the legal system to defend ownership of the kitchen against these encroachments.

Tenure security is also important for employment and livelihood. Field (2003) shows that introduction of title reform in eight cities in Peru increased the numbers of hours worked by households by 17 percent on average, as a result of families no longer having to leave a member safeguarding the homestead for fear of eviction.

Crime and violence

Slums are often perceived, sometimes fairly, as centres of crime and violence. Violent crimes take away lives and livelihoods, undermine social unity and threaten project staff. In Lima, communities had to deal with local youth gangs and terrorism in the shape of Sendero Luminoso. In Guatemala City, the Community Daycare Program was unable to open day care centres in some areas because of security issues. Crime, however, is not rampant in all urban areas. In Bangladesh, outside the major metropolitan areas, violent crime appears to be rare, with petty crimes such as theft being somewhat more common. Crime in many areas tends to illegal smuggling (alcohol, for example) and prostitution. In study sites in Bangladesh domestic violence is prevalent and practically accepted by the women themselves as a legitimate way for men to express their frustrations. In developing and operating projects, working with community residents, who live with the community's crime and violence every day, can help to outline a strategy to confront crime and reduce risks to beneficiaries and project staff.

Poor social networks and lack of cohesion

All these factors (diversity, tenure insecurity, mobility and crime), may weaken community cohesion and social networks. Programmes that depend on community interest or peer pressure, such as credit groups, may fail. Projects may also suffer, if residents have limited knowledge of other members of their community.

Although it is true that some aspects of urban living encourage "independence", others, such as relatively high education levels and relative ease of communication, may actually encourage group action. Urban protests against structural adjustment policies are solid evidence that urban residents can form effective groups quickly. In cities, social relations extend beyond the geographic bounds of the community. They are founded in ethnicity and kinship as well as politics, social issues, culture, religion, sports and employment. Illegal activities also form common connections among slum dwellers. Urban dwellers do have social networks. They may be different, but they are not necessarily weaker than those in rural areas.

Urban dwellers also usually have at least some experience in working together. In Peru, the women who ran the community kitchens had decades earlier joined together to invade the land and demand public services such as water and electricity. Funeral societies are common in Addis Ababa. Projects can take advantage of the structure, or at least the experiences, that these organizations provide.

Finally, just as projects depend on community cohesion to work, they may also be important means to strengthen community ties. As with mobility, the importance of that cohesion may vary with the project. Social unity may make little difference to individually targeted programmes, for instance, but may matter a great deal to community-based maintenance of infrastructure.

Projects and politics

The nature of urban living – the crowded conditions, scarcity of natural resources and investments required for public services – practically requires government intervention. In urban areas, government authorities tend to play larger roles in daily life than in rural areas. In cities, informing local authorities and organizations about project activities is vital. Actively involving them can also be beneficial, and can help leverage resources they may have. Projects should not overlook informal authorities, including crime lords and community and religious leaders, who often exert substantial influence on community activities.

For the most part, CARE's programmes in the case study countries dealt effectively with potentially troublesome local political relations. They kept government authorities at all levels involved and informed, even taking them on as partners. Maintaining good relations with local stakeholders and educating politicians and bureaucrats about the project can counter upheaval at the top. Legal agreements clearly outlined institutional roles, responsibilities and commitments.

The project's design and management should also be flexible enough to accommodate change. Project managers should assess how potential economic and political changes can affect the project, and incorporate an ability to respond into project management. Staff should be aware of continuously evolving economic, political and social conditions, and adjust the project as necessary. Changes by donors in funding priorities proved to be the biggest challenge to the operation and sustainability of projects reviewed, not local political changes.

Responses to programmatic challenges[11]

The final part of this paper presents a series of insights from our collaborative work with CARE into potential strategic responses to challenges in urban programming. It tries to illustrate that while urban livelihoods are complex, the complexities are manageable when actions follow some general principles. These principles also permit adaptation of the programme to respond to the challenges noted above.

Adapt to challenges by appropriately identifying needs, constraints, resources and levers

Programmes should enter communities cautiously. An institutional analysis can explore the influence of different community organizations, non-governmental organizations (NGOs) and political actors and the resources – human, financial and physical – available. This allows a programme to navigate more easily tricky political relations, focus on strategic interventions, facilitate processes and mobilize community and household human and financial resources. Use of a holistic analytical framework, such as a livelihoods approach that emphasizes connections among livelihood security areas, will help programmers get out of sectoral boxes in framing problems and devising solutions.

---

[11] Additional information on CARE's programmes can be found on IFPRI's Web site (www.ifpri.org).

Reduce complexity by focusing on a limited set of objectives, activities and location, and exploit comparative advantages

Urban "complexity" stays manageable when programmes refrain from attempting to address all problems of poor communities and instead try to unravel the complexity by focusing on a strategically chosen strand. Organizations must identify their own strategic niche and adapt to local conditions and the leverage resources it has. In Ethiopia, for instance, CARE understood that its comparative advantage was in building and maintaining roads, while other organizations such as World Vision were more experienced in building houses. In partnership, World Vision and CARE could bring both better housing and roads to these communities, instead of working against one another.

Manage diversity complexity by starting small, scaling up, learning and being flexible

Even if programmes understand the local environment and have an initially limited focus, conditions change and programmes must develop over time. Successful programmes, then, will start small and scale up as they learn-by-doing. Management processes, however, must exist to support such an approach, which involves institutional learning and flexibility to respond to new situations as they arise. Sustainable programmes will also welcome input, support and collaboration from beneficiaries and other stakeholders, and build capacity. CARE utilized these principles in Peru. Staff and beneficiaries learned together. The programme started by using the skills that the women already had (for example, how to cook) and built capacity in other aspects over time (such as staffing and inventory management).

Confront issues of sustainability and political uncertainty by involving and empowering stakeholders, tending to facilitation, not implementation

Experience now demonstrates that empowerment of local partners and of beneficiaries improves the probability of success and sustainability of programmes. Communities and local institutions should implement projects, with outsiders serving primarily as change agents and initial sources of expertise and financial resources. Beneficiaries in Ethiopia and Peru emphasized that they valued the fact that project staff respected them and believed in their capacities, even though they were poor. They also highlighted the importance of establishing well-known, fair rules that were enforced, and not favouring one individual or another because of greater wealth or political connections.

Ensure that donors and organizations help to create the economic, political and legal environment and project monitoring systems that promote such facilitation and sustainability[12]

Developing community capacity to manage programmes and access outside resources takes time, as does helping authorities recognize their own responsibilities to vulnerable populations and to the democratic process. Creating conditions for others to implement a project usually takes longer than if the organization simply implemented a project itself, but this latter approach does not create capacity or enhance the prospects for long-term sustainability.

Innovative financial arrangements should bring funding agencies closer to communities. Generally, donor aid goes through or must be approved by a national government, providing an obstacle to true decentralization and the building of design and management capacity at the local level. Project development guidelines and monitoring and evaluation

---

[12] See the special issue of *Environment & Urbanization* (Brief 3, April 2001) on Rethinking aid to urban poverty reduction: lessons for donors.

tools, such as logical frameworks, generally reflect an assumption that the recipient of the funds will implement, not facilitate, the project. Donors must change this approach to promote facilitation. They should pay greater attention to time frames needed for capacity building, employ phased indicators appropriate to the time frame, identify new indicators of process, facilitation and capacity building, and incorporate flexibility in the design of the project.

The Community Daycare Program in Guatemala: an example of an effective urban programme to assist working mothers and their children

The Community Daycare Program in Guatemala was designed to assist working parents, single mothers in particular, with low-cost, quality child care within their community. In this programme a group of parents select a woman from the neighbourhood and designate her as the care provider. She then provides care, hygiene and food for up to ten children in her own home in return for a small stipend provided jointly by the parents and the programme administration. The programme also provides cash to purchase food for beneficiary children, which is complemented by monthly food donations from the World Food Programme (WFP). These are usually 44 lb (approximately 20 kg) of maize, 1 gallon (approximately 4.5 litres) of cooking oil, and 13 lb (approximately 6 kg) of black beans – or six cans of fish).

IFPRI's evaluation of the programme in Guatemala City found that overall it was operating quite effectively, in spite of a few operational constraints. These included the lack of participation of the beneficiary parents (related to their heavy work and commuting schedule), and the extra demands on the care providers to go to receive their monthly payments and the food donations. The programme, however, proved to be an effective food aid targeting mechanism because it allowed poor working parents and their children to participate in spite of their busy schedule. The programme was also found to have a substantial positive impact on the diet of beneficiary children who consumed on average 20 percent more energy, protein and iron, and 50 percent more vitamin A than non-participants. There was no evidence of substitution at home and therefore the net benefits on the quality of the diet of participating children are substantial.

The programme also seemed to reach its targeted beneficiaries, i.e. poor urban working parents, and especially single mothers. Beneficiary mothers were slightly less educated, had fewer assets, lived in more precarious conditions, and were more likely to be single, compared to non-beneficiary working mothers from the same neighbourhoods. Probably as a result of their participation in the programme, beneficiary mothers were more likely to be employed in the formal sector and to receive work-related social and medical benefits. Their income was 30 percent higher than the income of working mothers who used other child care alternatives.

The Community Daycare Program is a feasible and efficient mechanism to target and deliver food assistance to poor urban children. It is clearly a type of programme with great potential and, if implemented successfully as it is in Guatemala City, can have a significant nutritional impact on children and on their family's food security. Moreover, the programme does effectively support working parents' efforts to seek and secure paid employment away from home, which in urban areas is essential to livelihood security. Its success in reaching single women also contributes to reinforcing these women's efficiency in managing their dual role as income generators and child care givers. Thus, the model of the Guatemala Community Daycare Program is particularly well suited for an urban environment because it addresses the unique characteristics of urban livelihoods.

A constraint often overlooked in urban programming is the inability of working parents to participate in programmes that require attendance or regular contacts with programme staff during the daytime when they are at work. Typical food assistance programmes that operate through maternal and child health programmes, for example, are likely systematically to exclude the working poor and even more important, single mothers. Urban programming needs to pay more attention to the particular needs of poor working women and design innovative approaches that will help them complement their basic livelihood strategies, rather than interfere with them.[13]

---

[13] Additional information on IFPRI's evaluation of the Community Daycare (*Hogares Comunitarios*) Program can be found in Ruel *et al.*, 2002; Ruel, 2001a; and on IFPRI's Web site (www.ifpri.org).

Bibliography

Aragrande, M. & Argenti, O. 2001. *Studying food supply and distribution systems to cities in developing countries and countries in transition.* Methodological and operational guide. Rome, FAO.

Argenti, O. 2000. Feeding the cities: food supply and distribution. Brief No. 5. *In* J. Garrett & M.T. Ruel, eds. *Achieving urban food and nutrition security in the developing world.* IFPRI 2020 Vision Focus 3. Washington, DC, International Food Policy Research Institute.

Arimond, M. & Ruel, M.T. 2002. *Progress in developing an infant and child feeding index: an example using the Ethiopia Demographic and Health Survey 2000.* Food Consumption and Nutrition Division Discussion Paper No. 143. Washington, DC, International Food Policy Research Institute.

Arimond, M. & Ruel, M.T. 2004. *Dietary diversity, dietary quality and child nutritional status: evidence from eleven Demographic and Health Surveys.* Washington, DC, Food and Nutrition Technical Assistance Project (FANTA).

Armar-Klemesu, M., Ruel, M.T., Maxwell, D., Levin, C. & Morris, S. 2000. Poor maternal schooling is the main constraint to good child care practices in Accra. *J. Nutrition*, 130: 1597-1607.

Asfar, R. 1997. Onus of poverty on women in the poorest settlements of Dhaka City. *In* K. Salahuddin, R. Jahan & M. Islam, eds. *Women and poverty.* Dhaka, Bangladesh, Women for Women.

Asian Development Bank (ADB). 1994. *Asian Development Outlook 1994.* New York, USA., Oxford University Press.

Basta, S. 1977. Nutrition and health in low income urban areas of the third world. *Ecology of Food and Nutrition*, 6: 113-24.

Blau, D.M., Guilkey, D.K & Popkin, B.M. 1997. Infant health and the labor supply of mothers. *J. Human Resources,* 31: 90-139.

CARE Bangladesh. 1998. *Urban livelihood security assessment in Bangladesh.* Report. Dhaka, Bangladesh.

CARE Tanzania. 1998. *Dar es Salaam urban livelihood security assessment.* Summary report. Dar es Salaam, United Republic of Tanzania.

de Haan, A. 2000. Urban livelihoods and labor markets. Brief No. 4. *In* J. Garrett & M.T. Ruel, eds. *Achieving urban food and nutrition security in the developing world.* IFPRI 2020 Vision Focus 3. Washington, DC, International Food Policy Research Institute.

Engle, P.L., Menon, P., Garrett, J. & Slack, A. 1997. Urbanization and caregiving: a framework for analysis and examples from Southern and Eastern Africa. *Environment and Urbanization,* 9(2): 253-270.

Engle, P.L., Menon, P. & Haddad, L. 1997. *Care and nutrition: concepts and measurement.* Occasional Paper No. 18. Washington, DC, International Food Policy Research Institute.

Ersado, L. 2003. *Child labor and school decisions in urban and rural areas: cross-country evidence.* Food Consumption and Nutrition Division Discussion Paper No. 145. Washington, DC, International Food Policy Research Institute.

Field, E. 2003. *Entitled to work: urban property rights and labor supply in Peru.* Harvard University. December. (www.dartmouth.edu/~economic/seminar%20papers/Fieldproplabor.pdf).

Funkhouser, E. 1996. The urban informal sector in Central America: household survey evidence. *World Development,* 24: 1737-51.

Garrett, J. 2002. *Livelihoods in the city: challenges and options for the urban poor.* Toward Eliminating Urban Poverty Seminar Series. Washington, DC, US Agency for International Development (USAID).

Garrett, J. 2004. *Living life: overlooked aspects of urban employment.* Food Consumption and Nutrition Division Discussion Paper No.171. Washington, DC, International Food Policy Research Institute.

Garrett, J. & Ersado, L. n.d. *A rural-urban comparison of cash and consumption expenditure.* Food Consumption and Nutrition Division Discussion Paper. Washington, DC, Food Consumption and Nutrition Division, International Food Policy Research Institute. (unpublished)

Garrett, J. & Ruel, M.T. 1999a. Are determinants of rural and urban food security and nutritional status different? Some insights from Mozambique. *World Development,* 27: 1955-76.

Garrett, J. & Ruel, M.T. 1999b. Food and nutrition in an urbanizing world. *Choices,* 10-15.

Garrett, J. & Ruel, M.T. 2000. *Achieving urban food and nutrition security in the developing world.* IFPRI 2020 Vision Focus 3.

Glick, P. & Sahn, D.E. 1998. Maternal labour supply and child nutrition in West Africa. *Oxford Bulletin of Economics and Statistics*, 60(3): 325-55.

Hight-Laukaran, V., Rutstein, S.O., Peterson, A.E. & Labbok, M.H. 1996. The use of breast milk substitutes in developing countries: the impact of women's employment. *American J. Public Health,* 86: 1235-40.

Hoddinott, J. & Yohannes, Y. 2002. *Dietary diversity as a food security indicator.* Food Consumption and Nutrition Division Discussion Paper No. 136. Washington, DC, International Food Policy Research Institute.

International Labour Organization. 1998. *The future of urban employment*. Geneva, ILO.

Johnson-Welch, C., Bonnard, P., Strickland, R. & Sims, M. 2000. *They can't do it all: a call for expanded investments in childcare*. Washington, DC, International Center for Research on Women. (unpublished)

Marcucci, P. 2001. *Jobs, gender and small enterprises in Africa and Asia: lessons drawn from Bangladesh, the Philippines, Tunisia and Zimbabwe*. SEED Working Paper No. 18. Geneva, International Labour Organization.

Massingarela, C. & Garrett, J. 2002. *Perfil de emprego nas zonas urbanas de Mozambique*. Maputo, Mozambique, Ministerio dos Planos e Financas.

Meagher, K. 1995. Crisis, informalization and the urban informal sector in sub-Saharan Africa. *Development and Change,* 26: 259-84.

Menon, P., Ruel, M.T. & Morris, S.S. 2000. Socio-economic differentials in child stunting are consistently larger in urban than in rural areas. *Food and Nutrition Bulletin,* 21: 282-9.

Morris, S.S., Levin, C.E, Armar-Klemesu, M., Maxwell, D. & Ruel, M.T. 2002. *Does geographic targeting of nutrition interventions make sense in cities? Evidence from Abidjan and Accra.* Food Consumption and Nutrition Division Discussion Paper No. 61. Washington, DC, International Food Policy Research Institute.

National Research Council. 2003. *Cities transformed: demographic change and its implications in the developing world.* Panel on Urban Population Dynamics. Washington, DC, The National Academies Press.

Popkin, B.M. 1994. The nutrition transition in low-income countries: an emerging crisis. *Nutrition Reviews,* 52: 285-98.

Popkin, B.M. & Doak, C.M. 1998. The obesity epidemic is a worldwide phenomenon. *Nutrition Reviews,* 56: 106-14.

Portes, A., Blitzer, S. & Curtis, J. 1986. The urban informal sector in Uruguay: its internal structure, characteristics and effects. *World Development,* 14: 727-41.

Pradhan, M. & van Soest, A. 1997. Household labor supply in urban areas of Bolivia. *Economic J.,* 79: 300-10.

Quisumbing, A., Hallman, K. & Ruel, M.T. 2003. *Maquiladoras and market mamas: women's work and childcare in Guatemala City and Accra.* Food Consumption and Nutrition Division Discussion Paper No.153. Washington, DC, International Food Policy Research Institute.

Reardon, T. & Berdegué, J. 2002. The rapid rise of supermarkets in Latin America: challenges and opportunities for development. *Development Policy Rev.,* 20: 371-88.

Reardon, T., Timmer, P., Barrett, C. & Berdegué, J. 2003. The rise of supermarkets in Africa, Asia and Latin America. *American J. Agricultural Economics,* 85(5): 1140-1146.

Ruel, M.T. 2000. Urbanization in Latin America: constraints and opportunities for child feeding and care. *Food and Nutrition Bulletin,* 21: 12-24.

Ruel, M.T. 2001a. Do subsidized child care programmes work? An operations evaluation in Guatemala City. *Food, Nutrition and Agriculture,* 29: 44-52. Food and Agriculture Organization of the United Nations (FAO).

Ruel, M.T. 2001b. The natural history of growth failure: importance of intrauterine and postnatal periods. *In* R. Martorell & F. Haschke, eds. *Nutrition and growth.* Philadelphia, USA., Nestlé Nutrition Workshop Series, Pediatric Program, Vol. 47, p. 123-58. Nestec Ltd, Vevey/Lippincott Williams & Wilkins.

Ruel, M.T., de la Briere, B., Hallman, K., Quisumbing, A. & Coj, N. 2002. *Does subsidized childcare help poor working women in urban areas?* Evaluation of a government-sponsored program in Guatemala City. Food Consumption and Nutrition Division Discussion Paper No. 131. Washington, DC, International Food Policy Research Institute.

Ruel, M.T., Garrett, J., Morris, S.S., Maxwell, D., Oshaug, O., Engle, P., Menon, P., Slack, A. & Haddad, L. 1998. *Urban challenges to food and nutrition security: a review of food security, health, and caregiving in the cities.* Food Consumption and Nutrition Division Discussion Paper No. 51. Washington, DC, International Food Policy Research Institute.

Ruel, M.T., Haddad, L. & Garrett, J. 1999. Some urban facts of life: implications for research and policy. *World Development,* 11: 1917-38.

Simon, P.B. 1998. Informal responses to crises of urban employment: an investigation into the structure and relevance of small-scale informal retailing in Kaduna, Nigeria. *Regional Studies,* 32: 547-57.

Smith, L.C. & Aduayom, D. 2003. *Measuring food insecurity using household expenditure surveys: new estimates from sub-Saharan Africa.* Paper prepared for presentation at the Workshop on Food Security Measurement in a Developing World Context with a Focus on Africa. 25th International Conference of Agricultural Economists, Durban, South Africa.

Smith, L.C., Ruel M.T. & Ndiaye, A. 2003. *Why is child malnutrition lower in urban than rural areas?* Evidence from 36 developing countries. Food Consumption and Nutrition Division Discussion Paper No. 176. Washington, DC, International Food Policy Research Institute.

Sutter, P. & Perine, C. 1998. *Urban livelihoods security assessment in Bangladesh.* Vol. 1, Main Report. Dhaka, Bangladesh, CARE Bangladesh.

Weatherspoon, D. & Reardon, T. 2003. The rise of supermarkets in Africa: implications for agrifood systems and the rural poor. *Development Policy Rev.,* 21: 333-55.

WHO/FAO. 2003. *Diet, nutrition and the prevention of chronic diseases.* Report of a Joint WHO/FAO Expert Consultation. Geneva, World Health Organization.

Winikoff, B., Castle, M.A. & Hight-Laukaran, V. 1988. *Feeding infants in four societies.* Contributions in Family Studies, No. 14. New York, USA., Greenwood Press.

World Health Organization (WHO). 1979. *Measurement of nutritional impact.* Geneva.

World Health Organization (WHO). 1985. *Energy and protein requirements.* Technical Report Series No. 724. Geneva.

World Resource Institute, United Nations Environment Programme, United Nations Development Programme & World Bank. *World Resources 1996-97. A guide to the global environment. The urban environment.* New York, USA., Oxford University Press.

Ypeij, A. 2000. *Producing against poverty: female and male micro-entrepreneurs in Lima, Peru.* Amsterdam, Amsterdam University Press.

Zhang, H.X. 1999. Female migration and urban labour markets in Tianjin. *Development and Change,* 30: 21-41.

Annex

Urban/rural differences in food insecurity in sub-Saharan Africa

Country	Survey year	% living in urban areas	Percentage of population that is energy deficient[1]			Number of people that are energy deficient			% energy deficient people contributed by urban areas
			National	Rural	Urban	National	Rural	Urban	
Burundi	1998	8	74.8	76.6	41.4	4 898 046	4 594 577	227 720	4.65
Ethiopia	1999	17	81.5	80.1	90.4	51 167 330	41 658 895	9 739 145	19.03
Ghana	1998	37	51.6	50.8	53.1	9 519 875	5 867 047	3 663 935	38.49
Guinea	1994	28	45.1	40.6	54.3	2 897 639	1 865 090	994 288	34.31
Kenya	1997	30	43.8	46.3	30.1	12 282 834	9 036 801	2 566 047	20.89
Malawi	1997	14	73.3	72.9	76.3	7 084 394	6 041 012	1 051 581	14.84
Mozambique	1996	35	60.4	63.0	50.7	9 802 920	6 638 005	2 886 596	29.44
United Rebuplic of Tanzania	2000	28	43.9	41.8	52.7	14 792 544	10 169 318	4 936 666	33.37
Uganda	1999	14	39.6	39.3	41.6	8 561 520	7 319 023	1 246 557	14.55
Zambia	1996	43	72.6	73.0	71.9	6 689 654	3 813 932	2 868 691	42.88

[1] In this study, household energy availability was computed using consumption/expenditure data from nationally representative data sets. Total household energy availability was calculated as the sum of energy available from foods acquired for consumption in and out of the home (see Smith and Aduayom, 2003 for additional information on the methodology used). A household was considered energy deficient if its total household energy availability was lower than its total energy requirements (calculated using WHO 1985 recommended intakes (60); and using energy requirements specific to each household member, based on his/her age and gender distribution, and using a "light" activity level). The percentage of people who are food energy deficient is then calculated as the percentage of sample individuals who live in food energy deficient households, with appropriate corrections for survey sampling designs.

Source: Smith and Aduayom, 2003.

Globalization, urbanization and nutritional change in the developing world

Michelle A. Mendez and Barry M. Popkin[1]

INTRODUCTION

Over the past 15 years, there has been increasing evidence that the structure of dietary intakes and the prevalence of obesity around the developing world have been changing at an increasingly rapid pace (Popkin, 2002b). While there is some evidence to link urbanization with these changes, less is understood about the role of globalization. Urbanization is accompanied by shifts in a broad array of elements such as access to mass media, modern technologies related to work and leisure and transportation, and enhanced access to a variety of foods across all seasons of the year. Many of these changes may be attributable as well to the increased flow of goods, services and information associated with globalization. Increased globalization may bring shifts in occupational structures as industries develop and expand in response to world markets; greater access to international mass media programming; and enhanced access to non-traditional foods as a result of changing prices and production practices as well as trade. Because of the multiple shared paths through which urbanization and globalization may influence food availability and choices in developing countries, it is difficult to unravel the effects of the two sets of forces on diet and health.

The clustering of populations in urban centres affects dietary patterns by changing the way that people interact with their environments, as well as by changing the environments themselves in ways that transform food production and distribution systems. For example, urban living is associated with occupational patterns less compatible with home food production and consumption, and often with limited land availability for cultivation. Urbanization brings infrastructure and resources such as improved transportation and refrigeration systems. Today, in developing countries undergoing rapid urbanization combined with globalization, the process includes changes in the sociocultural environment such as mass media marketing and the widespread availability of less traditional foods, which play an important role in influencing tastes and preferences (Chopra, Galbraith and Darnton-Hill, 2002; Lang, 1999; Evans *et al.*, 2001). Growing foreign investment has contributed to the rise of fast food restaurants and western-style supermarkets, which may also influence consumer food choices by offering greater variety, quality, convenience and competitive prices in high-value added foods, in addition to

[1] Barry M. Popkin, Ph.D.
Professor of Nutrition
Carolina Population Center
CB # 8120 University Square
University of North Carolina at Chapel Hill
Chapel Hill, NC 27516-3997
Tel.: (919) 966-1732
Fax: 919-966-9159 (backup: 6638)
E-mail: popkin@unc.edu

perceived higher social desirability (Regmi and Gehlar, 2001; Reardon, Timmer and Berdegue, 2003). These changes in the food environment are occurring at a rapid pace. As developing countries become more urbanized, the changes are expanding beyond large urban centres and into smaller cities and towns, mirroring the pattern that occurred over time in industrialized countries. For example, in China, western-style supermarkets are now found in smaller cities and towns along the eastern coast and in the interior (Reardon, Timmer and Berdegue, 2003).

Several studies in developing countries have shown in the past that, compared with rural diets, urban diets tended to include higher levels of milled and polished grains (e.g. rice or wheat, rather than corn or millet), foods higher in fat (more animal products), sugar, food prepared away from the home, and processed foods (Popkin and Bisgrove, 1988). Over time, migrants to urban areas tend to adopt urban dietary patterns, although the timing of such changes has not been studied (Popkin and Bisgrove, 1988). However, as infrastructure and resources typical of urban areas become more widespread, the extent to which "urban" dietary patterns are being adopted in rural towns is not known. Residents of many rural areas are likely to be increasingly exposed to environmental factors that affect food choices, particularly in highly urbanized countries. To understand fully the nutritional effects of urbanization and globalization, it may become increasingly important to examine trends in diet and overweight in evolving rural environments as well as in urban communities. Multidimensional measures that more directly capture heterogeneity and change in levels of "urbanicity" may provide insights into the effects of urbanized ecologies on diet beyond those that can be gained using prevailing measures such as static urban-rural designations or population size and density (Mendez *et al.*, 2003).

Little is known about how urbanization and globalization are affecting dietary patterns in lower-income groups (Drewnowski and Popkin, 1997; Popkin, 2002a). These forces may have positive effects on the poor by increasing incomes and reducing the prevalence of inadequate energy intakes and undernutrition (Sachs and Warner, 1995; Dollar, 2001). However, these effects may not be universal: several studies suggest that the benefits of globalization have been unequal, and that in some countries globalization has had little impact on poverty alleviation (Cook and Kirkpatrick, 1997; Cornia, 2001). Furthermore, along with reduced undernutrition, rising obesity has been observed in low-income groups in some developing countries (Monteiro, Wolney and Popkin, 2002; Monteiro *et al.*, 2003). This suggests that the poor are increasingly adopting obesogenic diet and activity patterns, but there are few data about the nature of changing dietary behaviour, or the extent to which behavioural changes may be attributable to living in urban or urbanizing environments. Understanding the health and nutrition effects of urban environments on the poor is increasingly important, as the process of urbanization in many developing countries has included a massive shift of less advantaged groups to urban areas. In fact, in some countries, as urban populations surpass rural ones, the number of persons defined as living in poverty is greater in urban compared to rural areas (Haddad, Ruel and Garrett, 1999). In this paper, we examine the types of shifts in food availability, dietary intake patterns and obesity that have taken place in developing countries during a period of rapid globalization and urbanization.

Between 1960 and 2000 the proportion of the developing country population living in urban areas doubled, from 21.6 to 40.4 percent (United Nations Population Division, 2002). Recent changes have been particularly rapid in China, where the urban population increased by 39.8 percent between 1980 and 1990 (from 19.6 to 27.4 percent) and by another 20.7 percent from 1990 to 2000 (reaching 35.8 percent). In the Middle East, Latin America and Oceania, the pace of urbanization is slower, but 65-75 percent of the population in these regions resided in urban areas by the year 2000. These population shifts have been accompanied by accelerated globalization, as illustrated by factors such as large increases in foreign direct investment (from US$24 billion to $170 billion in 1990-98), and a doubling of merchandise exports and imports in the past two decades (World Bank, 2001).

The first part of this paper presents shifts in the availability of key food groups during this period of rapid change. We present information on regional shifts in edible oils, animal source foods (ASFs), fresh fruit and vegetables, and added sugars. Using case study data from China, we examine changes in food group intakes in greater detail, assessing the extent to which potentially obesogenic dietary patterns are emerging in rural as well as in urban areas. To illustrate better the effects of urbanizing environments, we present data on dietary patterns in urban and rural areas that differ in terms of infrastructure and resources. This case study also explores how food group consumption patterns have changed in low- and high-income groups in urban and rural settings. Finally, we assess some implications of these global dietary shifts by describing levels of under- and overweight in women living in urban and rural areas of developing countries. We describe how the prevalence of each type of malnutrition varies across countries at different levels of urbanization, as well as how prevalence in low versus high socio-economic status (SES) groups varies with urbanization. Aspects of urbanization and globalization that influence physical activity in addition to diet play a major role in the ongoing transition from underweight to overnutrition, but are not the focus of this paper.

DATA AND METHODS
Global shifts in food available for consumption, 1961-2000
Changes in global food availability were calculated using food balance sheet data and population estimates for developing countries between 1961 and 2000. These data were obtained from the Food and Agriculture Organization of the United Nations (FAO, 2001) (apps.fao.org). For each year, 1961, 1970, 1980, 1990 and 2000, the mean food availability per capita was calculated for each region. This was based on 118 countries of the developing world: 44 in sub-Saharan Africa, 15 in the Middle East, 34 in Latin America and the Caribbean and 25 in the Far East (including China). The added sugar category includes sugars and sweeteners; fruit excludes wine; vegetables exclude potatoes; edible oils are vegetable oils; dairy includes milk, yoghurt and cheese; meat includes bovine, sheep, pig, goat, poultry and other (but excludes animal source fats such as lard); fish includes fish and seafood. Animal source foods combine eggs, meat and poultry, fish and dairy products, but exclude animal source fats such as lard.

The China case study
The case study uses data from the China Health and Nutrition Survey (CHNS) from 1991 to 1997. The CHNS was conducted in eight provinces across China. Multistage cluster sampling was used to select communities from areas that differ substantially with respect to economic and health status, as well as geography. Details on the sample and data collection methods have been published elsewhere (Entwisle *et al.*, 1995; Guo *et al.*, 1999), and are available online (www.cpc.unc.edu/projects/china/). Individual-level dietary intake data, collected using three consecutive 24-hour recalls, are used to estimate consumption trends in key food groups among Chinese adults aged 20 to 45 years. Added caloric sweetener data are not available as they are not found in the food composition table for China. Anthropometric data collected by trained interviewers were used to calculate body mass index (BMI) (weight in kg/height in m^2), with which participants were categorized as overweight or obese (BMI $\geq$ 25.0) or as underweight (BMI $\leq$ 18.5). Income was estimated based on earnings from market and non-market activities as well as

subsidies. Urbanicity was characterized using the China urbanization index, a multidimensional index of infrastructure and resources in ten categories: population size, population density, access to markets, transportation, communications/media, economic factors, environment/sanitation, health, education, and housing quality (Mendez *et al.*, 2003). The index was developed using data from community surveys, supplemented with household level information.

Nutritional status changes

To analyse changes in under- and overweight, we used national data sets from surveys conducted between 1992 and 2000 in 36 developing countries: 20 in sub-Saharan Africa, eight in Latin America and the Caribbean (including Brazil and Mexico), five in Asia (including China and India), and three in North Africa and the Middle East. Many demographic health survey (DHS) data sets are not used because of a lack of appropriate maternal anthropometry data. The China and Mexico data sets are from national health and nutrition surveys conducted by these countries in 1997 and 1999, respectively (see for references on these two survey systems: Rivera *et al.*, 2002; Popkin *et al.*, 1993). All other national data sets correspond to standardized USAID/Macro DHSs conducted between 1992 and 2000 (Boerma and Sommerfelt, 1993). We used only the most recent data for countries in which two or more DHSs were conducted in this period. DHS data sets were downloaded from www.macroint.com/dhs/ or obtained directly from the state statistical offices (SSOs) that conducted the surveys.

We restricted analyses in all data sets to non-pregnant women aged 20 to 49 years. The average sample size was 4 266, ranging from 1 460 in Bolivia to 21 171 in Peru, with a total of 157 844 women studied. Average non-response rates were less than 0.2 percent for weight and height measurements and less than 0.7 percent for questions on SES. In the case of the DHS data, most women were mothers of children under five years of age. All analyses presented in this article were age-adjusted to allow for differences in age distribution between, and within, countries (Ahmad *et al.*, 1999).

The overall prevalence of underweight (BMI $\leq$ 18.5) and overweight-plus-obesity (BMI > 25) was calculated for women in each country based on weight and height measurements. Prevalences were estimated for both urban and rural areas. We also calculated the social distribution of underweight and overweight-plus-obesity for each country, using country-specific indicators of SES – namely, the country's quartiles of the women's years of formal education. Since years of education are a numeric non-continuous variable, close to 25 percent of women in each country fall in the education quartiles. However, in some countries, women were highly concentrated in some education categories, and it was necessary to combine one or more quartiles. Prevalence figures were age-adjusted by the direct method, using the age distribution of the world population as a reference (Ahmad *et al.*, 1999). We used survey-specific sample weights, so all estimates are nationally representative (except for the China survey, which only represents eight provinces).

We first tested the significance of differences in overweight (and underweight) prevalence in urban versus rural areas. Next, we tested the differences in overweight versus underweight prevalence within both urban and rural areas. Finally, we examined the magnitude and direction of the associations between SES and prevalence of malnutrition (underweight or overweight-plus-obesity) in each country, by calculating age-adjusted prevalence ratios (with 95 percent confidence intervals), comparing the highest to the lowest education quartile within urban and rural areas.

RESULTS
Global shifts in food available for consumption, 1961-2000
Edible oils

Throughout the developing world, the availability of edible vegetable oils for consumption has nearly tripled (Figure 1). In some countries, the increase has been even more marked. For instance, availability of edible oils for consumption in China has risen sixfold over this period, while intakes in the rest of Asia and Oceania tripled. In the past two decades, edible oil availability continued to rise in Asia and Oceania. However, availability of oils in Latin America and the Middle East – already more than 65 percent higher than in other regions by 1990 – appears to have levelled off.

FIGURE 1
Regional trends in availability for consumption of edible oils, 1961-2000

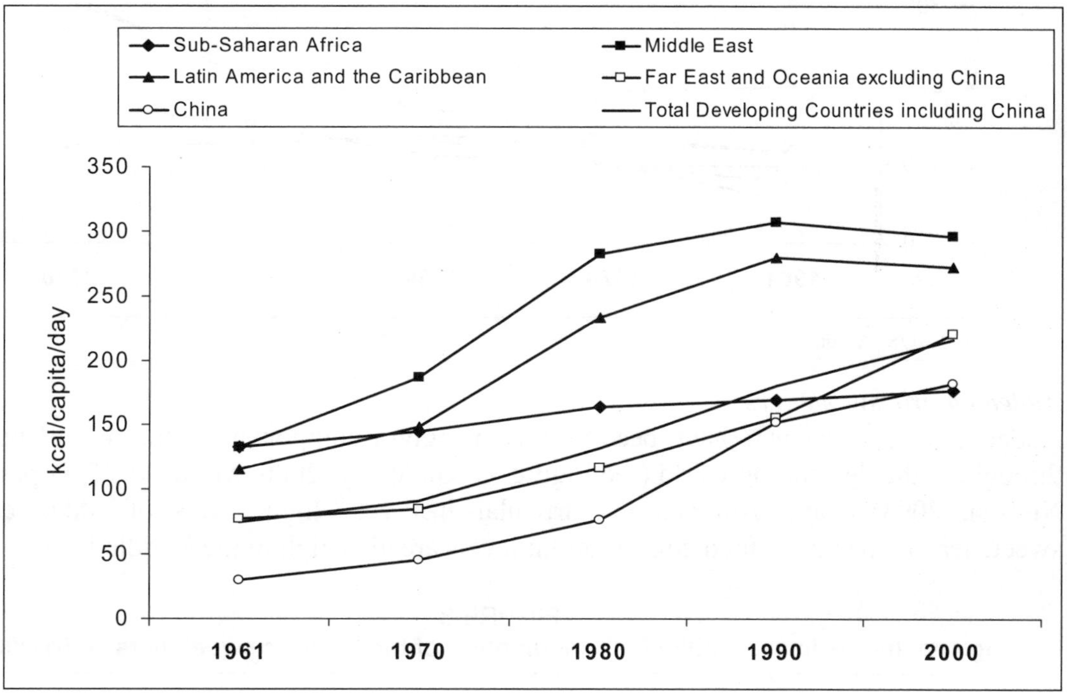

Source: FAOSTAT data.

Animal source foods

Figure 2 illustrates changes in world production of animal source foods (ASFs) available for human consumption, including eggs, meat (pork, all others), poultry, dairy and fish. There was an almost tenfold increase of ASFs in China, and overall a tripling of the amounts available for consumption in the developing world. In most regions, ASF intakes continued to increase rapidly in the past two decades: only sub-Saharan Africa and the Middle East did not experience substantial changes in animal food consumption over that period. However, levels of ASF consumption in the Middle East were already consistently higher than those in most other developing regions.

FIGURE 2
Regional trends in availability for consumption of total animal source foods, 1961-2000

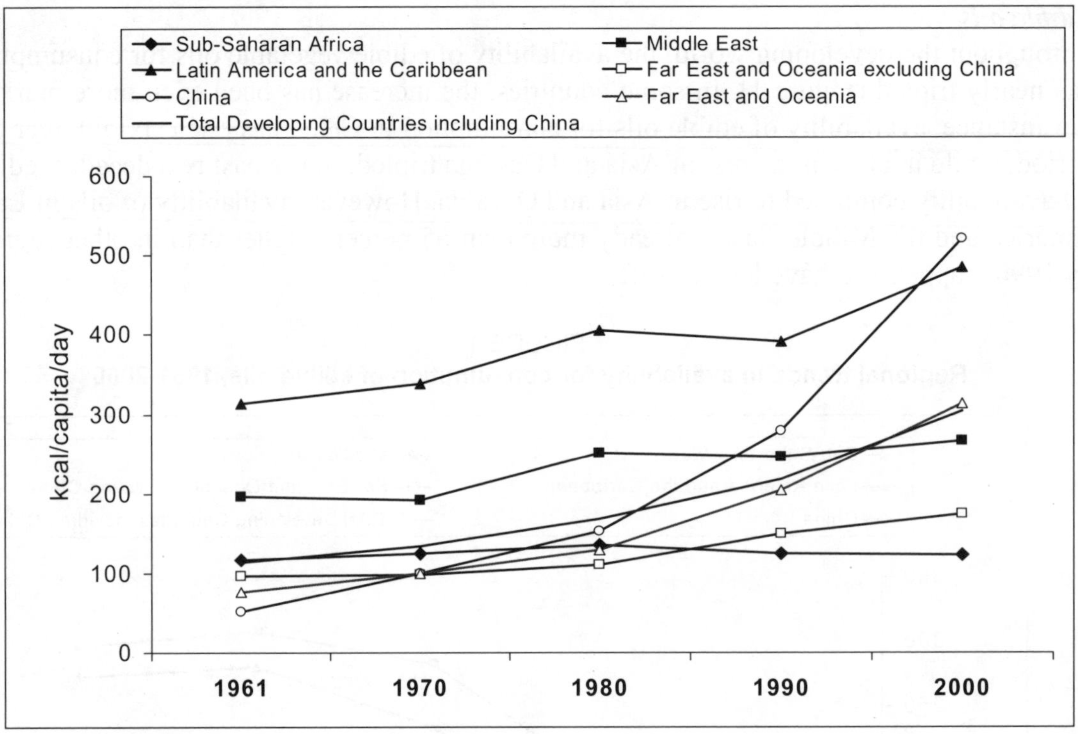

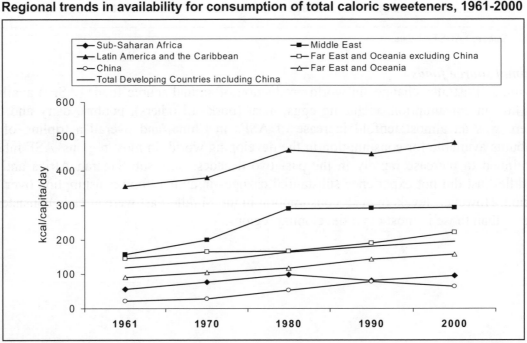

Source: FAOSTAT data.

Added caloric sweeteners

Added caloric sweeteners have become increasingly a component of the diet of persons throughout the developing world (see Figure 3) (Galloway, 2000; Mintz, 1977; Popkin and Nielsen, 2003). Latin America in particular has very high levels of added caloric sweeteners available for food consumption; levels are also high in the Middle East.

FIGURE 3
Regional trends in availability for consumption of total caloric sweeteners, 1961-2000

Source: FAOSTAT data.

Fruit and vegetables

Mean levels of fruit and vegetables (F&V) available for consumption in developing countries increased by about 72 percent, from 83 kcals/day in 1961 to 143 kcals/day in 2000 (Figure 4). Thus, changes in F&V availability were much less marked than shifts in edible oils (189 percent) or ASFs (169 percent).

FIGURE 4

Regional trends in availability for consumption of total fruit and vegetables (excluding potatoes), 1961-2000

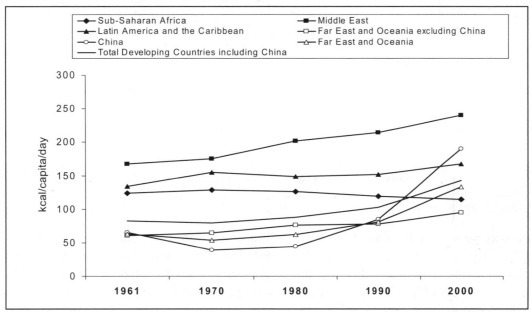

Source: FAOSTAT .data.

Energy

There is an increasing trend in the amount of energy available for consumption. Overall, the highest levels of energy available for consumption are found in the Middle East (see Figure 5). There has been a remarkably large increase in China over the past ten to 20 years: China now ranks second in terms of energy available for consumption, followed by Latin America and the rest of Asia and Oceania. Mean levels of food energy available are lowest in sub-Saharan Africa, by a considerable margin.

FIGURE 5

Regional trends in availability for consumption of total calories, 1961-2000

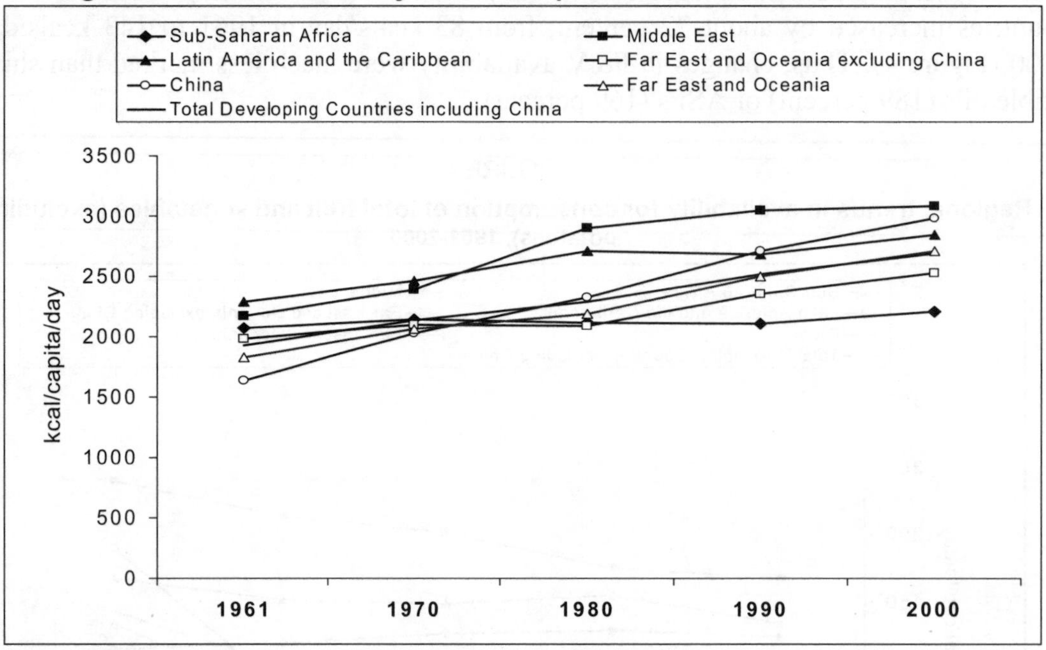

Source: FAOSTAT data.

Urbanization and dietary shifts in developing countries: the China case study

In only six years, between 1991 and 1997, there have been marked changes in the dietary intakes of Chinese adults, reflecting the large changes taking place in food availability (Table 1a; see also Du *et al.*, 2002a,b). Shifts in intakes of animal source foods have been especially pronounced, increasing by 23 percent in urban areas and by 27 percent in rural areas. Edible oil consumption has also increased substantially, again with larger increases in rural (19 percent) than in urban (11 percent) areas. As a result of these changes, the proportion of adults consuming high-fat (> 30 percent calories from fat) diets increased from 33.0 to 60.8 percent in urban areas, and from 13.5 to 29.3 percent in rural areas. Vegetable intakes have remained steady, changing very little in both urban and rural dwellers. Fruit intakes have more than doubled in both urban and rural areas, although intakes in both areas remain extremely low. As changes in fruit and vegetable intakes have been small, animal foods and oils – rather than healthier food choices – appear to have displaced cereals in both urban and rural communities. While the proportion of calories from cereals has fallen from 63.2 to 55.0 percent (-8.2 percent) and from 71.8 to 63.2 percent (-8.6 percent) in urban and rural areas respectively, calories from animal foods have increased by 1.6 and 2.5 percent, and from fats and sugars by 7.0 and 5.6 percent.

TABLE 1a
Shifts in consumption in the Chinese diet (China Health and Nutrition Survey, 1989-1997) for adults aged 20 to 45 (mean intake g/per capita/day)

	Urban			Rural		
	1991	1997	% change	1991	1997	% change
Animal foods (g)	151.1	185.8	23.0	84.9	107.8	27.0
Meat	71.1	83.3	17.2	39.9	45.3	13.5
Poultry	7.7	15.3	98.7	5.1	8.9	74.5
Fish	24.5	28.4	15.9	15.4	21.3	38.3
Eggs	44.3	47.6	7.4	38.4	45.5	18.5
Edible vegetable oils (g)	41.1	45.5	10.7	35.0	41.8	19.4
Vegetables (g)	304.4	309.5	1.7	360.9	363.5	0.7
Fruit (g)	17.2	35.2	104.7	7.8	15.9	103.8

Although some changes in food group intakes have been larger in rural than in urban areas, urban diets have remained consistently richer in ASFs and oils, and poorer in quantities of vegetables. As a result of the greater shifts in rural areas, however, urban-rural disparities in ASF and vegetable oil intakes have narrowed over time. Nevertheless, urban dwellers consume more than twice as much fruit as rural residents, and this disparity has not changed.

We conducted additional analysis using the CHNS urbanization index to take the level of urbanicity of both urban and rural areas into account (Table 1b). Dietary patterns across communities at different levels of urbanicity are explored in greater depth in a companion paper (Mendez *et al.*, 2003), but selected findings are presented here. In this analysis, it became clear that simple urban-rural disparities masked substantial heterogeneity in dietary patterns across differing environments. Dietary patterns in rural areas with very high urbanicity scores closely resemble diets in areas formally designated as urban, with high intakes of animal foods and oils. Only rural communities with very low levels of urbanicity have maintained low intakes of animal foods and edible oils.

TABLE 1b
Shifts in consumption in the Chinese diet (China Health and Nutrition Survey, 1989-1997) for adults aged 20 to 45 by level of urbanicity (mean intake g/per capita/day)

	Urban	Rural	Urban		Rural	
1997 dietary intakes			Low	High	Low	High
Animal foods (g)						
Low income	123.1	73.0	90.0	135.6	64.5	145.7
Middle income	176.1	104.6	160.5	182.4	93.8	170.5
High income	213.7	160.8	205.4	218.0	127.6	246.1
All	185.8	107.8	174.3	191.0	89.6	200.0
Plant fats (g)						
Low income	41.6	37.2	51.6	37.5	37.1	37.4
Middle income	43.8	43.4	49.8	41.2	43.9	40.7
High income	47.9	46.4	52.5	45.3	45.2	49.6
All	45.5	41.8	51.5	45.3	41.3	44.1

Over time, intakes of animal foods and oils increased much more quickly in lower- than in higher-income groups (see Table 2). Consumption of ASFs by adults in the lowest income tertile increased by 44 percent in both urban and rural areas, but by 20-25 percent in the highest income tertile. Similarly, consumption of vegetable oils increased several times faster in low- than in high-income adults. Thus, although higher-income groups have maintained higher intakes of these foods, the income disparity has narrowed considerably. In contrast to the large shifts for these foods in low-income groups, there was little change in vegetable intakes at any income level, and fruit consumption increased largely in high-income adults.

TABLE 2
Shifts in consumption in the Chinese diet (China Health and Nutrition Survey, 1989-1997) for adults aged 20 to 45 by income level (mean intake g/per capita/day)

	Urban			Rural		
	1991	1997	% change	1991	1997	% change
Animal foods (g)						
Low income	85.7	123.1	43.6	50.7	73.0	44.0
Middle income	150.3	176.1	17.2	89.4	104.6	17.0
High income	171.7	213.7	24.5	133.6	160.8	20.4
Edible oils (g)						
Low income	30.2	41.6	37.7	30.6	37.2	21.6
Middle income	40.1	43.8	9.2	34.7	43.4	25.1
High income	44.8	48.0	7.1	41.8	46.4	11.1
Vegetables (g)						
Low income	312.7	323.9	3.6	357.0	351.8	-1.5
Middle income	303.0	308.3	1.7	363.4	386.5	6.4
High income	303.0	305.5	0.8	364.1	352.5	-3.2
Fruit (g)						
Low income	8.7	7.8	-10.3	6.8	10.2	50.0
Middle income	9.6	19.0	97.9	8.4	20.7	146.4
High income	25.2	55.9	121.8	8.6	18.1	110.5

Global nutritional status changes
Current levels of overweight-plus-obesity (hereafter "overweight") among women in developing countries from different regions are shown in Figures 6 to 8, and in Table 3. In most countries, overweight has reached levels that are quite troubling, particularly in urban areas, where prevalence is generally highest. Among urban women across the developing world, overweight ranges from 10 to 70 percent of the population; levels are well over 20 percent in most countries. Prevalence of overweight in rural women ranges from 4.5 to 65.6 percent. There are, however, four countries where rural overweight exceeds urban overweight (Colombia, Kyrgyzstan, Turkey and Nigeria).

FIGURE 6

Prevalence of overweight in urban and rural areas of sub-Saharan Africa in women aged 20-49 years (BMI ≥25 for overweight)

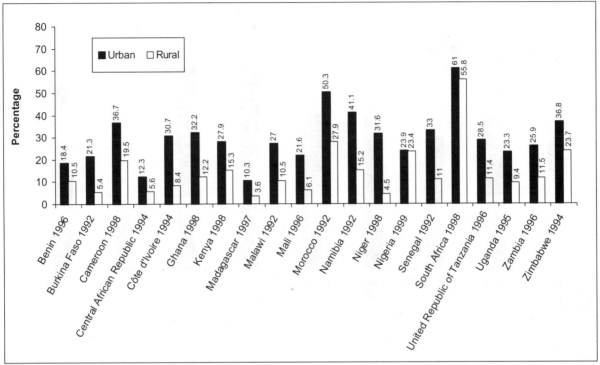

Source: Demographic and Health Surveys, weighted to be nationally representative. Age-standardized on the world population.

FIGURE 7

Prevalence of overweight in urban and rural areas of North Africa/WestAsia/Europe, Central Asia and South and Southeast Asia in women aged 20-49 years (BMI ≥25 for overweight)

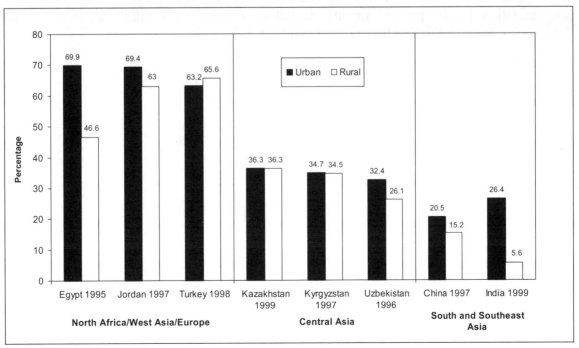

Source: Demographic and Health Surveys, weighted to be nationally representative. Age-standardized on the world population.

FIGURE 8
Prevalence of overweight in urban and rural areas of Latin America and the Caribbean in women aged 20-49 years (BMI ≥25 for overweight)

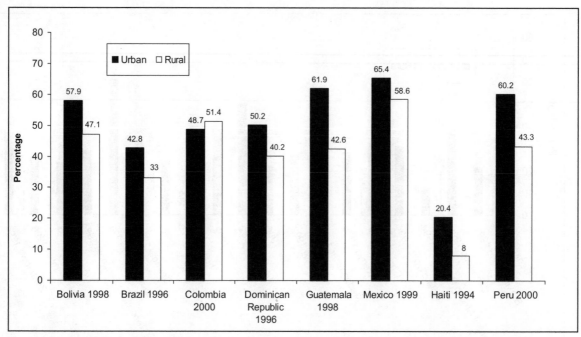

Source: Demographic and Health Surveys, weighted to be nationally representative. Age-standardized on the world population.

Throughout the developing world, overweight prevalence among women tends to be highest in countries where the greatest proportion of the population lives in urban centres (Figure 9). Furthermore, in highly urbanized regions – the Middle East and Latin America – the urban-rural disparity in overweight prevalence is relatively small. This disparity is also relatively small in many sub-Saharan African countries with high levels of urbanization (> 35 percent urban), including Benin, the Central African Republic, Morocco, Nigeria, South Africa, Zambia and Zimbabwe.

TABLE 3

Comparing overweight versus underweight prevalence by urban and rural areas

	Overweight	Underweight		Overweight	Underweight	
	Urban	Urban	P-value	Rural	Rural	P-value
Sub-Saharan Africa						
Low urbanization						
Burkina Faso 1992	21.3 (23.5, 19.1)	8.7 (10.2, 7.1)	0.00000	5.4 (6.4, 4.5)	15.5 (17.0, 14.1)	0.00000
Ghana 1998	32.2 (36.2, 28.2)	5.5 (7.5, 3.6)	0.00000	12.2 (13.8, 10.7)	12.6 (14.2, 11.1)	0.35647
Kenya 1998	27.9 (31.7, 24.0)	7.0 (9.2, 4.8)	0.00000	15.3 (16.6, 14.0)	12.1 (13.3, 11.0)	0.00029
Madagascar 1997	10.3 (12.8, 7.8)	14.1 (16.9, 11.2)	0.02548	3.6 (4.4, 2.8)	21.5 (23.3, 19.7)	0.00000
Malawi 1992	27.0 (30.4, 23.6)	5.8 (7.6, 4.0)	0.00000	10.5 (11.9, 9.1)	9.2 (10.5, 7.9)	0.09434
Mali 1996	21.6 (23.8, 19.4)	13.5 (15.3, 11.6)	0.00000	6.1 (7.0, 5.3)	14.6 (15.8, 13.4)	0.00000
Namibia 1992	41.1 (44.5, 37.6)	6.2 (7.9, 4.5)	0.00000	15.2 (17.0, 13.4)	16.5 (18.4, 14.7)	0.15984
Niger 1998	31.6 (34.7, 28.6)	12.1 (14.2, 10.0)	0.00000	4.5 (5.3, 3.7)	19.6 (21.1, 18.1)	0.00000
United Republic of Tanzania 1996	28.5 (31.5, 25.4)	8.6 (10.5, 6.7)	0.00000	11.4 (12.6, 10.3)	9.6 (10.6, 8.5)	0.00777
Uganda 1995	23.3 (25.9, 20.6)	6.6 (8.2, 5.0)	0.00000	9.4 (10.6, 8.3)	9.8 (11.0, 8.7)	0.31682
Zimbabwe 1994	36.8 (41.2, 32.3)	1.9 (3.2, 0.6)	0.00000	23.7 (25.8, 21.5)	4.9 (5.9, 3.8)	0.00000
High urbanization						
Benin 1996	18.4 (21.5, 15.4)	9.7 (12.0, 7.4)	0.00000	10.5 (11.9, 9.1)	15.5 (17.1, 13.8)	0.00001
Cameroon 1998	36.7 (32.9, 40.5)	5.2 (3.5, 7.0)	0.00000	19.5 (17.1, 21.9)	5.9 (4.4, 7.3)	0.00000
Central Afr. Rep. 1994	12.3 (14.6, 10.0)	13.6 (16.0, 11.2)	0.22467	5.6 (6.9, 4.4)	16.7 (18.8, 14.7)	0.00000
Côte d'Ivoire 1994	30.7 (33.3, 19.3)	5.0 (6.3, 3.8)	0.00000	8.4 (9.7, 7.2)	12.0 (13.5, 10.5)	0.00021
Morocco 1992	50.3 (53.1, 47.6)	2.6 (3.5, 1.8)	0.00000	27.9 (29.9, 26.0)	4.5 (5.4, 3.5)	0.00000
Nigeria 1999	23.9 (27.2, 20.7)	13.6 (16.2, 10.9)	0.00000	23.4 (25.4, 21.3)	13.3 (14.9, 11.6)	0.00000
Senegal 1992	33.0 (35.7, 30.2)	8.5 (10.2, 6.9)	0.00000	11.0 (12.4, 9.7)	14.4 (15.9, 12.9)	0.00062
South Africa 1998	61.0 (62.9, 59.1)	4.3 (5.0, 3.5)	0.00000	55.8 (58.1, 53.6)	5.7 (6.1, 4.1)	0.00000
Zambia 1996	25.9 (28.1, 23.6)	5.9 (7.2, 4.7)	0.00000	11.5 (12.7, 10.3)	9.9 (11.1, 8.8)	0.03174
North Africa/West Asia/Europe						
Egypt 1995	69.9 (71.6, 68.2)	0.7 (1.0, 0.4)	0.00000	46.6 (48.0, 45.1)	1.8 (2.2, 1.4)	0.00000
Jordan 1997	69.4 (71.1, 67.7)	1.6 (2.1, 1.2)	0.00000	63.0 (66.4, 59.6)	1.8 (2.7, 0.9)	0.00000
Turkey 1998	63.2 (66.0, 60.4)	2.1 (2.9, 1.3)	0.00000	65.6 (69.6, 61.6)	1.5 (2.6, 0.5)	0.00000 *(cont.)*

	Overweight	Underweight		Overweight	Underweight	
	Urban	Urban	P-value	Rural	Rural	P-value
Central Asia						
Kazakhstan 1999	36.3 (39.0, 33.6)	6.3 (7.6, 4.9)	0.00000	36.3 (39.8, 32.9)	6.0 (7.7, 4.3)	0.00000
Kyrgyzstan 1997	34.7 (37.3 32.0)	4.9 (6.1, 3.7)	0.00000	34.5 (36.6, 32.3)	4.4 (5.3, 3.5)	0.00000
Uzbekistan 1996	32.4 (34.6, 30.3)	7.0 (8.1, 5.8)	0.00000	26.1 (28.2, 23.9)	7.4 (8.7, 6.1)	0.00000
South and Southeast Asia						
China 1997	20.5 (23.0, 18.0)	7.4 (9.0, 5.7)	0.00000	15.2 (16.8, 13.6)	6.1 (7.2, 5.0)	0.00000
India 1999	26.4 (27.9, 24.8)	23.1 (24.6, 21.6)	0.00178	5.6 (6.2, 4.9)	48.2 (49.6, 46.7)	0.00000
Latin America and the Caribbean						
Bolivia 1998	57.9 (61.2, 54.5)	0.7 (1.2, 0.1)	0.00000	47.1 (51.0, 43.3)	0.6 (1.2, 0.0)	0.00000
Brazil 1996	42.8 (44.7, 40.8)	5.2 (6.0, 4.3)	0.00000	33.0 (36.5, 29.6)	9.3 (11.4, 7.2)	0.00000
Colombia 2000	48.8 (50.7, 46.7)	2.0 (2.6, 1.5)	0.00000	51.4 (54.5, 48.3)	2.1 (3.0, 1.3)	0.00000
Dominican Rep. 1996	50.2 (51.7, 48.6)	4.5 (5.2, 3.9)	0.00000	40.2 (42.1, 38.3)	6.2 (7.1, 5.2)	0.00000
Guatemala 1998	61.9 (65.5, 58.2)	1.5 (2.5, 0.6)	0.00000	42.6 (44.8, 40.3)	1.6 (2.2, 1.0)	0.00000
Mexico 1999	65.4 (66.4, 64.4)	1.5 (1.8, 1.2)	0.00000	58.6 (60.0, 57.1)	2.2 (2.6, 1.8)	0.00000
Haiti 1994	20.4 (23.2, 17.7)	16.5 (19.0, 13.9)	0.01855	8.0 (9.5, 6.5)	20.8 (23.1, 18.6)	0.00000
Peru 2000	60.2 (61.0, 59.4)	0.8 (0.9, 0.6)	0.00000	43.3 (44.3, 42.2)	0.7 (0.8, 0.5)	0.00000

Note: The statistical test compares overweight (% BMI ≥ 25) versus underweight (% BMI ≤ 18.5) in urban and in rural areas separately.

We compared the prevalence of underweight in urban versus rural areas (see Table 3). The overall pattern was to find more underweight in rural than in urban areas, although in many parts of the world these disparities were small (Central Asian Republics and Latin America, with the exception of Haiti, China and North Africa). In a large part of sub-Saharan Africa, as well as in India and Haiti, there was much more underweight in rural than in urban areas.

Perhaps the most notable finding in these recent data is that there is far more overweight than underweight among women in most developing countries (Figures 10 to 15).

FIGURE 9

The relationship of overweight prevalence with the proportion urban (BMI ≥25 for overweight)

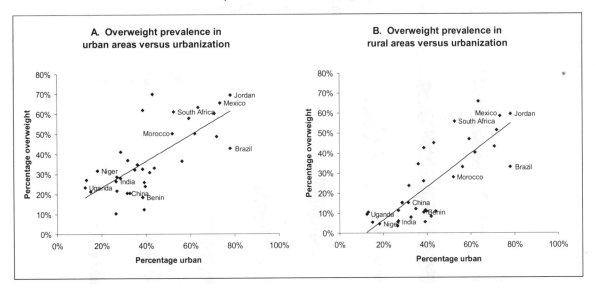

Source: Demographic and Health Surveys, weighted to be nationally representative. Age-standardized on the world population.

FIGURE 10

Comparison of overweight and underweight prevalence in urban areas of sub-Saharan Africa in women 20-49 years old (BMI ≥25 for overweight and BMI ≤18.5 for underweight)

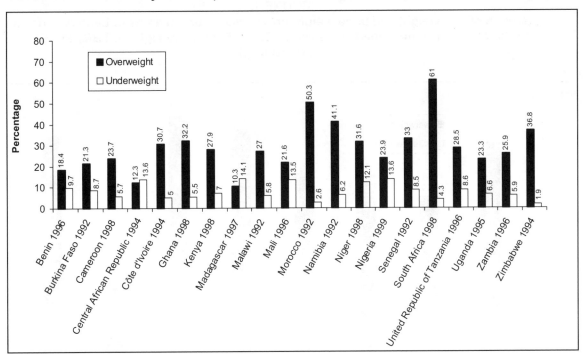

Source: Demographic and Health Surveys, weighted to be nationally representative. Age-standardized on the world population.

FIGURE 11

Comparison of overweight and underweight prevalence in urban areas of North Africa/WestAsia/Europe, Central Asia and South and Southeast Asia in women aged 20-49 years (BMI ≥25 for overweight and BMI ≤18.5 for underweight)

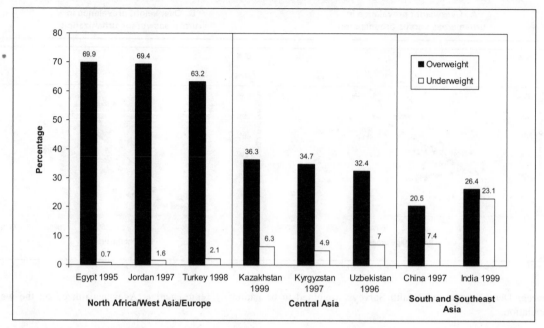

Source: Demographic and Health Surveys, weighted to be nationally representative. Age-standardized on the world population.

FIGURE 12

Comparison of overweight and underweight prevalence in urban areas of Latin America and the Caribbean in women aged 20-49 years (BMI ≥25 for overweight and BMI ≤18.5 for underweight)

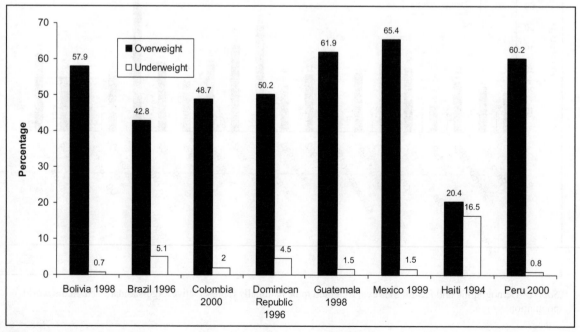

Source: Demographic and Health Surveys, weighted to be nationally representative. Age-standardized on the world population.

FIGURE 13

Comparison of overweight and underweight prevalence in rural areas of sub-Saharan Africa in women aged 20-49 years (BMI ≥25 for overweight and BMI ≤18.5 for underweight)

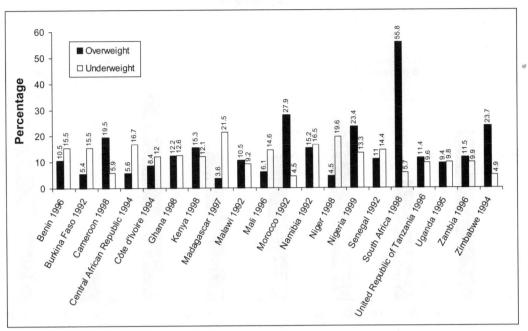

Source: Demographic and Health Surveys, weighted to be nationally representative. Age-standardized on the world population.

FIGURE 14

Comparison of overweight and underweight prevalence in rural areas of North Africa/WestAsia/Europe, Central Asia and South and Southeast Asia in women aged 20-49 years (BMI ≥25 for overweight and BMI ≤18.5 for underweight)

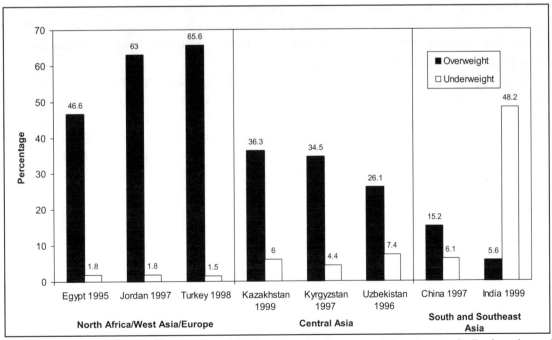

Source: Demographic and Health Surveys, weighted to be nationally representative. Age-standardized on the world population.

FIGURE 15

Comparison of overweight and underweight prevalence in rural areas of Latin America and the Caribbean in women aged 20-49 years (BMI ≥25 for overweight and BMI ≤18.5 for underweight)

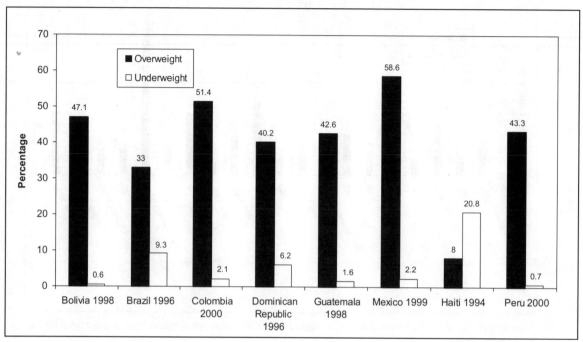

Source: Demographic and Health Surveys, weighted to be nationally representative. Age-standardized on the world population.

This predominance of overweight is found in most urban areas, and in many rural areas. The main exceptions are India, where close to half the rural women are underweight, and several countries in sub-Saharan Africa – especially in rural areas. In only two countries is there more underweight than overweight in urban areas, and these differences are small. By far, the primary problem of malnutrition found in urban women throughout the developing world is that of overnutrition.

We also explored the social distribution of overweight and underweight in urban and rural areas, using education as an indicator of SES. As expected, underweight status is predominantly a problem among low SES groups (not shown). In many countries, however, overweight status is now highly prevalent in low as well as in high SES groups. Indeed, especially in the most urbanized countries, overweight prevalence in the lowest SES women is similar or greater than in the higher SES groups (Figure 16).

FIGURE 16
The odds ratio of overweight prevalence among high education versus low education women
(BMI ≥25 for overweight)

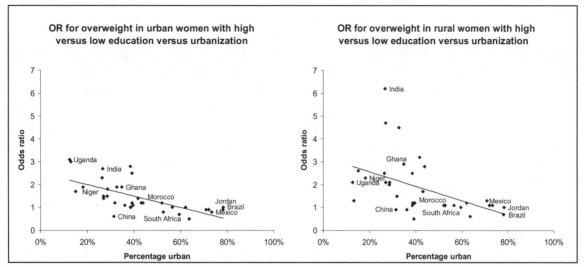

Source: Demographic and Health Surveys, weighted to be nationally representative. Age-standardized on the world population.

In the relatively short time frame between 1991 and 1997 (Table 4), there have been large increases in overweight prevalence in Chinese adults living in both urban and rural areas. Conversely, there were substantial declines in underweight throughout China; prevalence was < 5 percent in all areas by 1997. Overweight has increased in women and men in both urban and rural areas, although levels remained lower in rural China. Income disparities in overweight prevalence are very small in urban areas, although there is substantially more overweight in high-income than in low-income rural residents.

TABLE 4
Shifts in overweight and underweight prevalence in Chinese adults aged 20-45 years, 1991-1997 (overweight [% BMI ≥ 25]; underweight [% BMI ≤ 18.5])

	Overweight				Underweight			
	Urban		Rural		Urban		Rural	
	1991	1997	1991	1997	1991	1997	1991	1997
Male	12.4	27.4	6.4	13.1	5.7	2.0	4.4	2.4
Female	15.7	24.5	10.8	17.6	5.7	2.5	4.7	3.4
By income group								
Male								
Low	14.7	25.9	3.8	9.3	2.8	2.8	6.0	3.5
Middle	10.5	25.5	6.7	12.1	7.9	2.0	2.5	1.7
High	13.0	29.1	10.4	19.8	5.0	1.7	4.1	1.6
Female								
Low	14.7	24.4	8.2	14.4	5.4	3.4	6.5	4.9
Middle	18.4	25.5	12.2	18.1	6.0	2.0	4.0	3.8
High	14.0	23.9	13.3	24.1	5.6	2.7	2.7	1.2

CONCLUSIONS AND POLICY RECOMMENDATIONS

The effects of urbanization and globalization on dietary patterns and nutritional status in developing countries are complex. These forces are associated with potentially beneficial dietary shifts such as increases in energy sufficiency and greater consumption of fruit, but also appear to promote potentially obesogenic shifts such as increased intakes of edible oils, animal foods and caloric sweeteners. While there have been substantial reductions in undernutrition in this period of rapid development and social change, overweight has become an increasing problem. Among adult women, overweight now exceeds underweight in almost all developing countries, particularly in the most urbanized ones. Food availability and intake data suggest that adverse shifts in dietary composition are taking place at a much higher speed than potentially beneficial changes: there has been relatively little change in the levels of fruit and vegetables, but very large increases in edible oils, ASFs and added sugar and caloric sweeteners over short periods of time. Numerous studies have shown that consumption of energy-dense (high-fat, added sugar) foods tend to promote excessive energy intakes (Rolls, 2000). These adverse dietary shifts have undoubtedly contributed to the rise in overweight and obesity observed throughout the developing world.

Case study data from China indicate that consumption patterns closely reflect changes in food availability. There were large increases in dietary fats, oils and ASFs in the 1990s. As a result of these changes, mean intakes of ASFs in China have reached levels similar to the maximum amounts recommended in the United States guidelines and food pyramid (United States Department of Agriculture [USDA], 2000). In contrast, intakes of fruit and vegetables fall below recommendations, which would be in the range of 500-700 g/day (authors' calculations based on three fruit and four vegetable servings/day) – levels comparable to those reported for some Mediterranean countries (Moreno, Sarría and Popkin, 2002). In the past two decades, levels of fruit and vegetable availability in most regions have been relatively flat, with the exception of large increases reported for China. However, it is not clear to what extent the rise in reported availability of fruit and vegetables in China reflects patterns of human consumption. Between 1991 and 1997, fruit and vegetable availability in China nearly doubled, increasing from 324 to 580 g/day (88 to 152 kcals/day), while reported consumption in adults in the CHNS changed very little – from 354 to 369 g/day. This raises questions about the accuracy of the Chinese fruit and vegetable availability data. Worldwide, current availability of fruit and vegetables, especially in sub-Saharan Africa and the Far East, remains well below availability levels in Mediterranean countries such as Spain (249 kcals/day) and Greece (359 kcals/day) (FAO, 2001).

With globalization, many developing countries are experiencing large shifts in food imports. Between 1990 and 1998, there were large increases in trade in processed grain products, while trade in unprocessed bulk grains has declined (Regmi and Gehlar, 2001). Similarly, there have been large increases in trade in oils (Williams, 1984). At the same time, foreign direct investment in the food industry, notably supermarkets and fast food restaurants, has expanded several-fold in many countries (Reardon, Timmer and Berdegue, 2003; Bolling and Somwaru, 2001). For example, between 1989 and 1998, sales by food processing affiliates owned by the United States in South America grew from US$5 billion to $15 billion, and sales in Asia increased from $5 billion to $20 billion (Bolling and Somwaru, 2001). These shifts have been accompanied by marketing of brands and shifts in cultural norms that have influenced tastes (Chopra, Galbraith and Darnton-Hill, 2002). Urbanization is associated with occupations that involve spending more time away from home (Popkin and Bisgrove, 1988). Thus, in many urbanized countries, intakes of processed foods, ready-to-eat meals and snacks, and street vendor, restaurant and fast food meals have increased (Regmi and Gehlar, 2001). These eating patterns are associated with higher intakes of fat, sugars and energy.

Some of the reasons for the large shifts in edible oil consumption in developing countries have been written about elsewhere (Drewnowski and Popkin, 1997). Technological breakthroughs in the development of high-yield oilseeds and in the refining of high-quality vegetable oils greatly reduced the cost of baking and frying fats, margarine, butter-like spreads, and salad and cooking oils in relation to animal-based products (Williams, 1984). Worldwide demand for vegetable fats was fuelled by health concerns regarding the consumption of animal fats and cholesterol. Furthermore, a number of major economic and political initiatives led to the development of oil crops not only in Europe and the United States, but also in Southeast Asia (palm oils) and in Brazil and Argentina (soybean oils) (USDA, 1966).

Delgado has written perceptively about the ASF revolution in low-income developing countries, or the increase in demand for and production of meat, fish and milk (Delgado *et al.*, 1999, 2001; Delgado, 2003). As relative commodity prices decrease and incomes increase, people usually diversify their diets and shift towards higher priced commodities and processed convenience foods. While average income growth explains overall growth, urbanization and population growth also helps to explain the greater increase in ASF demand in developing countries relative to developed countries. From 1975 to 1999, animal products drove the expansion of production in developing countries, which now account for more than half of the world's meat production (Delgado, 2003). In contrast, growth in ASF production in the developed world is now flat – the market is saturated. Given that 81 percent of the world's people live in developing countries, small shifts in their diets result in huge changes in the world market. Since 1970, relative prices of food have dropped considerably, most dramatically for beef (Delgado, 2003). Because of market saturation and technological changes that increase productivity, the ASF revolution is projected to level off by 2020.

In many countries, large increases in the consumption of sugar have also been observed. Sugar is the world's predominant sweetener but there are marked increases in the consumption of high fructose corn syrup as well (Bray, Nielsen and Popkin, 2004). Increasing sugar and sweetener use has been linked with industrialization, and with the proliferation of processed foods and beverages that have sugar added to them (e.g. tea, coffee, cocoa and soft drinks). Elsewhere we review in far more detail the way the world's diet has changed with respect to added caloric sweeteners (Popkin and Nielsen, 2003).

As shown using data from China these emerging, potentially adverse dietary patterns are especially marked in urban areas. Compared to rural dwellers, urban residents continue to consume higher levels of fats and animal foods, together with lower intakes of vegetables. However, the dietary effects of urbanization and globalization appear to be expanding into areas designated as rural. With marked increases in oils and ASF consumption in rural areas, the disparity between urban and rural intakes has become smaller over time. Rural consumption of these foods is particularly high in areas that are highly urbanized in terms of infrastructure and resources. In a companion paper, we explore dietary patterns in different urban contexts in greater detail (Mendez *et al.*, 2003). Only areas with very low levels of urbanicity have maintained traditional diets that are low in fat and animal source foods. "Urban" dietary patterns are likely to become more common throughout developing countries as the process of rural development, or increased urbanicity in rural areas, continues.

Disturbingly, there is evidence that the adverse changes in dietary intakes associated with urbanization are taking place at all levels of SES, and probably contribute to the rising levels of low-income obesity observed in some developing countries. In China, although low-income adults consumed lower levels of animal foods and oils than higher-income adults, the rate of increase in ASFs and edible oil consumption is, overall, faster in low-income groups. Relatively high levels of overweight were observed in low SES women in numerous developing countries, resulting in relatively small disparities in overweight between high and low SES groups.

These dietary shifts have occurred together with increased sedentarism in occupational activity and commuting, as well as in the nature of leisure-time activity (e.g. from increased television watching) (Bell, Ge and Popkin, 2001, 2002; Hu *et al.*, 2002; Tudor-Locke *et al.*, 2002). Because of their tendency to promote overconsumption, the dietary changes currently taking place in developing countries may help to explain energy imbalance and obesity, as individuals fail to adapt their energy intakes to match reduced energy expenditure levels. Together, these shifts in diet and activity have contributed to the rising obesity observed throughout the developing world at all income levels and increasingly in rural areas. The high speed of change is also a concern, as individuals exposed to undernutrition earlier in life are also making these dietary shifts. Individuals with very poor nutrition in early life may be at greater risk of adverse consequences, including diabetes, cardiovascular disease or weight gain (Barker, 2001; Schroeder, Martorell and Flores, 1999; Sawaya *et al.*, 2003; Reddy, 2002).

In addition to obesity, the dietary changes associated with urbanization and globalization are of great concern because of the implications for risk of obesity-related chronic disease. Large increases in the prevalence of numerous obesity-related chronic diseases have been documented around the developing world, including diabetes and cardiovascular diseases (Kumanyika *et al.*, 2002; Yusuf *et al.,* 2001). A large body of evidence, including data from clinical trials, shows that diets lower in meats and fats, and richer in fruit and vegetables, reduce blood pressure and risk of diabetes incidence as much or more than costly pharmacological treatments (Knowler *et al.*, 2002; Vollmer, Sacks and Svetkey, 2001).

Researchers working in many developing countries have begun to move beyond documenting shifts in obesity to documenting the dietary and activity shifts underlying the ongoing nutrition transition as well. Studies in several other developing countries have described dietary trends similar to those described here (e.g. Shetty, 2002; Kosulwat, 2002). The need to develop policies appropriate for the current nutrition climate, in which overweight has become a major health issue in developing countries, has been highlighted (Uauy and Kain, 2002). In a few countries, policies and programmes to shift dietary practices in developing countries to address obesity in addition to undernutrition are being put in place, although the effectiveness of these efforts is as yet unknown (Coitinho, Monteiro and Popkin, 2002; Zhai *et al.*, 2002).

As part of its National Plan of Action for Nutrition, China has developed important educational tools such as the "Chinese pagoda", a set of dietary guidelines for Chinese residents (Zhai *et al.*, 2002). Schools have been asked to increase time allotted to physical activity. The government has used subsidies to promote urban vegetable consumption in northern areas of China, and to promote rural gardens. Promotion of pulse consumption has been identified as a strategy for maintaining protein quality, while providing an alternative to meat as a source of protein (Leterme and Carmenza Munoz, 2002). As part of its nutrition plan, China has developed policies to increase soybean production and consumption (Zhai *et al.*, 2002). While meat production has nearly kept pace with rising demand and consumption, increases in soybean production and consumption to date have been relatively small (Geissler, 1999). Despite the large shifts in consumption and availability, meat imports were 1.7 percent of the total supply in 1990, and 3.6 percent in 2001 (FAO, 2001). Meanwhile, estimated availability of pulses in China remains fairly low

(36.6 g/capita/day in 2001; FAO, 2001), similar to mean reported intakes of pulses in recent surveys (39 g/day in 1991 and 44.6 g/day in 1997, among CHNS adults).

Brazil has also developed a new national food nutrition policy, addressing the emergence of obesity rather than underweight as the major problem of adult malnutrition (Coitinho, Monteiro and Popkin, 2002; Monteiro, Conde and Popkin, 2004). In addition to continuing efforts to combat malnutrition, components of this policy include development of nutrition labels, regulation of health claims about foods, and the regulation of school meals, but their effectiveness remains unknown. However, even before these policies were implemented, there was a marked decline in the rates of increase in obesity among high SES women (Monteiro *et al.*, 2000). The researchers suggested that intensive mass media attention paid to the epidemic of obesity may have contributed to the decline. Television and print media programmes provided extensive information on the consequences of obesity, as well as on obesity prevention measures.

Developing countries may benefit from preventive measures that minimize further adverse shifts in diet, rather than attempting to reverse shifts after new dietary patterns are even more established as cultural norms. Given that adverse dietary and activity patterns appear to be widespread geographically and socio-economically, strategies with broad outreach are appropriate, for example by exploiting the use of mass media. The experience in Brazil suggests that mass media nutrition education efforts may be effective in reaching some population groups. Another important component of obesity prevention may involve working with the food industry. In the United States, increases in portion sizes in commercial food products may have contributed to higher intakes of energy-dense foods and exceed standard serving sizes (Young and Nestle, 2003; Nielsen and Popkin, 2003). Working with or regulating the restaurant and supermarket industries to maintain appropriate portion sizes may help to minimize excess intakes. Pricing has also been shown to play a key role in food choices in both developed and developing countries (French, 2003; Guo *et al.*, 1999). The use of subsidies or other incentives to ensure that fresh fruit and vegetables are affordable may help to promote healthier food choices. Since high intakes of meat are associated with increased risk of hypertension and cardiovascular disease, developing countries should continue to explore more effective agricultural and educational policies that promote the production and consumption of pulses as protein substitutes. Tastes and preferences begin to be established in early life (Hill, 2002). Therefore, schools may provide an important opportunistic venue through which preferences for more healthy options can be encouraged. Workplaces also provide an opportunity to encourage or provide opportunities for exercise and healthier diets, and efforts in some countries have targeted work sites (Doak, 2002). Dietary policies should be accompanied by programmes to address country-specific barriers to maintaining high levels of physical activity, such as efforts to facilitate safe active commuting, and the promotion of physical activity during leisure time.

Bibliography

Ahmad, O.B., Boschi-Pinto, C., Lopez, A.D., Murray, C., Lozano, R. & Inoue, M. 1999. *Age standardization of rates: a new WHO standard.* GPE Discussion Paper Series No. 31. Geneva, World Health Organization.

Barker, D., ed. 2001. *Fetal origins of cardiovascular and lung disease.* New York, USA., Marcel Dekker, Inc.

Bell, C., Ge, K. & Popkin, B.M. 2001.Weight gain and its predictors in Chinese adults. *Int. J. Obes.,* 25: 1079-1086.

Bell, A.C., Ge, K. & Popkin, B.M. 2002. The road to obesity or the path to prevention? Motorized transportation and obesity in China. *Obes. Res.,* 10: 277-283.

Boerma, J.T. & Sommerfelt, A.E. 1993. Demographic and Health Surveys (DHS): contributions and limitations. *World Health Statistics Qtly*, 46: 222-226.

Bolling, C. & Somwaru, A. 2001. US food companies access foreign markets though direct investment. *Food Rev.,* 24(3): 23-28 (www.ers.usda.gov/publications/FoodReview/septdec01/).

Bray, G.A., Nielsen, S.J. & Popkin, B.M. 2004. Consumption of high-fructose corn syrup in beverages may play a role in the epidemic of obesity. *Am. J. Clin. Nutr.,* 79(4): 537-543.

Chopra, M., Galbraith, S. & Darnton-Hill, I. 2002. A global response to a global problem: the epidemic of overnutrition. *Bull. World Health Org.,* 80: 952-958.

Coitinho, D., Monteiro, C.A. & Popkin, B.M. 2002. What is Brazil doing to promote healthy diets and active lifestyles? *Public Health Nutr.,* 5(1A): 263-267.

Cook, P. & Kirkpatrick, C. 1997. Globalization, regionalization and third world development. *Regional Studies,* 31(1): 55-66.

Cornia, G.A. 2001. Globalization and health: results and options. *Bull. World Health Org.,* 79: 834-841.

Delgado, C.L. 2003. Rising consumption of meat and milk in developing countries has created a new food revolution. *J. Nutr.,* 133: 3907S-3910S.

Delgado, C., Rosegrant, M., Steinfeld, H., Ehui, S. & Courbois, C. 2001. Livestock to 2020: the next food revolution. *Outlook on Agr.,* 30(1): 27-29.

Delgado, C., Rosegrant, M., Steinfeld, H., Ehui, S. & Courbois, C. 1999. *Livestock to 2020: the next food revolution.* Food, Agriculture and the Environment Discussion Paper No. 28. Washington, DC, International Food Policy Research Institute (IFPRI).

Doak, C. 2002. Large-scale interventions and programmes addressing nutrition-related chronic diseases and obesity: examples from 14 countries. *Public Health Nutr.,* 5(1A): 275-277.

Dollar, D. 2001. Is globalization good for your health? *Bull. World Health Org.,* 79: 927-833.

Drewnowski, A. & Popkin, B.M. 1997. The nutrition transition: new trends in the global diet. *Nutr. Rev.,* 55: 31-43.

Du, S., Lu, B., Zhai, F. & Popkin, B. 2002a. A new stage of the nutrition transition in China. *Public Health Nutr.,* 5(1A): 169-174.

Du, S., Lu, B., Zhai, F. & Popkin, B. 2002b. The nutrition transition in China: a new stage of the Chinese diet. *In* B. Caballero & B.M. Popkin, eds. *The nutrition transition: diet and disease in the developing world.* London, Academic Press.

Entwisle, B., Henderson, G.E., Short, S., Bouma, J. & Fengying, Z. 1995. Gender and family businesses in Rural China. *Am. Sociol. Rev.,* 60: 36-57.

Evans, M., Sinclair, R.C., Fusimalohi, C. & Liava'a, V. 2001. Globalization, diet and health: an example from Tonga. *Bull. World Health Org.,* 79(9): 856-862.

Food and Agriculture Organization of the United Nations (FAO). 2001. *Food balance sheets* (apps.fao.org). Accessed June 2002.

French, S.A. 2003. Pricing effects on food choices. *J. Nutr.,* 133(3): 841S-843S.

Galloway, J.H. 2000. Sugar. *In* K.F. Kiple & K.C. Ornelas, eds. *The Cambridge World History of Food,* p. 437-449. Vol. I. New York, USA., Cambridge University Press.

Geissler, C. 1999. China: the soyabean-pork dilemma. *Proc. Nutr. Soc.,* 58(2): 345-353.

Guo, X., Popkin, B.M., Mroz, T.A. & Zhai, F. 1999. Food price policy can favorably alter macronutrient intake in China. *J. Nutr.,* 129: 994-1001.

Haddad, L., Ruel, M.T. & Garrett, J.L. 1999. Are urban poverty and undernutrition growing? Some newly assembled evidence. *World Dev.,* 27: 1891-1904.

Hill, A.J. 2002. Developmental issues in attitudes to food and diet. *Proc. Nutr. Soc.,* 61(2): 259-266.

Hu, G., Pekkarinen, H., Hanninen, O., Yu, Z., Huiguang, T., Zeyu, G. & Nissinen, A. 2002. Physical activity during leisure and commuting in Tianjin, China. *Bull. World Health Org.,* 80(12): 933-938.

Knowler, W.C., Barrett-Connor, E., Fowler, S.E., Hamman, R., Lachin, J., Walker, E. & Nathan, D. 2002. Reduction in the incidence of type 2 diabetes with lifestyle intervention or metformin. Diabetes Prevention Program Group. *N. Engl .J. Med.,* 346(6): 393-403.

Kosulwat, V. 2002. The nutrition and health transition in Thailand. *Public Health Nutr.,* 5(1A): 183-189.

Kumanyika, S., Jeffery, R.W., Morabia, A., Ritenbaugh, C. & Antipatis, V. 2002. Obesity prevention: the case for action. *Int. J. Obes. Relat. Metab. Disord.,* 26(3): 425-436.

Lang, T. 1999. Diet, health and globalization: five key questions. *Proceedings of the Nutrition Society,* 58(2): 335-343.

Leterme, P. & Carmenza Munoz, M.L. 2002. Factors influencing pulse consumption in Latin America. *Br. J. Nutr.,* 88 (Suppl 3): S251-255.

Mendez, M,, Stookey, J.D., Adair, L.S. & Popkin, B. 2003. *Measuring urbanization and its potential impact on health: the China case.* Chapel Hill, North Carolina, United States. (unpublished manuscript)

Mendez, M., Du, S. & Popkin, B.M. *Urbanization, income and the nutrition transition in China: a case study.* Paper prepared for the FAO Technical Workshop on Globalization of Food Systems: Impacts on Food Security and Nutrition, 8-10 October 2003, Rome.

Mintz, S. 1977. Time, sugar and sweetness. *In* C. Counihan & P. Van Esterik, eds. *Food and culture: a reader,* 77: 357-369. New York, USA., Routledge.

Monteiro, C.A., Conde, W.L., Lu, B. *et al.* 2003. *Is obesity fueling inequities in health in the developing world?* (submitted for publication)

Monteiro, C.A., Conde, W.L. & Popkin, B.M. 2004. The burden of disease due to under- and overnutrition in countries undergoing rapid nutrition transition: a view from Brazil. *Am. J. Public Health,* 94(3): 433-4.

Monteiro, C.A., Wolney, L.C. & Popkin, B.M. 2002. Is obesity replacing or adding to undernutrition? Evidence from different social classes in Brazil. *Publ. Health Nutr.,* 5(1A): 105-112.

Monteiro, C. A., Benicio, M.H.D.A., Conde, W.L. & Popkin, B.M. 2000. Shifting obesity trends in Brazil. *Eur. J. Clin. Nutr.,* 54: 342-346.

Moreno, L.A., Sarría, A. & Popkin, B.M. 2002. The nutrition transition in Spain: a European Mediterranean country. *Eur. J. Clin. Nutr.,* 56: 992-1003.

Nielsen, S.J. & Popkin, B.M. 2003. Patterns and trends in food portion sizes, 1977-1998. *JAMA,* 289(4): 450-453.

Popkin, B.M. 2002a. An overview on the nutrition transition and its health implications: the Bellagio meeting. *Publ. Health Nutr.,* 5(1A): 93-103.

Popkin, B.M. 2002b. The shift in stages of the nutrition transition in the developing world differs from past experiences! *Publ. Health Nutr.,* 5(1A): 205-214.

Popkin, B.M. & Nielsen, S.J. 2003. The sweetening of the world's diet. *Obes. Res.,* 11: 1325-1332.

Popkin, B.M. & Bisgrove, E.Z. 1988. Urbanization and nutrition in low-income countries. *Food Nutr. Bull.,* 10 (1): 3-23.

Popkin, B.M. & Du, S. 2003. Dynamics of the nutrition transition toward the animal foods sector in China and its implications: a worried perspective. *J. Nutr.,* 133: 3898S-3906S.

Popkin, B.M., Keyou, G., Zhai, F., Guo, X., Ma, H. & Zohoori, N. 1993. The nutrition transition in China: a cross-sectional analysis. *Eur. J. Clin. Nutr.,* 47: 333-346.

Reardon, T., Timmer, C.P. & Berdegue, J.A. 2003. The rise of supermarkets in Latin America and Asia: implications for international markets for fruits and vegetables. *In* A. Regmi & M. Gehlhar, eds. *Global markets for high value food products.* Agricultural Information Bulletin, USDA, Economic Research Service. Washington, DC. (in press)

Reddy, K.S. 2002. Cardiovascular diseases in the developing countries: dimensions, determinants, dynamics and directions for public health action. *Publ. Health Nutr.,* 5(1A): 231-237.

Regmi, A. & Gehlar, M. 2001. Consumer preferences and concerns shape global food trade. *Food Rev.,* 24(3): 2-8.

Rivera, J.A., Barquera, S., Campirano, F., Campos, I., Safdie, M. & Tovar, V. 2002. Epidemiological and nutritional transition in Mexico: rapid increase of non-communicable chronic diseases and obesity. *Publ. Health Nutr.,* 5(1A): 113-122.

Rolls, B.J. 2000. The role of energy density in the overconsumption of fat. *J. Nutr.,* 30(2S): 268S-271S.

Sachs, J.D. & Warner, A. 1995. Economic reform and the process of global integration. *Brookings Papers on Economic Activity, 25th Anniversary Issue,* 1: 1-64.

Sawaya, A.L., Martins, P., Hoffman, D. & Roberts, S. 2003. The link between childhood undernutrition and risk of chronic diseases in adulthood: a case study of Brazil. *Nutr. Rev.,* 61(5 Part 1): 168-75.

Schroeder, D.G., Martorell, R., & Flores, R. 1999. Infant and child growth and fatness and fat distribution in Guatemalan adults. *Am. J. Epidemiol.,* 149(2): 177-185.

Shetty, P.S. 2002. Nutrition transition in India. *Publ. Health Nutr.,* (1A): 175-182.

Tudor-Locke, C., Neff, L.J., Ainsworth, B.E., Addy C. & Popkin B. 2002. Omission of active commuting to school and the prevalence of children's health-related physical activity levels: the Russian Longitudinal Monitoring Study. *Child Care Health Dev.,* 28(6): 507-512.

Uauy, R. & Kain, J. 2002. The epidemiological transition: need to incorporate obesity prevention into nutrition programmes. *Public Health Nutr.,* 5(1A): 223-229.

United Nations Population Division. 2002. *World urbanization prospects: the 2001 revision.* (www.un.org/esa/population/publications/wup2001/WUP2001Annextab.pdf). Accessed 19 July 2003.

US Department of Agriculture (USDA). 1966. *US fats and oils statistics, 1909-65.* Statistical Bulletin No. 376. Economic Research Service. Washington, DC.

US Department of Agriculture (USDA). 2000. *Dietary guidelines for Americans.* Center for Nutrition Policy and Promotion (www.health.gov/dietaryguidelines/dga2000/document/contents.htm).

Vollmer, W.M., Sacks, F.M. & Svetkey, L.P. 2001. New insights into the effects on blood pressure of diets low in salt and high in fruits and vegetables and low-fat dairy products. *Curr. Control Trials Cardiovasc. Med.,* 2(2): 71-74.

Williams, G.W. 1984. Development and future direction of the world soybean market. *Q. J. Intl. Agr.,* 23: 319-337.

World Bank. 2001. *World Development Report 2000/2001: attacking poverty.* New York, USA., Oxford University Press.

Young, L.R. & Nestle, M. 2003. Expanding portion sizes in the US marketplace: implications for nutrition counseling. *J. Am. Diet. Assoc.,* 103(2): 231-234.

Yusuf, S., Reddy, S., Ounpuu, S. & Anand, S. 2001. Global burden of cardiovascular diseases. Part I. General considerations, the epidemiologic transition, risk factors, and impact of urbanization. *Circulation,* 104(22): 2746-2753.

Zhai, F., Fu, D., Du, S., Ge, K., Chen, C. & Popkin, B. 2002. What is China doing in policy-making to push back the negative aspects of the nutrition transition? *Public Health Nutr.,* 5(1A): 269-273.

The growing global obesity problem: some policy options to address it

Josef Schmidhuber [1]

INTRODUCTION

The last two centuries have seen a fundamental transformation of diets in essentially all affluent countries. At the beginning of this transformation was the agro-industrial revolution of the nineteenth century, which provided people with the expertise to produce more, the income to consume more, and increasingly sophisticated food products. The modernization of agriculture has played a pivotal role in bringing about change. The rigorous application of scientific advances to traditional agriculture, mechanization, genetic improvements and the development of fertilizers and pesticides enabled a doubling and redoubling of food production within the time span of a few decades. In fact, productivity growth was so strong that growth in production comfortably exceeded growth in demand and afforded a rapidly growing population more and better food at declining real prices. Agricultural productivity growth also promoted the industrialization of the then largely agrarian societies. It helped accumulate capital, free up labour and provide ever more and more nutritious food. Eventually, a virtuous circle was created where productivity growth, rising incomes and better nutrition became mutually supportive and thus spurred overall economic development[2]. At least for the nineteenth century, however, these developments remained largely limited to industrial countries.

It took more than a century before the agro-industrial revolution started to reach the first developing countries. With the beginning of the 1960s, the same factors that had initiated the agro-industrial revolution in the developed world in the previous century got a foothold in the food and agricultural sectors of parts of the developing world. The combination of modern varieties, expansion of irrigation, more and improved input supplies and the widespread mechanization of production made more food available to consumers in developing countries. Since the early 1960s, the average calorie availability in the developing world has increased from about 1 950 to 2 680 kcals/person/day while protein availability nearly doubled from about 40 to 70 g/person/day. The prevalence of undernourishment declined from 37 percent in 1970 to 17 percent in 2000 and, while more than 840 million of people (FAO, 2003) are still food insecure, this is more often the result of adverse local production conditions, war and civil strife, a lack of income and of access to food rather than the inability of the world as a whole to produce and provide enough food.

[1] Josef Schmidhuber
Global Perspectives Studies Unit
Economic and Social Department
Food and Agriculture Organization of the United Nations
Tel.: (39) 06 5705-6264
E-mail: Josef.Schmidhuber@fao.org.

[2] Fogel (1994) estimates that half of the overall economic growth in France and England in the nineteenth century was a result of better nutrition.

As in the industrial world of the nineteenth century, consumers in developing countries have benefited the most from advances in agricultural productivity. In real terms, food prices have declined to the lowest levels in history and, together with gains in broader economic growth, have enabled consumers today to eat better while spending less and less of their budget on food. However, not all countries and regions have benefited from these advances. In parts of the developing word, notably in sub-Saharan Africa, these advances have not even started to yield a meaningful impact. But in many developing countries, the progress in access to providing more, better and cheaper food has been impressive.[3] The rapid decline in real food prices has allowed consumers in developing countries to embark on food consumption patterns that were reserved for consumers in industrialized countries at much higher gross domestic product (GDP) levels. Today, a consumer in a developing country can purchase more calories than ever before and more than consumers in industrialized countries ever could at comparable income levels. In China, for instance, consumers today have about 3 000 kcals/day and 50 kg of meat per year (FAO, 2004) at their disposal – at less than US$1 000 nominal income per year (World Bank, 2002).

In addition to falling real prices of food, rapid urbanization has affected and will continue to affect consumption patterns. Essentially the entire population growth over the next 30 years will be urban. Urbanization creates a new and improved marketing and distribution infrastructure; attracts supermarkets and their sophisticated food handling systems (cold chains, etc.); makes for better roads and ports, thus improving the access of foreign suppliers and the importance of imports in the overall food supply; and, all in all, will promote a globalization of dietary patterns. Most important from a nutrition perspective, these changes include not only a shift towards higher food energy supplies but also a shift towards more fats and oils and more animal-based foodstuffs, and thus higher intakes of saturated fat and cholesterol.

The shifts in consumption patterns and lifestyles have resulted in a rapid increase in the prevalence of obesity and related non-communicable diseases (NCDs) in developed countries. Many developing countries are in the process of undergoing a similar nutrition transition (see WHO, 2003), with probably even more adverse health impacts. The main compounding factor of these nutritional changes is a phenotypic and genotypic predisposition towards developing obesity and NCDs. The phenotypic predisposition is the result of rapid transition from hunger and undernourishment towards overnutrition and affluence. There is ample empirical evidence that hunger and malnutrition "programme" the next generation to develop a more efficient energy metabolism and thus to have a higher propensity to develop obesity and related NCDs (see Delisle, 2002 for a comprehensive discussion). In addition, populations of developing countries have on average a genetic predisposition towards developing obesity and NCDs (thrifty *genotype,* Miller and Colagiuri, 1994).

The combination of: (i) the rapid nutrition transition with a rapidly declining share of expenditure on food as a percentage of total expenditure/income; (ii) urbanization; (iii) the shift in diet towards more animal products; and (iv) the phenotypic and genotypic predisposition towards a more efficient metabolism and NCDs could spark a rapid increase in the prevalence of obesity and NCDs in developing countries over the next generations.

---

[3] While not all developing countries have benefited from rapid income growth and nor have they experienced the same rapid socio-economic transformations that come with rapid industrialization and urbanization, the number of countries that are in the process of a profound transformation of their food economies is steadily increasing. As population giants such as China, India, Indonesia, Brazil and Mexico are among the most rapid transformers, the nutrition transition affects a large and growing share of the developing world's population.

The human and economic toll could be dramatic and, for many, the exit from food poverty may be associated with a straight entry into health poverty. This means that, while fewer people will suffer from hunger and chronic undernourishment, more will have health problems related to obesity and NCDs. The impacts will be felt more strongly than in developed countries as fewer consumers in developing countries will be able to afford the needed medical treatment even if they can afford more food. Many NCDs have a lethal impact if left untreated.

The rapid increase of NCDs also suggests that some of these concerns have already become a reality, at least in *developed* countries. Phenotypic and genotypic predisposition for obesity and NCDs in *developing* countries, in conjunction with the rapid nutrition transition towards higher calorie availabilities in general and more livestock products in particular, suggest that their populations may have to cope with an even bigger problem in a shorter period of transition. The policy messages emerging from these links are straightforward. First, all efforts that help fight hunger today and improve the nutritional situation of women of child-bearing age have the potential to yield an extra dividend for coming generations. Second, nutritional education and supplementary feeding programmes for pregnant women that ensure a balanced and healthy diet are even more important than hitherto assumed.[4] Third, policy-makers in developed and developing countries alike have to think about possible policy measures that can help contain a growing obesity problem without thwarting progress in fighting hunger.

As far as the fight against hunger is concerned, there is no shortage of programmes and projects that could provide or at least promise success. But policy approaches that could help contain or reverse the global obesity problem are rather new. The various proposals and their pros and cons are being discussed at the moment in many developed countries (for example, Australia, the United States of America and the United Kingdom of Great Britain and Northern Ireland).[5] The remainder of this paper aims to shed some light on the various proposals and will also try to assess possible interactions and incompatibilities with other policy measures. It will first look at the effects of price interventions, both at the level of primary commodities and final consumer goods (tax on fat food), then examine the possibilities of tax on excess body weight (tax on fat people), and finally present some experience gathered with a combination of various measures in integrated nutritional programmes. The discussion of the various policy options includes an examination of their effectiveness and efficiency, and an evaluation of their pros and cons and their compatibility with other policies. However, the presentation and discussion of possible policy measures will be limited to a few instruments; the focus will be placed on policy measures that have received particular prominence in the current public discussion in developed countries and in developing countries in rapid economic and nutrition transition; no claim is being made that the selection of instruments is comprehensive or representative.

---

[4] They could be of critical importance in those developing countries where the prospects for a rapid increase in calorie availability combined with a more efficiently "programmed" metabolism could result in a disproportionate increase in obesity and related NCDs.

[5] For the United Kingdom, see for instance: news.bbc.co.uk/1/hi/uk/2988314.stm; for the United States: www.usatoday.com/life/2002/2002-02-19-diet.htm; for Australia: www.consumerfreedom.com/headline_detail.cfm?HEADLINE_ID=1960.

FOOD PRICE INTERVENTIONS

One of the most popular proposals to come to grips with the growing obesity epidemic and associated public health costs has been the proposal of a tax on energy-rich foodstuffs.[6] These proposals are now being discussed by health officials and public policy-makers with a view to identifying their *effectiveness* in reaching their stated objectives, their *efficiency* relative to other measures, and their shortfalls and side-effects. In principle, interventions could take place at two different levels. The first would be to influence producer prices for food, i.e. interventions at the agricultural producer level. There is a long history of such interventions in Organisation for Economic Co-operation and Development (OECD) countries and an equally long debate about the effects and problems that have emerged with such interventions on agriculture, but relatively little has been said about consumers and food consumption. The second entry-point for price interventions would be at the consumer price level. These interventions are currently largely limited to surcharges in the form of value-added tax (VAT) and total or partial exemptions from such VAT surcharges. The following will try to shed some light on possible impacts of the two types of intervention and will try to provide answers that arise in the context of policy interventions.

The case for food price interventions

The basic case for food price interventions rests on the notion that higher prices could provide a means to reduce excess food consumption, which is in turn associated with significant societal externalities. Put differently, the price of food energy set by a free market reflects the cost of producing the food rather than true cost (which is the production cost plus the external costs of treating NCDs such as coronary heart disease (CHD) or non-insulin dependent diabetes mellitus (NIDDM)). If food markets fail to capture the full costs of excess consumption, a tax – set at the level where production cost plus tax will equal the production cost plus external costs – would provide an economically efficient solution.

But there may be important rejoinders to the tax argument. For instance, that a tax on excess food consumption could be a regressive tax as it creates an extra burden on people with higher calorie needs or lower incomes. Moreover, interventions on food prices in a system of increasingly freer trade in food and agriculture are likely to create incompatibilities with commitments taken elsewhere, notably those taken within the World Trade Organization (WTO). Not liberalizing trade means foregoing efficiency gains to be had from a better allocation of production, which would need to be taken into account in the overall cost-benefit analysis of such a tax. How effective and efficient these taxes are in practice, and how compatible they are with other policy reforms will be discussed in the following section.

Price interventions at the producer level: "a tax on primary products"

As already mentioned, producer price interventions for food products are a commonly used tool of agricultural policies in developing and developed countries alike. Numerous studies have analysed their impacts on agriculture, farm households, incomes, the environment or rural development. But relatively little is known about their impacts on consumers and food consumption patterns. In fact, many analyses simply assume that changes in producer

---

[6] For details of a recent debate at governmental level on a tax on fatty foods in the United Kingdom, see for example: www.theage.com.au/articles/2004/02/19/1077072753005.html?from=storyrhs or news.bbc.co.uk/1/hi/health/3502053.stm.

prices are fully transmitted to the consumer level or that consumers are implicitly assumed to change their consumption patterns according to a change in producer prices.

Interventions at the producer level have been subject to controversial policy debates, particularly those associated with higher border protection, intervention price systems and export subsidies. Any suggestion to increase such measures for the sake of possible health benefits would therefore add to an already contentious debate and should be most carefully vetted before any inference is drawn.

Much of the rationale put forward by the proponents of agricultural price interventions rests on the observations that countries with massive support to agriculture, high producer prices and high border protection are benefiting from relatively moderate prevalence levels for obesity. This relationship is depicted in Figure 1, which in fact suggests that the OECD countries with the highest Producer Support Estimate rates (PSE) (Japan, the Republic of Korea, Norway and Switzerland) have the lowest prevalence rates of obesity, while Australia, New Zealand and the United States, all with low or middling levels of protection, are burdened with relatively high prevalence rates of obesity. The question that arises in this context is whether this relationship is of a causal nature, i.e. whether it is a matter of correlation or causation.

FIGURE 1
Support for agriculture and the prevalence of obesity

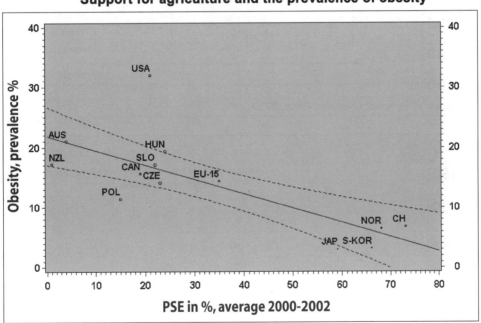

Source: International Obesity Task Force (IOTF) and OECD; FAO, Global Perspectives Studies Unit, 2003.

A necessary condition for a causal relationship is that a price increase at the level of the protected agricultural product has a substantial impact on final consumer prices. The question therefore is how and to what extent prices are transmitted along the food chain and to what extent the value share of farm products affects the final consumer price. A number of empirical studies help to find an answer to this question (e.g. Wohlgenant). These studies show that: (i) the value share of primary products in the final consumer good has been declining over time (with rising value share of services included in the product); and (ii) that there are considerable differences across commodities (for example, very low for wheat/bread and high for eggs). The high service element in the differences also means that the margins between producer and consumer prices are typically much higher in developed than in developing countries. For some products at least, an increase in the producer price in a developed country (regardless of whether through higher border protection, higher support prices or a combination of the two) may therefore not create a sizeable increase in consumer prices. This suggests that a change (increase) in producer prices for food would in general be a rather blunt tool to change food prices at the consumer level and thus have little influence on food demand. Figure 2 should help explain the channels that affect the transmission of prices from producers to consumers.

FIGURE 2
Examples of the agricultural price formation at support levels and processing margins

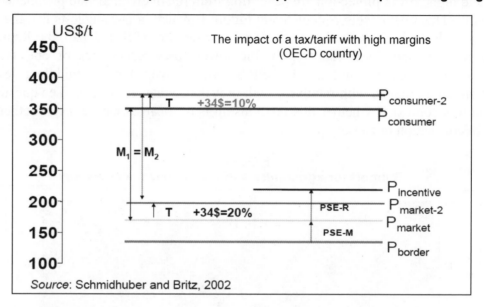

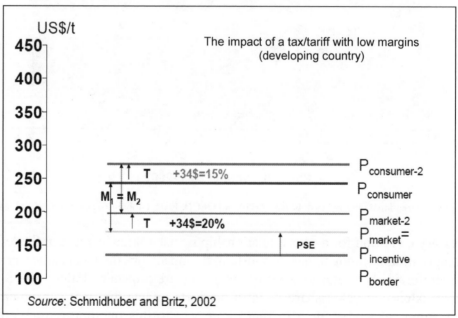

The upper pane of Figure 2 depicts the main factors that affect the *horizontal* and *vertical* price transmission for food products in a *developed* country (Schmidhuber and Britz, 2002). What is referred to as the horizontal transmission is essentially the transmission of primary product prices across the border from international markets to the domestic commodity market. In many OECD countries, this process is often heavily affected by agricultural policy measures. In this process, the internal price formation starts from a (low) border price that is raised, e.g. through a tariff, to the level of the domestic market price. For producers, this market price is further increased (e.g. through a direct transfer) to the level of the farm incentive price, which drives the level of input applications and allocated area. The domestic market price is where the vertical price transmission process starts. It starts with a wholesale operation (cooperative), pooling supplies from farmers; the primary products (cereals) are then further processed at various stages (flour, bran, etc.); intermediate products are further refined (different types of flour), added to other products and eventually sold as the final consumer good (bread, breakfast cereals, etc.) by a retailer (supermarket, bakery). In this multistage process, the various agents often add considerable margins for the processing or marketing services they provide. As a result, the value share of primary good (wheat) eventually accounts for only a small share of the final value of consumer good (bread)[7,8].

The situation is quite different where primary products account for a larger value share in the final consumer good (Figure 2, lower pane); not an atypical case for the price formation in many *developing* countries. Any price increase at the producer level would translate into a more substantial increase in consumer prices and, where consumers are price responsive, result in a reduction of consumption. Higher consumer prices for food in developing countries, however, may also mean that – other things being equal – undernourishment may increase. It also explains, although does not justify, why many developing countries have chosen to tax their agriculture to the benefit of (urban) consumers rather than protecting it.

From the consumer point of view, the impacts of low shares on the final product is in effect described by Marshall's theory of derived demand (Marshall, 1920), i.e. that demand is typically fairly inelastic where the primary commodity forms only a small component of the final good. It may therefore be more efficient to levy a tax directly at the consumer level, again distinguishing the impacts of low and high price elasticities of demand.

Price interventions at the consumer level: a tax on "fat food"
A similar, although in its impacts somewhat different, approach to address the growing obesity problem is the proposal to levy a tax directly on consumer prices of food. Particularly in developed countries, the discussion has recently advanced from the theoretical proposition to examining actual and operational issues. Public health officials[9] in particular have been proposing concrete measures to increase the costs of energy-dense and "saturated fat rich" foods by adding an extra tax on energy-rich food or reducing the food VAT exemptions that are still in place in many countries.

While enthusiasm among public health advisors for such a tax is understandable, issues pertaining to the economic effectiveness and the operational efficiency of such measures in reducing obesity are less clear. Again, the effectiveness of such a measure depends crucially on how responsive consumers of these foods are to price changes induced by

---

[7] Notable consumer price impacts are only likely if tariffs are extraordinarily high and/or processing and marketing margins are very small. Rice in Japan could be a case for more significant impacts on consumer prices, except that consumers in Japan have shown little responsiveness in their consumption of rice.

[8] In Figure 2 (upper pane), the margin between producer and consumer prices is assumed to be 100 percent. For cereals, the margin may exceed 500 percent and more, while it should be less than 100 percent for eggs.

[9] Dr Martin Breach, spokesperson for the British Medical Association, for instance, proposed a 17.5 percent VAT on high-fat foods. The Australian Medical Association is promoting similar measures.

(higher) taxes. The elasticities used in the FAO@2030 model[10] in Figure 3 give an idea of the general link between income levels and the responsiveness of demand with respect to income levels. They show a clear and strong decline of income elasticities with rising incomes and thus suggest that rich consumers are likely to react much less to a tax on certain foods than poor consumers.

FIGURE 3
Income elasticities at different income levels

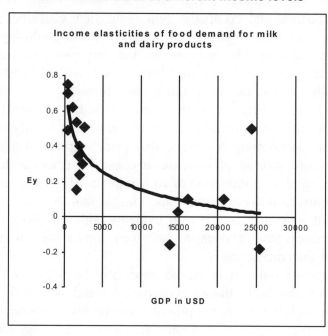

Source: Schmidhuber and Britz, 2002.

In general, income elasticities decline with rising incomes and even become negative (inferior goods) once a certain income level is exceeded. In tandem with lower income elasticities, price elasticities tend to decline (in absolute values) with rising incomes.[11] A detailed study by the US Department of Agriculture (USDA) (Regmi *et al.*) fully confirms the theoretical expectation with ample evidence from more than 100 countries. As depicted in Figure 4, rising incomes are associated with a sharp decline in own price elasticities from -0.9 in low-income countries to close to zero in the top range of the high-income countries.

---

[10] A description of the model is available in Schmidhuber and Britz, 2002.
[11] Falling income elasticities do not necessarily mean that price elasticities are also falling with higher incomes. In fact, it is possible to construct a globally well-behaved demand system with low-income elasticities as well as high own and cross-price effects. In reality, however, low-income elasticities for food are also associated with low price and cross-price effects.

FIGURE 4
Price elasticities for food across income ranges

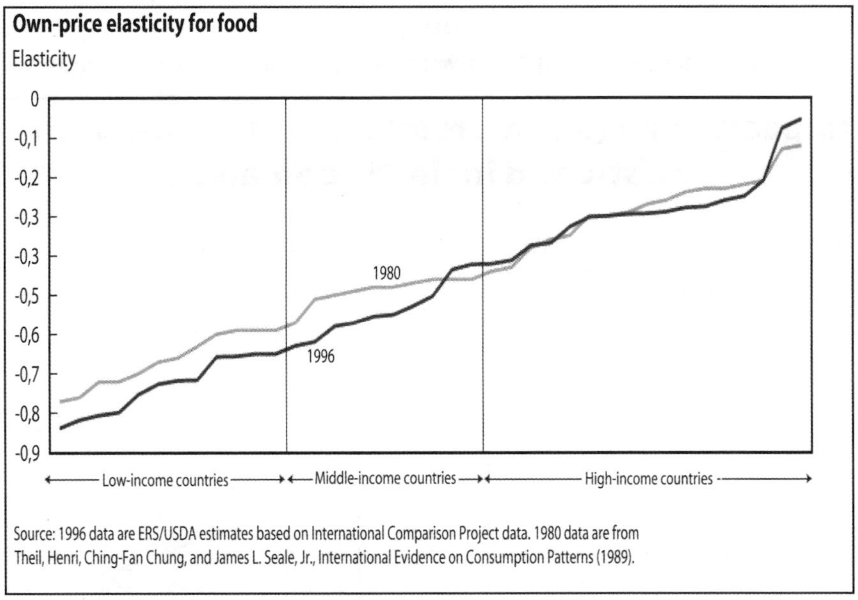
Own-price elasticity for food
Elasticity
0
-0,1
-0,2
-0,3
-0,3
-0,5
-0,6
-0,7
-0,8
-0,9
1980
1996
Low-income countries
Middle-income countries
High-income countries
Source: 1996 data are ERS/USDA estimates based on International Comparison Project data. 1980 data are from Theil, Henri, Ching-Fan Chung, and James L. Seale, Jr., International Evidence on Consumption Patterns (1989).

Source: Regmi et al, 2001.

The results of this research are summarized in Seale, Regmi and Bernstein (2003). They confirm many of the results obtained and established by earlier studies, notably that: (i) low-income countries spend a greater portion of their budget on necessities, such as food, while richer countries spend a greater proportion of their income on luxuries, such as recreation; (ii) low-value staples, such as cereals, account for a larger share of the food budget in poorer countries, while high-value food items, such as dairy and meat, constitute a larger share of the food budget in richer countries; and (iii) low-income countries are more responsive to changes in income and food prices and, therefore, make larger adjustments to their food consumption pattern when incomes and prices change. However, Seale, Regmi and Bernstein (2003) also found that adjustments to price and income changes are not made uniformly across all food categories. Staple food consumption changes the least, while consumption of higher-value food items such as dairy and meat changes the most. Additionally, the results indicate that when price changes are accompanied by equivalent income changes, wealthier low-income countries and middle-income countries make the most adjustments to their food demand (Seale, Regmi and Bernstein, 2003).

Assuming the basic relationships between food demand, incomes and prices, the principal impacts of a change in food prices, e.g. through a tax, can be examined. Figure 5 depicts the demand response to a tax on excess calories with price elastic (right pane) and price inelastic (left pane) demand. Where demand is inelastic (rich consumers, left pane of Figure 5), a tax on fat food will bring about only a small reduction in demand, thus only providing a small contribution to reducing food intakes and possibly obesity. In fact, the impact of the tax on demand will decline with the elasticity, while the tax revenues will increase. This low-responsiveness situation characterizes many food markets in developed countries, particularly where income differences within an economy are relatively small. The effect could be quite different in middle-income developing countries or in developed countries where incomes are less evenly distributed. Here a tax on excess calorie consumption – applied uniformly across all income strata – would do little to reduce obesity in the high-income-low elasticity strata but could have a consumption-contracting effect on poor elastically reacting consumers.

FIGURE 5
Impacts of a tax on food with elastic and inelastic demand

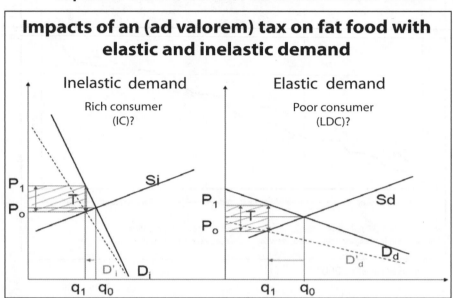

There is empirical work that – by and large – confirms these theoretical expectations. In China, for instance, Guo *et al.* (1999) documented the possible reactions of consumers to price changes in various food items across a range of income strata. They found that: (i) consumers in low-income strata are more responsive to price changes for certain food items than rich consumers. For example, pork consumers in the poorest strata are reacting three times as elastically as consumers in the richest strata; and (ii) "an increase in the price of a food tends to drive consumption away towards its substitutes". They finally conclude that "increases in food prices have much less favourable effects for the poor" (Guo *et al.*, 1999).

Where income elasticities are low but substitutability between the various foodstuffs is high, a price-induced reduction of consumption in a given good is associated with higher consumption of its substitutes. In such a situation, taxes may well help to direct consumption of single food components in the desired direction, but the impacts on overall energy intake are likely to be limited. If, for instance, calories from animal fats are being taxed, consumption of vegetable oils and fats is likely to increase.[12] Numerous other side-effects could result.

A tax on animal fats, for instance, should promote the production and consumption of so-called "light" products (light yoghurts, low fat milk, etc.), while consumers would tend to reduce foodstuffs with high calorie contents. But the excess fat is likely to surface elsewhere in the food chain either domestically or abroad. One vent for surplus in many developed markets is the fast food and snack food industry that adds extra fat and sugar to many of its products, including ice cream, hamburgers and French fries. If these "junk" foods were to be taxed, the fat and sugar added currently to ice creams and hamburgers would occur elsewhere in the food chain. If not domestically, the high calorie parts of a

---

[12] As King (2002) puts it: "If the government regulates the content of, say, fast food, people will find fat elsewhere".

foodstuff could be exported and end up in developing countries. A case in point is poultry meat, where rich economies already consume predominantly the lean parts (breasts), while the fattier parts (leg quarters, wings) are primarily exported, with possible adverse effects on the food consumption patterns and agricultural economies of those countries that import them.

Another problem with a tax on excess calorie consumption is that in practice such a tax would have to be imposed on food items rather than on nutrients (energy) directly. As food items typically contain a group of different nutrients, a tax on a food item rather than on a nutritional component could bring about undesired side-effects. Guo *et al.* (1999), for instance, found that higher pork prices in China may indeed help reduce the intake of energy and saturated fatty acids of rich consumers but may cause an undesired fall in protein consumption by the poor.

A look at excess body weights and dietary energy supply (DES) levels across countries seems to confirm the described impacts of a food tax on overweight and obesity. The left pane of Figure 6 depicts the DES levels and *male overweight*[13,14] in those countries for which OECD and the International Obesity Task Force (IOTF) provide information. It may help to illustrate a number of different issues that characterize the relationship between dietary energy supplies and excess body weight across different populations. First, it suggests that a considerable overweight/obesity problem can exist even where food supply levels are low on average. Second, the prevalence of excess body weight increases with the average food availability. Third, once the DES exceeds a certain level (about 3 300 kcals/person/day), there is no more increase in the prevalence of overweight. In fact, if obesity estimates were included, the curve would be flatter. The latter reflects the fact that a large share of calories above 3 300 calories is likely to be wasted. All in all, the relationship between food availability and excess body weight resembles a typical input-output function (agricultural production function, diminishing production increments per unit of additional applications of an input, e.g. fertilizer, beyond a certain level).

The tax on fat food (input) – in the context of an input-output function – helps to illustrate the possible impact of a change in input prices (tax on fat food) on the level of output (excess body weight). The right pane of Figure 6 combines the impacts of a tax on excess food energy intake in the input market with the likely effects on the output market (excess body weight). It underlines that the small impacts of the tax on actual food availability are even further reduced as the tax is effective in the flat part of the food energy/body weight curve. The flat part of the curve reflects the fact that a high DES is associated with high levels of waste; societies with more than 3 300 kcals also waste a lot more food and may thus not experience such a rapid increase in the prevalence of excess body weight.

---

[13]   Male overweight was chosen because of the larger sample size, which also included low-income countries.

[14]   A look at the prevalence of excess body weight across different income strata within a country would have been preferable, but was – in the absence of data - impossible.

FIGURE 6
Impacts of a food tax on excess body weight

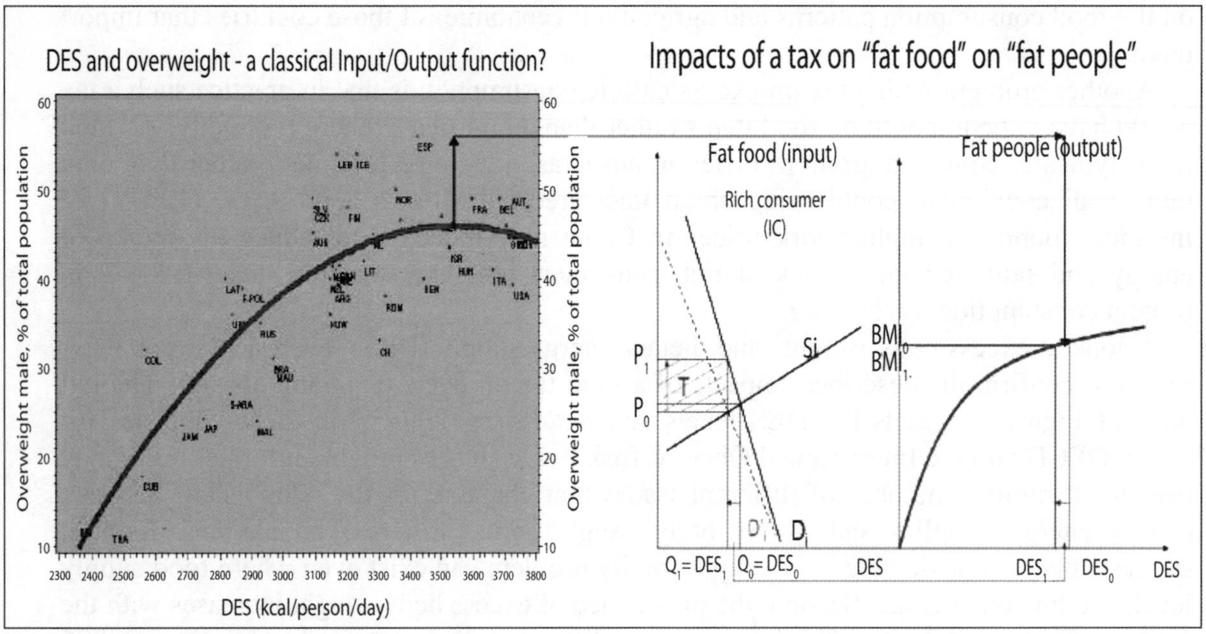

Source: OECD/FAO/IOTF 1991-2001
FAO. Global Perspective Studies Unit. 2003

Waste is in fact usually the most elastic form of utilization and may therefore be the first to be reduced when prices rise (through tax). Again, this buffer is likely to be more (less) pronounced where incomes and food availability are high (low). As DES levels climb above the 3 300 kcals threshold, the largest part of the incremental food availability is likely to be wasted. This means that a tax on excess calorie consumption (e.g. on calorie-rich foods) may primarily reduce the level of waste in rich countries/for rich consumers while it may affect more directly the poorer consumers with lower waste levels. In the worst case (elastic poor and inelastic rich consumers and large income disparities), a tax on food may do little about obesity and increase undernourishment. In the best case (high level of equality, low food demand responsiveness), it will have a small impact on obesity, reduce waste to a certain extent and be an effective means to collect money that could be used to finance programmes for nutrition education.

As shown above, the link between calorie availability and excess body weight of Figure 6 is based on a cross-country (intercountry) analysis of available data. It was also mentioned that an intracountry analysis of excess body weight would have been preferable but had to be dismissed because of a lack of income-stratified obesity data. The problem with the cross-country data is that they may not be representative of the obesity distribution within a country. In fact, there is growing evidence that – within rich countries – excess body weight is increasingly a problem for poorer consumers, who rely heavily on the cheap but empty calories of the fast food industry. Nestle (2003), for instance, claims that obesity is increasingly becoming a problem of the poor who are disproportionately high consumers of cheap dietary energy. In this case, a tax on certain energy-rich food items ("junk food") could in fact have a curbing impact on consumption. The problem is of course whether poor consumers in developed countries have alternatives that they could resort to in the case of an extra tax on such food items.

Nevertheless, the disadvantages of food price interventions are likely to outweigh their advantages in reducing or reversing the trend towards a higher prevalence of obesity. For rich consumers, inelastic demand will limit the desired impacts on food demand, while for poor consumers high prices may create an added food insecurity problem. That said, targeted price interventions at the consumer level can have an impact on food consumption patterns if: (i) they are targeted; (ii) demand is reasonably elastic; and (iii) consumers have a choice to shift to healthier foods. Where marketing and processing costs are high and taxes are applied to the final consumer good, the tax revenues could be considerable, the impacts on primary agriculture would be small and thus the trade distortions would be minimal. Where processing margins are small and demand is elastic, tax revenues would be small and the risk of creating adverse impacts on food security could be considerable.

A TAX ON EXCESS BODY WEIGHT: "TAX ON FAT PEOPLE"

The low effectiveness and efficiency of a tax on energy-dense foods in reducing excess body weight in affluent societies, its potential for creating added trade problems and the risk of increasing food insecurity in poor societies or poor segments of rich societies pose the question of a more effective alternative. One of the most frequently discussed options is a tax on excess body weight rather than on excess calorie consumption. Colloquially, this proposal is being referred to as a tax on "fat people" as opposed to a tax on "fat food".

While such a proposal may sound exotic at first, in practice it is not. In fact, there are already various forms of incentives or disincentives in place that aim to reduce excess body weight (or prevent increases in excess body weight). However, none of these measures are referred to as a tax on fat people. Health insurances, for instance, offer discounts on premiums for clients with normal body weights. Car insurers have started to offer discounts to normal weight customers as there is growing evidence that obese drivers have a higher risk of causing an accident. Even fast food chains introduce implicit taxes on overweight people by rejecting obese job applicants (Greenhouse, 2003). On the incentive side, employers offer free access to gyms to their employees even during working hours as there is ample evidence that excess body weight reduces the productivity of their staff and increases disability and sick leave claims (Figure 7). In the United States, probably the most important incentive to reduce excess body weight was brought about by a new policy of the Internal Revenue Service (IRS, 2002), stating that "obesity is medically accepted to be a disease in its own right". For taxpayers, this now means that treatment specifically for obesity can be claimed as a medical tax deduction.[15]

---

[15] "Uncompensated amounts paid by individuals for participation in a weight-loss program as treatment for a specific disease or diseases (including obesity) diagnosed by a physician are expenses for medical care that are deductible under §213, subject to the limitations of that section."

FIGURE 7
Economic costs of obesity

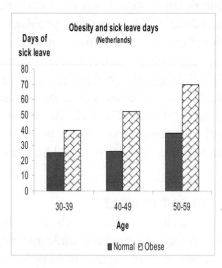

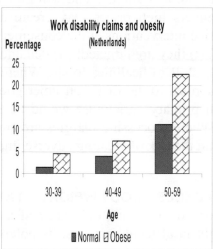

Source: Narbro *et al.*, 1996.

The basic case for these measures rests on the social costs that overweight people cause for society (Figure 7). To the extent that obesity creates external costs for society, a tax on fat people could be perceived as a "Pigouvian" tax that helps bring private costs (low premium and low perception of personal health damage) in line with the social costs for society, i.e. higher health expenditures, lower productivity or more disability claims. To the extent that obesity is a question of nurture rather than nature, such a tax would essentially reflect the application of the "polluter pays principle" for obesity. The crucial questions for practical policy implementation are: (i) whether such a tax on the "output" (excess body weight) would be more efficient and more effective than a tax on the "input" (excess food consumption); (ii) what differential impacts such measures would have on rich and poor consumers, food availability and food security; and (iii) to what extent obesity is a condition caused primarily by phenotypic and genotypic predisposition or whether it is predominantly the result of a food energy imbalance (calorie intake in excess of calorie expenditure).

There are a number of reasons that suggest that a tax on excess body weight would be both more effective and more efficient than a tax on excess food energy intake. First, a tax on excess food energy would address only the calorie intake side of the dietary energy imbalance but leave the calorie expenditure side completely unaddressed. When calorie requirements are high because of physical work, exercise or a less efficient metabolism, a tax on food may create additional private costs without creating a societal benefit. On the contrary, the extra food costs may reduce workers' productivity, lower their physical activity and thus create an extra cost for society. Poor consumers would be hardest hit. A tax on fat people would avoid that problem as it directly taxes the result of the dietary energy imbalance rather than only the energy input side. Moreover, a tax on excess body weight should not have any trade distorting impact, as there is simply no need to maintain the food tax distortion through a price wedge for food at the border. Finally, to the extent to which the tax on excess body weight lowers food demand, food prices may actually fall and thus afford an added advantage to poorer consumers. But a tax on excess body weight may not be without pitfalls. Most important, lower body weights *per se* are not a guarantor for a healthier diet and lifestyle. In fact, there is no shortage of unhealthy ways to reduce excess body weight.

The discussion on the various price and tax intervention mechanisms suggests that there are considerable differences in the efficiency and effectiveness of these measures in helping to reduce the prevalence of obesity. Probably the least efficient and least effective measure would be an intervention at the producer price level. It would also be the measure least compatible with other policy objectives, notably freer trade. While probably more efficient, a tax on consumer prices of food may also cause undesirable side-effects, notably where income inequality is large and where low-income strata react elastically to changes in food prices. A direct tax on excess body weight should be the most efficient and effective measure, but will not be sufficient on its own.

There is also growing evidence (Barker, 1994) that the effect of a phenotypic or genotypic predisposition can crucially affect the occurrence and degree of obesity. Moreover, a high prevalence of obesity in a given generation can be the result of a higher prevalence of undernourishment in the parent generation, and countries that undergo a rapid nutrition transition may suffer most. In this case, the "polluter pays" principle would certainly not apply and could in fact represent a grossly unfair policy measure.

INTEGRATED HEALTH AND NUTRITION PROGRAMMES

The preceding discussion suggested that there is no simple or single solution. Instead, there is growing evidence that it will take a combination of policy instruments to address the problem of obesity and related NCDs successfully. Such an integrated programme has, for instance, been launched in Norway and has – overall – yielded very positive results. The details of the programme are available from Norum (1997). Without repeating the details, the correlates of success were: (i) a strong legal and institutional foundation of a population-wide effort in a national organization, i.e. the National Nutritional Council (NNC); (ii) a robust scientific and empirical backing;[16] and (iii) a combination of measures (from food price interventions to nationwide food education programmes) embracing a great number of stakeholders. Practical experience in Norway also suggests that there can be a considerable time-lag between the implementation of various measures and the first measurable success.

The Republic of Korea provides another example of a successful nutrition programme. Details are available from Lee, Popkin and Kim (2002). Kim, Moon and Popkin (2000) find that food energy intake and obesity levels in the Republic of Korea are approximately half of what might be expected in a country at that economic level, while vegetable intake is much higher than might be expected. Lee, Popkin and Kim (2002) suggest that a number of factors have contributed to this outcome. First, there has been a strong movement to retain traditional diets and food preparations. At the heart of this movement is a training programme, which has been offered by the Rural Development Administration since the 1980s. The Home Management Division of the Rural Living Science Institute (Suwon, Republic of Korea) has trained thousands of extension workers to provide monthly training sessions in cooking methods for traditional Korean foods, such as rice, *kimchi* (pickled and fermented cabbage) and fermented soybean products. The programme appears to reach a significant component of the newly married women in the Republic of Korea, but exact statistics are not available. At least to a certain extent, food consumption was also curbed by higher food prices, which were backed by domestic producer price support and border measures. The same combination of food traditions, educational programmes and higher food prices may help to explain the positive nutritional outcome in Japan where, as in

---

[16] For example, the "Oslo Study" or the health surveys of the National Health Screening Service.

Norway and the Republic of Korea, the prevalence of obesity and NCDs remained much lower than in other countries of comparable development and income levels (see Figure 1).

SUMMARY AND CONCLUSIONS

This paper has analysed some of the currently discussed policy options to reduce or avoid food-related causes of excess body weight and NCDs. The analysis included various options, from food price interventions at various levels to integrated nutrition programmes. Interventions at the producer price level have been identified as the least efficient and the least effective in changing nutritional outcomes and reducing excess body weight. They are also unlikely to be compatible with efforts to liberalize agricultural trade. Consumer price interventions are likely to be more efficient – at least in developed countries – particularly as their effects are not diluted by huge processing margins. But what plagues all price interventions is the fact that those consumers who should reduce excess energy intake are likely to be the least responsive to price increases and will thus not alter their consumption patterns only because food is more expensive. Alas, the opposite holds for poor countries or poor consumers in rich countries where higher food costs could bring about or aggravate undernourishment problems.

Probably more effective and efficient than a tax on food would be a direct tax on excess body weight, i.e. a tax on obesity itself. In fact, many developed countries have already instituted such taxes, mostly in the form of penalties for extra body weight or incentives (premiums/tax brakes) to lose excess body weight. The main advantages are: (i) no negative side-effects on food markets; (ii) compatibility with other policy measures; and (iii) no penalty for consumers who need high-energy intake levels because of a higher calorie expenditure. Moreover, the tax would not only have fewer side-effects but be more effective and efficient as it addresses the excess body weight problem from both sides of the energy balance: the calorie intake side and the calorie expenditure side. The main drawbacks are possible difficulties in the actual implementation and the fact that a lower body weight in itself is no guarantor for a healthier diet.

The discussion of the various price intervention mechanisms also underlined that there is no single measure that is sufficient to address the problem. Where progress towards a healthier diet – and in the sequel a healthier population – has become reality, the underlying policy changes included a broad spectrum of measures. These measures encompassed not only price interventions and premiums but also measures to enhance nutrition transparency and education. But even for such integrated programmes, progress is not immediate and even in developed countries decades may pass before tangible impacts are produced. The diversity and complexity of successful approaches, the time-lag between policy measures and their impacts, the accelerating nutrition transition and predisposition to develop obesity and NCDs underline the urgency for action in developing countries.

Bibliography

Barker, D.J.P. 1994. *Mothers, babies and disease in later life.* London, BMJ Publishing Group.

Barker, D.J.P. 1995. Fetal origins of coronary heart disease. *British Medical Journal*, 311: 171-174.

Bruinsma, J., ed. 2003. *World agriculture: towards 2015/2030. An FAO perspective.* Rome, FAO and London, Earthscan.

Delisle, H. 2002. *Programming of chronic disease by impaired fetal nutrition. Evidence and implications for policy and intervention strategies.* WHO Report. WHO/NHD/02.3. Geneva, World Health Organization.

FAO. 2003. *The State of Food Insecurity in the World 2003.* Rome.

FAO. 2004. FAOSTAT data (faostat.fao.org).

Fogel, R. 1994. Economic growth, population theory and physiology: the bearing of long-term processes on the making of economic policy. *American Economic Rev.*, 84(3): 369-95.

Greenhouse, S. 2003. Obese people are taking their bias claims to court. *New York Times*, 3 August.

Guo, X., Popkin, B.M., Mroz, T.A. & Zhai, F. 1999. Food price policy can favorably alter macronutrient intake in China. *J. Nutrition*, 129: 994-1001.

Internal Revenue Service (IRS). 2002. Ruling 2002-19. Part 1, Section 213 – Medical, dental, etc. expenses. 26 CFR 1.213-1 (also §262; 1.262-1.) and Rev. Ruling 2002-19.

Kim, S., Moon, S. & Popkin, B.M. 2000. The nutrition transition in South Korea. *American J. Clinical Nutrition,* 71: 44-53.

King, A. 2002. A tax on fat? *EconLog*, 17 November.

Kynge, J. & Dickie, M. 2003. China encourages mass urban migration. *Financial Times*, 27 November.

Lee, M-J., Popkin, B.M. & Kim, S. 2002. The unique aspects of the nutrition transition in South Korea: the retention of healthful elements in their traditional diet. *Public Health Nutrition,* 5: 197-203.

Marshall, A. 1920. *Principles of economics.* 8th ed. Book 5, Chapter 6: (2). London, Macmillan.

Miller, J. & Colagiuri, S. 1994. The carnivore connection: dietary carbohydrate in the evolution of NIDDM. *Diabetologia,* 37: 1280-1286.

Narbro, K., Jonsson, E., Larsson, B., Waaler, H., Wedel, H. & Sjöstrom, L. 1999. Sick leave and disability pension before and after treatment for obesity. A report from the Swedish Obese Subjects (SOS) study. *Int. J. Obesity*, 23(6): 619-624.

Nestle, M. 2003. Have fat, will sue. *Financial Times* (suppl.), 14 December.

Norum, K.R. 1997. Some aspects of Norwegian nutrition and food policy. *In* P.S. Shetty & K. McPherson, eds. *Diet, nutrition and chronic disease. Lessons from contrasting worlds.* Wiley.

Popkin, B.M. 1993. Nutritional patterns and transition. *Population and Development Rev.,* 19: 138-157.

Regmi, A., Deepak, M.S., Seale, J.L. & Bernstein, J. 2001. Cross-country analysis of food consumption patterns. In *Changing structure of global food consumption and trade.* Agriculture and Trade Report. WRS-01-1. Market and Trade Economics Division, Economic Research Service, US Department of Agriculture.

Schmidhuber, J. & Britz, W. 2002. *The impacts of OECD policy reform on international agricultural commodity markets: first results of a quantitative assessment based on the @2030 model.* Schriften der Gesellschaft für Wirtschafts- und Sozialwissenschaften des Landbaues e.V., Band 36, Münster-Hiltrup.

Seale, J.L., Regmi, A. & Bernstein, J. 2003. *International evidence on food consumption patterns.* Electronic Report from the Economic Research Service (ERS). Technical Bulletin No. 1904, October.

Shetty, P.S. 1997. *Diet, lifestyle and chronic disease. Lessons from contrasting worlds. In* P.S. Shetty & K. McPherson, eds. *Diet, nutrition and chronic disease. Lessons from contrasting worlds.* Wiley.

Smil, V. 2000. *Feeding the world – A challenge for the twenty-first century.* Cambridge, Massachusetts and London, MIT Press.

UN-HABITAT. 2003. *Challenge of slums.* Global Report on Human Settlements in 2003. United Nations Human Settlements Programme and London, Earthscan.

World Bank. 2002. *World Development Indicators.* CD-ROM.

World Health Organization (WHO). 2003. *Nutrition in transition: globalization and its impact on nutrition patterns and diet-related diseases* (www.who.int/nut/trans.htm).

Impact of globalization on food consumption, health and nutrition in Nigeria

Kolawole Olayiwola[1], Adedoyin Soyibo and Tola Atinmo

INTRODUCTION

Globalization refers to the way in which developments in one region can rapidly come to have significant consequences for the security and well-being of communities in quite distant regions of the globe. As there can be no island of prosperity in an ocean of economic instability, globalization expresses the widening scope, deepening impact and speeding up of interregional flows and networks of interaction within all realms of social activity from the cultural to the criminal (McGrew, 2000).

Globalization is a force that can neither be halted nor ignored. This implies greater difficulties for countries trying to isolate themselves from the world marketplace. It offers growth prospects to national economies if they satisfy its requirements in terms of flexibility and competitiveness, which include designing and implementing domestic policies to meet global requirements (International Monetary Fund, 1997). It is argued that countries can be exposed to new technologies and ideas, which can create jobs, improve incomes and reduce poverty. This is predicted to have a positive influence on the health and nutritional status of people across the world. There is the presence of the perpetuation of social vulnerability (Bahalla and Lapeyre, 1999). Also, advances in information technology may have profound effects that directly influence health (Daulaire, 1999). The glamorization of self-serving and unsustainable lifestyles is one of the effects of the spread in information technology, which may negatively affect health status and worsen poverty.

In Nigeria, the institution of various reforms, starting with the Structural Adjustment Programme (SAP) of 1986 and membership in the World Trade Organization (WTO) placed the country under the umbrella of globalization. The resultant deterioration in the human development indices is a source of serious concern in the country. In absolute terms, the urban poverty level increased from 17.2 percent in 1980 to 58.3 percent in 1996 (Soyibo, Alayande and Olayiwola, 2001). The nutritional status of the average Nigerian remained precarious as the country consistently recorded deficit average per capita calorie intake. Food deficits of 31 percent and 20 percent in 1980 and 2000 respectively were recorded (Okojie *et al.*, 2001). A number of pertinent questions come to mind in relation to the extent to which globalization has impacted on food consumption, health and nutrition in Nigeria and how the country can take advantage of globalization to improve the health and nutrition status of its people. These are some of the issues this paper addresses.

---

[1] Kolawole Olayiwola
  Economic Policy Unit
  Development Policy Centre
  Ibadan, Nigeria
  Tel.: 234-802-350-4408
  Fax: 234-281-03283
  E-mail: kolaolay@yahoo.co.uk

We also discuss the conceptual approach and methodology adopted by the paper, while highlighting Nigeria's position in the globalizing world. We analyse the role of globalization on dietary change and lifestyles in Nigeria, trends in malnutrition in urban areas, and discuss trends in health status in the urban environment. Finally we examine government-sponsored nutrition programming in the country, and present our conclusions.

CONCEPTUAL FRAMEWORK
Conceptual framework for analysing linkages between globalization, food consumption, health and nutrition

The framework focuses on the linkages between the different strands of globalization and components of poverty, nutrition and health as identified in the literature. Thus, it focuses on openness to international trade/trade agreements, capital flows, migration, information technology and technology diffusion and discusses how each of these can be linked to problems of poverty, nutritional and health status (Figure 1).

The framework shows that openness to international trade will lead to greater integration into the global market which, in turn, could increase exports, output and income. This would reduce poverty by expanding the opportunities of the poor in terms of ownership or access to productive resources, infrastructure, financial services and social networks. It will also allow countries to concentrate on those activities in which they enjoy comparative advantage and subjects firms to healthy foreign competition. Therefore, the poor can gain from the advantages of trade liberalization by specializing in the production of goods that make use of their abundant, low-cost and unskilled labour.

International trade agreements affect the health status and general well-being of people. For example, trade-related aspects of intellectual property rights allow access to essential life-saving drugs that are non-affordable by low-income countries, regardless of the level of their public health expenditure. Innovations as inspired by the duo of large market and intellectual property rights ensure adequate rewards of innovators. While trade can contribute to improved welfare through increased drug availability, the associated negative externality of possible infections carried across borders could adversely affect not only people's health, but also their general well-being.

With the employment generation potential of globalization, women are likely to become more involved in the labour force. The potential helpful or harmful effect this may have on child health is a subject needing more research, especially where adequate child care institutions are lacking. Migration can lead to improved nutritional and health status through movement of people across national borders, which is expected to ease labour bottlenecks and lead to transfer of technological knowledge. The process of globalization can help to improve the skills of the poor through technology diffusion and capital flows. Transnational migration may be a drain on the brain power of countries, but may also lead to significant cash remittances returning home.

FIGURE 1
Linkages between globalization, food consumption, health and nutrition

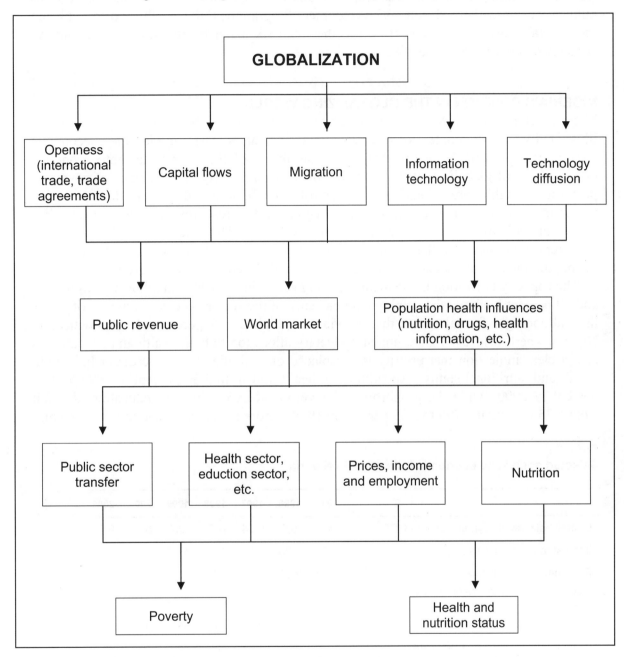

Methodological approach

Globalization has an impact on various elements of the economy: international trade, capital flows, migration, communication and information technology as well as technology diffusion. To the best of our knowledge, there is no study, as yet, that has assessed the impact of globalization on food, nutrition and health in Nigeria. Accordingly, we shall adopt an indirect approach, by analysing the impact of globalization on these issues, in relation to policy development, generation of ideas and disparate intervention programmes in the country.

As globalization is not new, some authors conceive of internationalization, liberalization and policy reforms as forms of globalization. We shall adopt a historical approach. The current globalization efforts are viewed to have started the liberalization and reforms efforts of SAP, which began in 1986. We have used secondary data and the results from many other studies in this paper. Data for our analysis are based on various publications of the United Nations Development Programme (UNDP), the World Bank and the Central Bank of Nigeria (CBN), together with six major health and nutrition surveys conducted between 1990 and 2003.

NIGERIA'S POSITION IN THE GLOBALIZING WORLD

The dismal picture of Nigeria's vulnerability to poverty in the globalizing era can be illustrated within the context of macroeconomic indicators. The Nigerian macroeconomic environment portends a picture that limits the ability of the poor to tap into economic opportunities of globalization that can free them from poverty. The balance of payments position is highly precarious in the face of huge external debt and debt servicing requirements (Table 1). This tends to limit the amount of resources available to revitalize the collapsing basic social and economic infrastructure. The country has also witnessed persistent high rates of inflation in the 1990s. Inflation contributes to the vulnerability of the population because it undermines investment and impedes economic growth.

The capacity utilization in the manufacturing sector in the 1990s that hovered around 29 and 39 percent hindered the employment capacity of the sector. The consequence of this is the ballooning informal sector that provides as high as 75 percent of employment in Nigeria. The low level of government budgetary allocation to both health and education is also a clear indication that priority is not placed on activities that have direct links with health and nutritional status. Expenditure on health fell from 3.30 percent in 1995 to 2.92 percent in 2000, while the proportion of government expenditure to education also fell from 6.33 percent in 1995 to 3.33 percent in 1999, before it was increased to 5.87 percent.

TABLE 1
Selected social and economic indicators in Nigeria

	1995	1996	1997	1998	1999	2000	2001
Overall balance of payment as % of GDP	-3.1	-5.6	0.04	-7.7	-9.7	6.3	0.5
Interest rate differentials (%)	7.57	8.03	12.3	11.6	17.7	16.0	19.2
Government expenditure on health (% of total)	3.30	2.57	1.71	2.80	1.71	2.92	4.39
Government expenditure on education (% of total)	6.33	8.12	3.92	5.05	3.33	7.07	5.87
Life expectancy	52	53	53	54	54	54	54
Infant mortality rate (per 1 000 births)	114	114	114	75	75	75	75

Source: Central Bank of Nigeria, 2001.

In terms of trade performance, the value of exports that rose rapidly from US$3.47 billion in 1973 to a peak of US$26.10 billion in 1980 fell drastically to US$12.88 billion in 1999 (Oyejide, 2001). However, the value of imports rose from US$6.04 billion in 1980 to a continuous rise of US$8.59 billion in 1999. This clearly shows that globalization had a more expansionary impact on imports than exports in Nigeria. The consequence of this development is deteriorating terms of trade during this period (Figure 2).

FIGURE 2
Behaviour of Nigeria's terms of trade (1995 = 100)

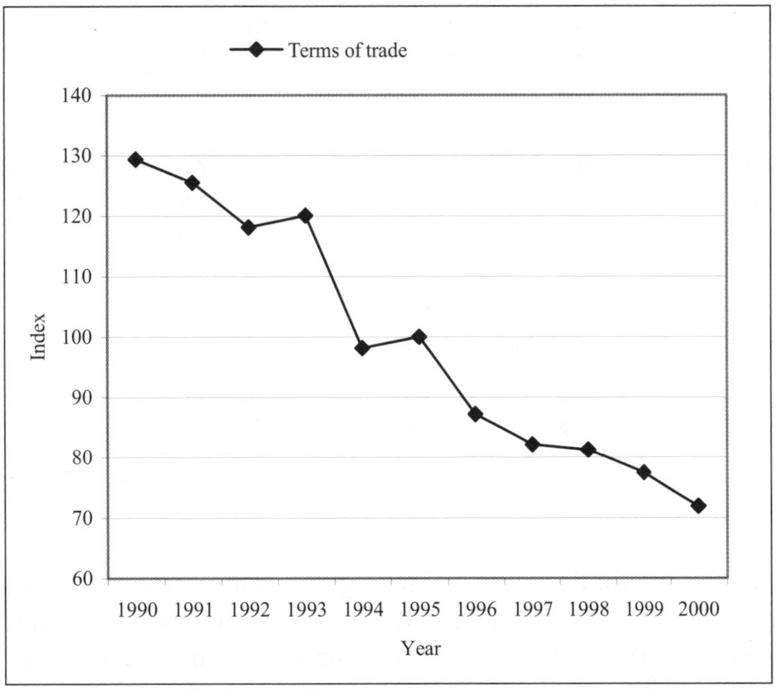

Source: Central Bank of Nigeria, 2002.

In order to provide an understanding of the environment within which globalization is taking place in Nigeria, an overview of the political and institutional developments is helpful. This is based on the economic intelligence ranking of countries between 1993 and 1997, but projected to 2002. The political environment is based on two major indicators – political stability and political effectiveness (see Olayiwola, 2003). This is selectively shown in Table 2.

Table 2 shows that Nigeria ranks lowest among the African countries included in the survey. The country has become politically unstable since 1993 when a presidential election was annulled. The governance outlook of the country took a different turn with the return to democratic rule in 1999. Nigeria also falls below average in terms of political effectiveness.

In the context of the Human Development Index of UNDP (2001), welfare seems to have improved in Nigeria from 0.322 in 1990 to 0.400 in 2000. The level of urbanization rose from 31 percent in 1985 to over 43 percent in 2000. As the urban population increased from 29.6 million in 1985 to 68.9 million in 2000, the rural population followed suit as it increased from 65.6 million to 90.3 million during the same period. This trend in urbanization is associated with problems of unemployment and lack of basic services such as water, sanitation and health care (Mabogunje, 1974). These problems arise because of the obvious mismatch between the growth of the urban population and available resources. The second problem is the character of urban growth, as a result of rural-urban migration. For example, Lagos city in Nigeria witnessed a remarkable increase in population from 5.83 million in 1985 to 12.89 million in 2000 (Abumere, 2001).

TABLE 2
Political environment ranking of countries, 1998-2002

Country	Political stability	Political effectiveness	Overall political environment	Total score	Rank
Netherlands	9.6	9.3	9.4	8.82	1
United Kingdom	8.2	9.6	9.0	8.77	2
United States	8.2	7.4	7.8	8.59	4
South Africa	6.0	5.1	5.7	6.31	37
Egypt	5.5	5.1	5.3	5.91	41
Indonesia	3.3	3.6	3.5	5.63	47
Algeria	4.2	4.0	4.1	4.73	57
Nigeria	2.4	1.8	2.0	4.17	58
Iraq	1.5	1.8	1.6	2.03	60
Average	**6.9**	**6.1**	**6.5**	**6.78**	
Median	**6.9**	**5.9**	**6.5**	**6.83**	

Source: Adapted from Olayiwola, 2003.

The indicators of another dimension of globalization, information technology, are also considered. According to the International Telecommunication Union, teledensity was 34.38 in Europe in 1997, 30.38 in the Americas, 6.02 in Asia and 1.85 in Africa. In 1998, Nigeria had the lowest teledensity (4), compared to South Africa (115), Senegal (16) and Côte d'Ivoire (12). Cellular density (as a percentage of total telephone lines) for the Americas was 6.92 (18.6 percent), in Europe 4.57 (11.7 percent), in Asia 1.35 (18.3 percent) and in Africa 0.17 (8.4 percent). The number of mobile telephones per 1 000 people in Nigeria was 0.01 in 1998. This number was insignificant compared to that of South Africa (56), Indonesia (5) and Egypt (1). The number of personal computers per 1 000 persons was 5.7 in Nigeria compared to 47.4 in South Africa, 9.1 in Egypt and 11.4 in Senegal (Table 3). As of 2000, the number of Internet hosts per 1 000 people was the smallest in Nigeria (0.01) compared to that of the Republic of Korea (60.03), South Africa (39.17), Indonesia (1.0) and even Senegal (0.32). In terms of television sets per 1 000 people, the Nigeria figure of 66 in 1998 was only better when compared to Senegal (41) whose GDP is less than one-third of the country (Olayiwola, 2001).

Nigeria has recorded a rising profile of cyber cafes and Internet usage. From a mere 17 cafés in 1998, the number increased to no less than 1 500 cafés in 2003. There were 153 350 Internet users in 2001. Moreover, Nigeria accounted for the largest Internet usage in 2001 in West Africa. Nearly one out of every two West African users of the Internet was a Nigerian. However, Internet penetration was 0.08 percent of the entire population. Access to electricity is very low in the country. Less than 30 percent of the population has access to electricity. As of 1997, the consumption per capita of electric power was 84 kWh in Nigeria, a marginal increase from 77 kWh in 1990. But in the context of transmission and distribution loses, the Nigerian figure of 32 was more than triple that of the Republic of Korea (4) and South Africa (8).

TABLE 3
Communication, information, science and technology indicators[1]

Country	Daily newspapers	Radio	TV	Telephone mainlines	Mobile phones	Personal computers	Internet host
United States	215	2 146	847	661	256	459	1 938
United Kingdom	329	1 436	645	557	252	263	321
Indonesia	24	156	136	27	5	8	1
Korea, Rep.	393	1 033	346	433	302	157	60
South Africa	32	317	125	115	56	47	39
Nigeria	24	223	66	4	0	6	0.01
Côte d'Ivoire	17	164	70	12	6	4	0.42
Senegal	5	142	41	16	2	11	0.32
Egypt	40	324	122	60	1	9	0.73

[1]Per 1 000 persons in various years (1996-2000).
Source: World Bank, 2000.

In spite of this relatively poor performance when compared with other countries, overall the country can be said to have witnessed significant performance in attracting foreign investment since the advent of representative democracy in 1999, compared to the military dictatorship of the previous 15 years. In the last four years, a total foreign investment of over N70 billion has come into the country. In the area of Information and Communication Technologies (ICTs), four global systems of mobile communication operators have provided an additional 2 million lines within two years. Although Nigeria's cost of mobile calls is one of the highest in the world because of the poor state of infrastructure, competition in the market in the next few years is expected to bring down the costs. The number of motor vehicles increased threefold from four to 12 per 1 000 people in 1980 to 1987, and the number of passenger cars also increased from three per 1 000 people to seven per 1 000 people. This was not matched by corresponding kilometres of paved roads, which increased marginally from 3 km per 1 000 km road to 7 km per 1 000 kilometre road. The resultant effect of this is the increase in traffic accidents from 123 per 1 000 in 1980 to 732 per 1 000 in 1998. Moreover, the number of air passengers has also decreased tremendously. International passengers decreased from 228 516 in 1994 to 40 166 in 1998. The same situation occurred with domestic passengers; they decreased from about 4.4 to 0.92 million during the same period.

ROLE OF GLOBALIZATION AND URBANIZATION ON DIETARY CHANGE AND LIFESTYLES
Globalization (trade liberalization) and trends in food supply
A cursory look at the aggregate food consumption shows some improvement within the period under consideration. The per capita calorie availability of the average Nigerian has fluctuated over the years. This situation tends to mirror the domestic production of staple crops. The index of food crop production increased from 90.74 in the period 1980-1984 to 296.44 in 1998-2002 (Table 4). This increase in domestic production did not translate into increased food supply because of two major factors. First, farm food losses remained consistently high throughout the same period.

TABLE 4
Per capita calorie availability and index of food production in Nigeria

Year	Index of food crop production	Average per capita calorie availability	Deficit/surplus of per capita calorie availability (%)
1975-1979	99.98	1 761	-27.2
1980-1984	90.74	1 680	-30.6
1985-1989	135.62	2 024	-16.3
1990-1994	245.12	2 200	-9.1
1995-1997	285.40	1 942	-19.7
1998-2002	296.44	2 043	-18.4

Source: Okunmadewa *et al.*, 1999; Central Bank of Nigeria, 2002.

Second, an upward trend in consumer price indices is generally noticeable and this is more pronounced in the period after 1986 and also in 1993-1995 (Table 5). The price situation of food items was in general more favourable before 1986 than thereafter. With measures in place to discourage importation, particularly of food items and with the devaluation of currency by the deregulated exchange rate, prices of consumer items rose astronomically after 1986. This implies low purchasing power of the people, especially wage earners, thereby adversely affecting the food security situation in the 1986-2000 period. The food price index increased from 3 044 in 1998 to 4 560 in 2002 and this increase was more pronounced in the urban areas, where it increased from 2 944.2 to 4 562.10 during the same period.

TABLE 5
Average food prices and food imports in Nigeria

	1970-74	1975-80	1981-85	1986-92	1993-95	1998-2002
Consumer price index (1985 = 100)	11.74	30.97	73.66	226.03	1 125.68	3 837
Total import (N million)	1 176.6	6 621.3	7 858.2	33 594.4	281 594.9	1 051 960
Food import (N million)	104.6	823.1	1 308.7	2 256.2	29 798.8	123 644
Food import as % of total import	8.8	11.8	17.2	9.0	9.7	11.75

Source: Central Bank of Nigeria, 2002.

Although there were increases in production, especially since 1986, these have been inadequate to feed the country, which therefore meant importation of food. The country's share of food imports in total imports generally increased during the decade of the 1990s. The average value of food imports increased from N823.1 in 1975-1980 to N123 643.62 in 1998-2002, as the share of food imports also jumped to 11.75 percent in 2002 (Table 5). The implication of this is that Nigeria consistently complemented domestic food production with imports. This paints a picture of significant dependence on food imports, which is strategically risky and financially expensive.

Other developments on the issue of globalization and dietary change are the importance of street foods and the emergence of fast food chains in Nigeria. Akinyele (1998) had previously shown that civil servants, skilled and unskilled and low-income families constitute the major patrons of street foods since they have to eat at least one meal outside the home. He found that two-thirds of the population's daily meals are bought from vendors and fast food chains. Street foods constituted at least one-third of their daily nutrient intakes. Street foods and fast foods contributed between 53.2 to 92.6 percent of the total nutrient intake of people of 21-40 years old, the primary consumers of these foods. People under 20 consume street and fast foods because of their sporadic quest for food at any time of the day. Ready to eat foods accommodate their lifestyle more than foods that must be taken home and prepared.

The changing role of women and urbanization on child care and feeding
Child care is influenced by women's health status, the time that mothers spend with their children, breastfeeding practices, complementary feeding, and the cultural beliefs and practices that influence these behaviours. It is therefore worthy to note that adequate income, greater food availability and expanded health services are necessary for improved nutrition, and these factors will not bring improved nutrition unless households are able to take advantage of them. Alayande, Olayiwola and Olaniyan (2000) had shown that women in formal employment in Nigeria had increased by 65 percent. The implication of this is that women's "heavy burden of production and reproduction" and high maternal mortality rates limit their capacity to care for their children. The dual demands of work outside and within the home leave women with less than four hours per day for child care. In a survey conducted by Akinyele (1998), 43.9 percent of working mothers kept their older children at home. Some made use of the available community child care centres (12 percent), while 12 and 5 percent kept their children in fee-paying nursery schools or in the custody of househelp.

Infant and child feeding practices generally are not appropriate for good nutrition. Tradition and/or women's economic responsibilities lead to low rates of exclusive breastfeeding (EBF) and the early introduction of complementary feeding. The rate of EBF increased from 2 to 20 percent during 1990-1999 for infants up to three months, but it is still low (National Population Commission, UN Population Fund and US Agency for International Development, 2000). A decade ago most mothers did not practise EBF and did not think that it was feasible. Although 96 percent of infants in Nigeria are breastfed, the median duration of EBF is less than one month and that of full breastfeeding is just over two months.

The urban rates of breastfeeding infants within an hour or a day of birth are higher than the rural rates (74 percent of urban mothers breastfeed within a day, versus 63 percent of rural mothers). This difference is attributed to the Baby-Friendly Hospital Initiative that operates mainly in urban hospitals as well as urban women's greater access to health education about breastfeeding (National Population Commission, UN Population Fund and US Agency for International Development, 2000).Women's education also affects breastfeeding: 71 percent of urban mothers with primary and secondary education breastfed their infants within one day of birth, versus 58 percent of mothers with no education. However, infants are breastfed longer in rural than urban areas: 77 percent of rural infants are breastfed at 12-15 months, versus 59 percent of urban infants (Federal Office of Statistics and United Nations Children's Fund [UNICEF], 1999). Overall, the issue in Nigeria is to promote EBF in order to give children a better nutritional start in life.

TRENDS IN MALNUTRITION IN URBAN AREAS
Stunting
The effects of globalization such as improvement in information, education and the communication activities of health promotion seem to have influenced infant breastfeeding positively in Nigeria. However, the gains appear diminished by early introduction of complementary infant formula.

A survey undertaken by the Federal Office of Statistics (FOS) in 1990 found that 43 percent of preschool children were stunted. It also reported that a higher proportion of children in rural areas are more malnourished than those in urban areas. The Federal Ministry of Health (FMoH) and Social Services and USAID (1993) showed that the prevalence of stunting among children declined slightly from 43 percent in 1990 to 40 percent in 1993. The Federal Government of Nigeria (FGN) and UNICEF (1994) also reported an increase in the prevalence of stunting from 43 percent in 1990 to 52 percent in 1994. FOS and UNICEF (1999) indicated that the prevalence of stunting decreased to 32 percent in 1999 and also showed that stunting is more prevalent in rural than urban areas. FGN *et al.* (2003) indicate that the prevalence of stunting is still high at 42 percent, and comparable to the previous rates reported between 1990 and 1999 (Table 6).

TABLE 6
Trends in stunting and wasting in children, 1990 - 2003

Survey year	Age	Stunting (%)			Wasting (%)		
		Total	Urban	Rural	Total	Urban	Rural
1990	< 5 years	43	35	46	9	7	10
1993	6 months-6 years	40	35	45	21		
1994	< 5 years	52	-	-	11		
1999	< 5 years	32	23	38	16	14	16
1999	< 3 years	46	42	47	12	11	13
2003	< 5 years	42	36	44	9	8	10

Sources: The surveys used in the analysis include the 1990 Nigeria Demographic and Health Survey (NDHS) undertaken by the Federal Office of Statistics and IRD/MACRO International published in 1992; the 1993 National Micronutrient Survey (NMS) published by the Federal Ministry of Health and Social Services and USAID in 1993; the 1994 Participatory Information Collection Study (PICS), published by the Federal Government of Nigeria and UNICEF in 1994; the 1999 Nigeria Demographic and Health Survey (NDHS), published by the National Population Commission, UN Population Fund and US Agency for International Development in 2000; the 1999 Nigeria Multiple Indicator Cluster Survey (MICS) published by the Federal Office of Statistics and UNICEF in 1999; and the 2003 Nigeria Food Consumption and Nutrition Survey published by the Federal Government and partners in 2003.

This analysis of stunting shows that the situation in Nigeria has not improved in the past decade. This is probably a result of the problems of poverty and food security in the country, which worsened during the era of globalization, particularly in rural areas.

Wasting
FOS and IRD/MACRO International (1992) reported that 9 percent of preschool children were wasted with a higher prevalence rate in rural areas. The prevalence of wasting reported by the FMoH and Social Services, USAID (1993) data was 21 percent, twice as high as in 1994 and 1990. This increase reflects short-term deficiencies in nutrition, and suggests a sudden worsening of food insecurity probably due to a sharp accentuation of poverty in the absence of any climatic or human disaster as reported by FOS and UNICEF (1999). FGN *et al.* (2003) also indicated a decline in the national prevalence of wasting or

acute undernutrition to the 1990 level of 9 percent (Table 6). The conclusion is that there has been a gradual decline in the prevalence from 1993 to 2003, although the current level of 9 percent is still not satisfactory.

Underweight

FOS *et al.* (1992) found that 36 percent of schoolchildren were underweight with the prevalence rate about 50 percent higher in the rural areas and the northern zones. FMoH and Social Services, USAID (1993) reported a higher rate of 39 percent and that regional disparities had worsened with one out of every two preschool children in the north underweight. With FGN and UNICEF (1994) data, the rate of underweight declined to 28 percent, while in FOS and UNICEF (1999), there was a decline from 36 percent in 1990 to 30 percent in 1999. The National Population Commission (NPC), UN Population Fund and US Agency for International Development (2000) found that 27 percent of children under three were underweight. FGN *et al.* (2003) reported the rate to decline from 36 percent in 1990 to 25 percent in 2003. In summary, the prevalence of underweight among preschool children was reduced by about 30 percent between 1990 and 1993. According to the current estimate, one out of every four preschool children is underweight.

Women's nutritional status

The close link between maternal undernutrition, low birth weight, and childhood stunting and underweight is only now being revealed with its intergenerational implications. The national surveys provide little information about undernutrition in women in general or pregnant and lactating women.

TABLE 7
Women's nutritional status

	Height <145 cm (%)	Body mass index (BMI) <18.5 (%)	
	NPC *et al.*, 2000	NPC *et al.*, 2000	FGN *et al.*, 2003
Total	7	16	12
Urban	6	15	12
Rural	7	17	13
Mothers' education			
None	9	20	
Primary	5	14	
Secondary	4	12	

Source: compiled by the authors from National Population Commission, UN Population Fund and US Agency for International Development, (2000); FGN *et al.* (2003).

FOS and IRD/MACRO International (1992) reported a national prevalence of short stature of 7 percent in women, with considerable regional variation, but very few urban-rural differences. The prevalence of thinness in women was 16 percent. There was a slightly higher proportion of mothers with low BMI in rural areas (17 percent) than in urban areas (15 percent), and there were also significant regional disparities with the northeast having 25 percent of mothers with low BMI, compared with 20 percent in the southwest, 18 percent in the northwest, 8 percent in the central zone and 7 percent in the southeast.

FGN *et al.* (2003) also used BMI data from women (aged from 15 to 49) as an indicator of their nutritional status. Twelve percent of the women were thin or undernourished and there were no significant urban-rural differences. However, the prevalence of malnutrition among women in the north was almost twice the rate in the south.

Trends in micronutrient deficiencies, 1993-2003

Three key micronutrient deficiency disorders, vitamin A deficiency (VAD), iron deficiency anaemia (IDA) and iodine deficiency disorders (IDD) are common in many parts of Nigeria. Two national surveys provide data (Table 8) on the prevalence of these micronutrient deficiencies from 1993 to 2003. These are (i) National Micronutrient Survey (FMoH and Social Services, USAID, 1993); and (ii) National Food Consumption and Nutrition Survey (FGN et al., 2003).

TABLE 8
Prevalence (percentage) of micronutrient deficiencies in children and women

Children					
FMoH, 1993	Southeast	Southwest	Northwest	Northeast	All children
VAD	15	24	48	50	33
IDA	6	6	13	15	12
IDD	2	0.3	2	3	2
FGN, 2003	Dry savannah	Moist savannah	Humid forest	Urban/rural	All children
VAD	31	20	26	20/27	27
IDA	34	20	15	28/20	22
IDD	3	5	2	3/6	4
Women					
FMoH, 1993	Southeast	Southwest	Northwest	Northeast	All women
IDA	10	5	4	20	9
IDD	0	5	5	0.7	3
FGN, 2003	Dry savannah	Moist savannah	Humid forest	Urban/rural	All women
VAD	20	15	9		13
IDA	23	20	22	11/11	13
IDD	5	7	7	2/5	6

Source: compiled by the authors from FMoH and Social Services, USAID (1993); FGN et al. (2003).

Vitamin A deficiency

According to FMoH and Social Services, USAID (1993), almost one in every three children was vitamin A deficient. FGN et al. (2003) reported the rate to range from 20 to 31 percent for children under five (Table 8). It also reported the rate of 9 to 20 percent for pregnant women. The regional variation of VAD prevalence may be attributed to food consumption patterns in Nigeria, particularly the variation in the consumption of foods rich in vitamin A among people living in different ecological zones. These foods, especially green leafy vegetables, fruit and palm oil are much more prominent in diets in southern Nigeria.

Iron deficiency anaemia

FMoH and Social Services, USAID (1993) reported a prevalence rate of IDA to be 12 percent in children. The northwest and northeast had the highest rate of 13 percent and 15 percent respectively. FGN et al. (2003) reported an increased national prevalence rate of 22 percent among preschool children with the dry savannah having the highest prevalence of 34 percent and the humid forest the lowest rate of 15 percent. FMoH and Social Services, USAID (1993) reported a national prevalence of 9 percent of IDA in women of reproductive age with the northeast having the worst rate of 20 percent followed by the southeast with 10 percent. This rate had increased to 13 percent as reported by FGN et al. (2003). Moreover, the dry savannah had the highest rate of 23 percent while the moist savannah had the lowest rate of 20 percent (Table 8). The data available show that iron deficiency anaemia is still a serious problem that must be addressed in view of its implications for child survival and pregnancy outcome.

Iodine deficiency disorders
FMoH and Social Services, USAID (1993) reported the national prevalence rate of IDD in children to be 2 percent. There was insignificant difference among the zones. FGN *et al.* (2003) results show that the national prevalence of IDD among these preschool children is 4 percent with insignificant agro-ecological zonal differences. FMoH and Social Services, USAID (1993) also measured IDD in women and defined it in terms of the visible goitre rate. The national prevalence rate was 3 percent with the northwest and southwest having the highest rate of 5 percent. FGN *et al.* (2003) reported a national prevalence rate of 6 percent in women using urinary iodine as the indicator. Both the humid forest and moist savannah had the highest rate of 7 percent but there were no rural-urban differences. The review of micronutrient deficiencies in Nigeria suggests very little direct impact of globalization on these deficiencies in the country, which are mostly a result of ecological differences. However, external funding that in part helped to conduct these studies can be seen to have some positive effect at least in giving basic data about the situation. The next level of assistance can take this as a starting-point.

TRENDS IN HEALTH STATUS IN THE URBAN ENVIRONMENT
The anthropometric data show that rural children's rates of stunting, wasting and underweight were consistently higher than urban rates from 1990 to 2003. More than one-third of the urban population has consistently suffered from chronic malnourishment since 1990. However, there is little contrast in urban wasting rates, which have been 7 to 10 percent since 1990. Urban underweight rates have increased from 20 percent in 1990 to 27 percent in 2003. In the context of urban women's nutritional status, based on height and thinness indices, 12 percent of urban women are currently undernourished (FGN *et al.*, 2003).

Micronutrient deficiency rates also vary along the urban/rural continuum, according to FGN *et al.*, 2003. This is the only survey that has information on *urban/rural* micronutrient deficiency rates, so there are no other data for comparison or to establish trends. The data show that micronutrient deficiencies exist in the urban sector. Urban children have a VAD rate of 20 percent and a slightly higher IDA rate of 37 percent. Urban women's VAD and IDD rates are 14 and 18 percent respectively.

Disease is another indicator of health status. Of particular interest are diarrhoeal, water-borne, infectious and non-communicable diseases. Lack of clean water, sanitation facilities and adequate shelter are associated with these diseases and this is an underlying cause of poor health status. The proportion of urban population that has access to pipes in residence increased from 2.44 percent in 1990/91 to 24 percent in 1999 (Development Policy Centre [DPC], 2002). During the same period, the proportion of the population with access to public taps increased marginally from 21 to 26 percent. The contrast is the case of boreholes, when the proportion fell drastically from 12 to 1.68 percent. In the area of sanitation, the main types in urban populations are private flush toilets, traditional pit toilets and bush or dung hills. The proportion of population with access to pit latrines fell drastically from 74 to 46 percent, but there is a significant increase in the proportion of the population sharing and using bush and dunghills, which increased from 4 and 8 percent to 12 and 10.6 percent respectively. Moreover, the accumulation of refuse in the urban sector is a breeding ground for various diseases. In some selected cities in Nigeria such as Lagos,

Ibadan and Kano, the volumes of solid waste generation increased from 786 079, 440 956 and 402 133 tonnes in 1990 to 998 081, 559 882 and 535 186 tonnes in 2000, respectively (Abumere, 2001).

Nigerians are also vulnerable to idiosyncratic shocks, especially health risks. Infectious diseases characterize the Nigerian epidemiological pattern, which has been worsened by malnutrition and high fertility in recent times. The Nigerian epidemiological environment is dominated by the prevalence of malaria. This problem is further aggravated by the existence of drug-resistant malaria. The occurrence of resistance to malaria drugs moved from 2 percent in 1992 to 40 percent in 1996, while resistance varied between 20 and 50 percent all over the country in 1999 (DPC, 2002).

In urban Nigeria, the incidence of sexually transmitted infections (STIs) is on the increase, especially in the slums. Gonorrhoea, chlamydia, genital herpes and warts were ranked among the ten most reported notifiable diseases in 1999. The reason adduced for the increase is the problem of self-medication, which is widely practised with respect to STIs. The presence of commercial sex workers, who routinely use antibiotics, and men using orthodox and/or traditional medication, make these diseases more prevalent.

The incidence and burden of HIV/AIDS are on the increase in the country. HIV prevalence has increased progressively among the general population, using antenatal clinic attendees as proxy, from 1.8 percent in 1991 to 5.4 percent in 1999. High-risk groups in Nigeria, with higher prevalence of HIV than the general population, include commercial sex workers, people infected with STIs, long-distance drivers and urban people. The national HIV/AIDS database shows a progressive increase in the number of cases recorded yearly, from 962 cases in 1989 to 10 296 in 1999 for medical laboratories, and from eight cases in 1989 to 8 633 cases in 1999 for health facilities. The cumulative data showed a total of 32 515 for laboratories, and 24 557 for health facilities. In Nigeria by the end of 1999, there were 2.7 million people living with HIV/AIDS (with a range of 2.1 to 3.2 million), including 1.4 million women and 120 000 children. The estimate also indicates that there were up to 1.4 million AIDS orphans in 1999. The prevalence rate, estimated to be 1.8 percent in 1993, increased by more than 100 percent within a year to 3.8 percent in 1994, to 4.5 percent in 1996 and to 5.4 percent in 1999 (Lambo, 2003).

Globalization eases access to funds from different countries for HIV/AIDS and major diseases of public health concern such as tuberculosis and malaria. Some initiatives are the Global Fund for fighting AIDS, tuberculosis and malaria; the High Indebted Poor Countries Initiatives and other private sector actors; non-governmental organizations (NGOs)such as the Corporate Council on Africa; Abbot Laboratories; Bristol Myers Squibb; and foundations such as the Bill and Melinda Gates Foundation, MetLife, Rockefeller and the John D. and Katherine MacArthur Foundations (Lambo, 2003). The Bill and Melinda Gates Foundation has committed a substantial grant to the AIDS Prevention Initiatives in Nigeria (APIN). Similarly, a number of multilateral initiatives combating micronutrient deficiencies are in place, led by UNICEF and implemented by government agencies and NGOs in Nigeria.

GOVERNMENT-SUPPORTED NUTRITION PROGRAMMING IN NIGERIA
The policy context
We first review briefly a number of policy options aimed at enhancing the nutritional status of Nigeria.

Launching of the National Policy on Food and Nutrition

The National Policy on Food and Nutrition was drafted in 1995, adopted by the government in 1998 and finally launched in November 2002. The policy is expected to serve as a framework to guide the identification and development of intervention programmes aimed at addressing the problems of food and nutrition across different sectors and levels of Nigerian society.

Development of the Nigeria PROFILES

PROFILES, a computer-based nutritional policy analysis and advocacy tool, was developed with existing nutrition data to make an effective case for attention and resources to be allocated to combat malnutrition. This was to be updated with data generated by the Nigeria Food Consumption and Nutrition Survey, 2001.

Universal salt iodization

The introduction and implementation of a policy of universal salt iodization (USI) has proved effective in overcoming IDD. The success of USI can be gauged by the fact that in 1995, it was reported that 97 percent of all food grade salt manufactured in Nigeria was iodized and by 1999, 98 percent of Nigerian households were using the salt.

Vitamin A fortification of flour (wheat/maize), sugar and vegetable oil

The government has published standards for flour (wheat/maize), sugar and vegetable oil, including levels of fortification with vitamin A. These products were selected on the basis of their importance in the national food market and the food consumption habits of the population. The proposed standards were signed into law, making it mandatory for manufacturers to fortify these products. The National Agency for Food and Drug Administration and Control and the Standards Organization of Nigeria are monitoring the implementation of the law and compliance.

Re-establishment of the National Committee on Food and Nutrition (NCFN)

The NCFN was established to coordinate nutrition activities across the sectors and to mobilize resources for nutrition. It has remained dormant over the last few years but has since become active again.

Options to improve food security and nutrition

Strengthen the National Committee for Food and Nutrition

The consensus is that the NCFN is being revived and is the key government institution for the future, despite its problematical history. The committee's appointed nutritionist needs support for advocacy, and the NCFN needs strengthening and aid to provide strong leadership for improved nutrition in Nigeria. Strengthening includes training on nutrition, as well as vehicles, computers and a communication system.

Relocate the NCFN under the Presidency

The NCFN should be under the Presidency and the Food and Agriculture Organization of the United Nations (FAO) should support the move. FGN involvement in nutrition is critical and this involvement includes recognition of the negative relationship between nutrition and HIV/AIDS that affects the availability and productivity of labour, and therefore also affects agricultural production and food supplies. Relocating the NCFN under the Presidency is necessary to put nutrition and its critical issues on the national agenda, so as to mobilize the attention, funding and action required for progress. The

National Planning Commission (NPC) where the NCFN is at present located has neither the budget nor the expertise in nutrition to assist the NCFN to coordinate nutrition activities effectively.

Coordinate policy-making
This should improve government understanding of the spiral effects of policy and the need for coordinating policy in order to avoid unforeseen and negative effects on food security. The obvious issue in Nigeria is the spiral effect of policies for oil that drive the national economy and ultimately affect all three components of food security – availability, access and utilization.

Nutrition and HIV/AIDS
Nutrition and HIV/AIDS are two parts of a single problem that must be addressed in order to improve Nigeria's food security. The distribution of malnutrition and HIV/AIDS overlaps in the country. HIV/AIDS-affected households need support to access production technologies and economic options to help them maintain their food security and HIV/AIDS-affected people need access to the food and medications necessary to help them remain well-nourished and productive as long as possible.

Build capacity for government data collection
The need to strengthen government capacity for the systematic collection, analysis and distribution of nutrition and health data is critical. The data collection system should include a Geographic Information System to collect data on environmental factors, agricultural production and HIV/AIDS seroprevalence in order to map regional vulnerability to food insecurity. Capacity building should be done through FGN and its civil servants with the objective of strengthening existing government institutions, and not creating parallel donor systems.

Increase academic expertise in nutrition
There is the potential to increase expertise in nutrition in Nigeria's universities through support for higher education. Education in nutrition may be available through a programme such as the US Department of State's "Azikwe Professional Fellowships" that provide short-term training in the United States for Nigerian professionals. Education on the nutrition-HIV/AIDS relationship and its negative effects on nutrition, food security and agricultural production should be a key topic in nutrition education.

Educate women
The consensus is that educating women about key issues that affect child nutrition is essential for addressing widespread child malnutrition in Nigeria. The education could include teaching women about the links between nutrition and disease.

School feeding programmes
The FMoH's Department of Community Development and Population Activities is planning a school-feeding programme and looking for partners to support it. FAO could provide non-commodity support for the programme as well as nutrition education for women and children in the communities where it operates. One option to promote girls' attendance in school is to give their families a food ration to replace the labour they lose by the girls attending school.

Community-based child growth monitoring: the Honduras "Integrated attention to children" model

Honduras historically has been a low-income country with a malnourished population. More than ten years ago it implemented a community-based child growth monitoring system that has been successful at maintaining good nutritional status in children under the age of two. The system is based on training community health workers to collect accurate growth data and to transmit it to the community when negative changes require a response. The community transmits the information to the municipal mayors, who work with NGOs and government agencies to organize a response. The Honduran government's long-term investment of time and resources is reported as the key to making this system a success. The system could be adapted for Nigeria, based on government commitment to a pilot programme.

Supplements and fortification

The current efforts to provide vitamin A supplements and the options of fortifying flour, sugar and oil should be supported. One option in fortification is to promote the participation of small and medium enterprises that would make fortified flour readily available in rural areas. Fortifying salt with iron, like iodization, is a possibility in the future that is under research outside Nigeria.

Increase agricultural productivity

Agricultural productivity, including the production of roots and tubers through the International Institute of Tropical Agriculture programme, should be increased. This includes diversifying crop production to support dietary diversity, as well as improving storage and processing techniques, marketing networks and roads. The universal aim to increase agricultural productivity in order to improve food security must take HIV/AIDS into account.

Improved food storage, preservation, processing and safety

Post-harvest losses vary between 15 and 40 percent of the total crop production. These could be reduced by improved food storage, preservation, processing and safety at the household level. One option is to educate women on simple, low-level technology. Donor agencies could provide support for advocacy using various media strategies.

CONCLUDING REMARKS

This paper shows that there appears to be a limited direct impact of globalization through the usual roots of trade, migration and information technology at the household level; level of care-providing activities; and the nature of the health environment, including access to health services. The paper demonstrates that in the case of nutrition intervention programmes, funding for policy development and data collection has generally been obtained from donor agencies such as FAO and UNICEF. In particular, the results of these studies are useful in prescribing best practices. As an example, a USAID study prescribed the Honduras "Integrated attention to children" model of community-based child growth monitoring as an approach that Nigeria could adopt and adapt.

Besides funding of HIV/AIDS intervention by APIN and other international agencies, Nigeria should consider fast-tracking the use of regional initiatives to raise funds for combating HIV/AIDS, following the example of the Commonwealth Regional Health Community Secretariat of East, Central and Southern Africa (ECSA). For this purpose, the

West African Health Community may need to be energized and enhanced to perform this singular act.

In conclusion, the impact of globalization on food, nutrition and health in Nigeria has improved with democratic governance. But in the area of trade, migration, ICTs and capital inflows, there is a lot still to be accomplished. Many laudable national policies on information technology, nutrition and health are not yet properly implemented. Therefore, Nigeria runs a high risk of social and economic exclusion if drastic steps are not taken to improve information infrastructure and provide and encourage a conducive business environment. All these issues are basic challenges faced by the government, the private sector, civil society and the international communities.

Bibliography

Abumere, S.I. 2001.The challenges of urbanisation in sub-Saharan Africa. *In* S. Abumere & A. Soyibo, eds. *Development policy and analysis: a book in honour of Akinlawon Ladipo Mabogunje,* p. 85-144. Ibadan, Nigeria, Daybis Limited.

Akinyele, I.O. 1998. Street foods and their contribution to the food security and nutritional status of Nigerians. *West African J. Foods and Nutrition,* 1(1): 6-20. September.

Alayande, B.A, Olayiwola, K. & Olaniyan, O. 2000. The effect of nutrition in the productivity of rural women in Nigeria. *African J. Econ. Policy,* 8(1): 95-114.

Ayeni, B. 2001. Is urbanisation in Nigeria a constraint on development? *In* S. Abumere & A. Soyibo, eds. *Development policy and analysis: a book in honour of Akinlawon Ladipo Mabogunje,* p. 27-49. Ibadan, Nigeria, Daybis Limited.

Bahalla, A. S. & Lapeyre, F. 1999. Global integration and social exclusion with special reference to Poland and Hungary. *European J. Development Res.,* 11(1): 101-124.

Central Bank of Nigeria (CBN). 2001. *Annual report and statement of account.* Abuja.

Central Bank of Nigeria (CBN). 2002. *Statistical bulletin.* Abuja.

Daulaire, N. 1999. Globalization and health. *Development,* 42(4): 22-24.

Development Policy Centre (DPC). 2002. *Nigeria Development Report 2001.* Ibadan, Nigeria.

Federal Government of Nigeria (FGN) & UNICEF. 1994. *The nutritional status of women and children in Nigeria.* Participatory Information Collection Study. Nigeria, UN Children's Fund. 111 pp.

Federal Government of Nigeria (FGN), IITA, USAID, USDA and UNICEF. 2003. *Nigeria Food Consumption and Nutrition Survey 2001.* 138 pp.

Federal Ministry of Health (FMoH) and Social Services, USAID. 1993. Vitamin A Field Support Project and Opportunities for Micronutrient Interventions. 1996. *Nigeria, National Micronutrient Survey 1993.* 107 pp.

Federal Office of Statistics (FOS) & UNICEF. 2000. *Nigeria multiple indicator cluster survey 1999.* Lagos, FOS. 164 pp.

Federal Office of Statistics & IRD/MACRO International. 1992. *Nigeria demographic and health survey 1990.* Columbia MD, United States. 244 pp.

International Monetary Fund (IMF). 1997. *World economic outlook. 1. Global economic prospects and policies.* Washington, DC.

Lambo, E. 2003. *Resource mobilization for an expanded and comprehensive resource response to HIV/AIDS and its implications.* Nairobi, Apex Publications Limited for the Commonwealth Regional Health Community Secretariat, Arusha, United Republic of Tanzania.

Mabogunje, A.L. 1974. *Cities and social order.* Inaugural lecture. Ibadan, Nigeria. University of Ibadan.

McGrew, A. 2000. Sustainable globalization: the global politics of development and exclusion in the new world order. *In* T. Allen & A. Thomas, eds. *Poverty and development into the 21st century*, p. 345-364. Oxford, United Kingdom, Oxford University Press.

National Population Commission (NPC), UN Population Fund & US Agency for International Development. 2000. *Nigeria demographic and health survey 1999.* Abuja, NPC. 321 pp.

Okojie, C., Ogwumike, F.O., Anyawu, J.C. & Alayande, B.A. 2001. *Poverty in Nigeria – An analysis of gender issues, access to social services and the labour market.* Collaborative research report submitted to the African Economic Research Consortium (AERC), Nairobi.

Okunmadewa, F., Olomola, A. & Adubi, B. 1999. *Trade liberalisation and food security: situation analysis in Nigeria.* DPC Research Report, No. 17. Ibadan, Nigeria, Development Policy Centre.

Olayiwola, K. 2001. *The economics of information technology and business development in Nigeria.* Selected paper for the Conference on Technology and Development in Africa, held at the College of Engineering and the Centre for African Studies, University of Illinois at Urbana-Champaign, United States. 25-28 April.

Olayiwola, K. 2003. *Positioning Nigeria in the knowledge society in a globalising world.* Selected paper for the 2003 Annual Conference of the Nigerian Economic Society. August. Ibadan, Nigeria.

Oyejide, T.A. 2001. *Nigerian trade policy in the context of regional and multilateral trade agreements.* DPC Research Report, No. 27. Ibadan, Nigeria, Development Policy Centre.

Pinstrup-Andersen, P., ed. 1990. *Macroeconomic policy reforms, poverty and nutrition: analytical methodologies.* New York, Cornell Food and Nutrition Policy Program, Monograph 3. 314 pp.

Soyibo, A., Alayande, B. & Olayiwola, K. 2001. Poverty alleviation strategies in Nigeria. *In* S. Abumere & A. Soyibo, eds. *Development policy and analysis: a book in honour of Akinlawon Ladipo Mabogunje,* p. 173-212. Ibadan, Nigeria, Daybis Limited.

United Nations Development Programme (UNDP). 2001. *Human Development Report.* New York, USA, Oxford University Press.
World Bank. 2000. *World development reports: attacking poverty 2000/2001.* Washington, DC.

Globalization, urbanization and nutritional changes in South Africa

Mickey Chopra[1]

INTRODUCTION

The relationship between globalization, urbanization and nutritional changes is one that is receiving increasing attention. South Africa is a particularly interesting case because until the late 1980s the apartheid political regime placed extensive restrictions on the ability of the non-white population to live in many urban centres. The abhorrence of the racist political system also meant that South Africa became a pariah nation sheltered from many of the forces of globalization impacting on most other countries. The last 15 years have witnessed a remarkable transformation not just of the political system, leading to freedom of movement and rapid urbanization, but also the full integration of South African capital into the international markets. Even in this relatively short period these changes have begun to have an impact on the dietary habits and health of South Africans. This paper will briefly review the socio-economic and demographic changes that have resulted and then suggest ways in which these macrolevel changes are influencing dietary intakes and ultimately levels of overweight, obesity and mortality.

Historical background

The victory of the Nationalist Party in 1948 ushered in the apartheid state that systematically discriminated against the majority black population. Some commentators have pointed out that the new regime merely codified a practice that had been going on for many years (Marais, 1998). For example, the 1913 Native Land Act had designated 13 percent of the available land as the only areas that the black population could purchase and reside in. But there is little doubt that the accession to power of the Nationalist Party signified the victory of a particular Afrikaner nationalist ideology. Much has been written about the political and ideological nature of apartheid; however, less prominent is the useful role the political superstructure played for Afrikaner capital in South Africa during this time. Post-war South African economy was dominated by the mineral and agricultural sectors that depended upon a regular supply of cheap and relatively unskilled labour that the apartheid laws were able to supply. The apartheid state actively assisted in the supply and reproduction of such labour: "Massive forced removals saw the labour tenant system replaced by a contract labour system. Between 1960 to 1982, 3.5 million people were forcibly removed by the state. About 700 000 more people were removed from urban areas declared 'white'" (Marais, 1998, p. 22).

[1] Mickey Chopra
Senior Lecturer
University of the Western Cape
School of Public Health
PO Bag x 17
Bellville 7535
Western Cape, South Africa
Tel.:27 21 959 2809
E-mail: mchopra@uwc.ac.za

The creation of "homeland" areas served as dumping grounds for unemployed workers and allowed the cheap reproduction of labour. It also served as a useful way of diffusing and marginalizing any discontent. Strict influx control measures prevented Africans from being physically present in many urban centres. Under this apartheid institutional framework, the market acted "like a malevolent invisible hand, working to the advantage of white workers and capitalists, and widening the wage differentials between black and white workers" (McGrath, 1990). The ratio of per capita incomes of white to black people rose from 10.6:1 in 1947 to 15:1 in 1970 (McGrath, 1990). However, by the late 1980s the contradictions in the system began to unravel. One pertinent example was the increasing defiance of the pass laws – it is estimated that between 1986 and1990 more than 3.5 million Africans illegally moved from the homelands into "informal" urban settlements (SA Urban Foundation, 1991). Large-scale revolts coupled with continuing economic decline forced the Nationalist Government to negotiate a settlement with the African National Congress ultimately leading to its democratic election in 1994.

South Africa post-apartheid

The recent 2001 census counted 44.8 million people living in South Africa, a rise of nearly 10 percent since the 1996 census. Figure 1 shows the demographic profile of the country from the last census. This census also reveals the continuing migration of people from rural to urban centres. More than 60 percent of the population now live in urban centres. The last five years alone have seen more than 3 million people migrate from rural to urban areas. While there are important economic differences between rural and urban areas (20 percent higher unemployment levels and worse infrastructure in rural areas), researchers have also found that the relatively cheap cost of transport (for travel between rural and urban areas) and the existence of family networks in urban areas encourage this urban migration.

FIGURE 1

Percentage of the total South African population in each five-year age group by sex, October 2001

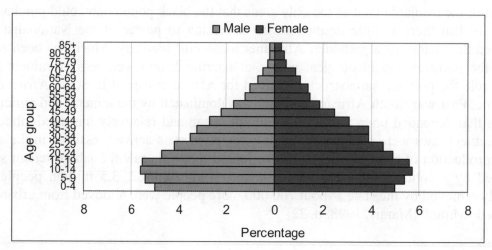

Source: Census 2001

Socio-economic transformation

While the political transformation in South Africa has received the most international attention, it has been the economic transformation that has probably most affected the lives of ordinary South Africans. Not only has South Africa become exposed to the forces of global capital and markets but the economic policy pursued by the government very closely follows that proscribed by the Bretton Woods institutions. South Africa is classified as a middle-income country with an average income of US$1 753 per capita (UNDP, 2001). Despite the reasonable average income, there are high levels of poverty. Depending on the poverty line and the methodology used there are various estimates of the extent of poverty. Statistics South Africa estimate that 52 percent of households were living in poverty in 1996 and that the Gini coefficient for South Africa is currently 0.58, the second highest in the world (Statistics South Africa, 1996).

The rapid dismantling of tariffs has resulted in sharp declines in employment, especially in the textile and manufacturing sectors. On the other hand, the depreciation of the currency has led to increases in some sectors such as tourism. Overall it has been estimated that over one million jobs have been lost, predominantly among artisans and unskilled workers (Figure 2).

FIGURE 2
Percentage of the employed aged 15 to 65 years by occupational category, October 1996 and October 2001

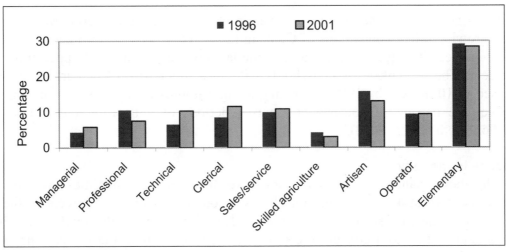

Source: Census 1996 and 2001.

This led to a significant growth in unemployment from 33.0 percent in 1996 to 41 percent in 2001 (Statistics South Africa, 2003). This increase has disproportionately affected the majority of the African population with unemployment increasing from 42.5 to over 50 percent in just five years (Figure 3). The loss of jobs in the formal sector is giving rise to so-called informal sector jobs. These include activities such as hawking, food retailing and home-based manufacturing. There is some debate as to whether this is an economically healthy development. The example of Silicon Valley is often cited as a way in which less regulated and smaller firms can achieve far greater flexibility in response to a global market. However, studies of most informal economies in Africa have shown that it is extremely difficult for small companies to grow without significant external inputs that in the present climate of reduced state investment are usually not forthcoming. In most cases the informal economy is a survival strategy rather than an engine for growth (Potter, Binns and Elliot, 1999).

FIGURE 3
Official unemployment rates by population group and sex, October 1996 and October 2001

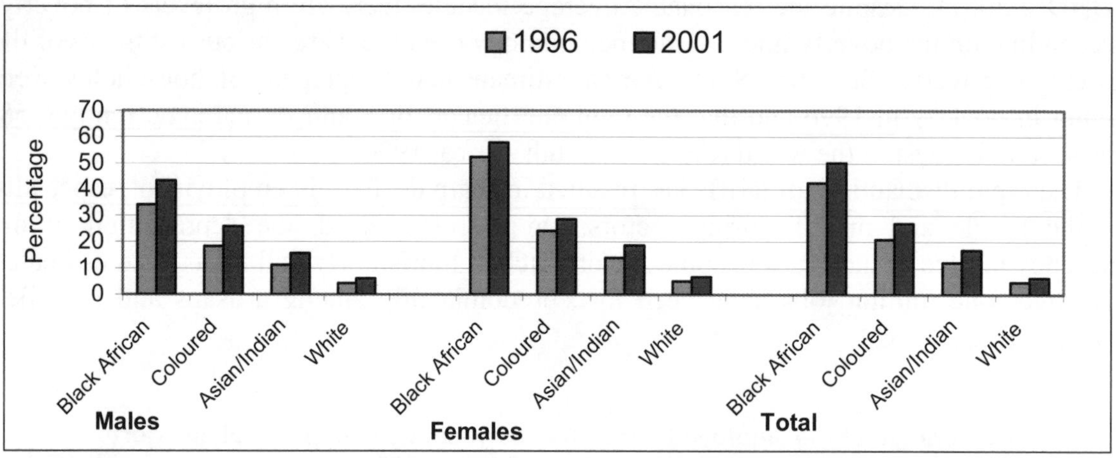

Source: Census 1996 and 2001.

Nearly one in six of the population lives in shacks. The highest proportion is in the rapidly growing urban populations of Gauteng (25 percent). Access to piped water inside the home appears to have become worse in the last few years and has dropped from 45 to 39 percent. The percentage of households without a toilet was 12 percent in 1996 and decreased to 10 percent by 1999, indicating a slight improvement in access to sanitation. Moreover, 22 percent of households reported periods of hunger by the end of 1999 (Statistics South Africa, 2002).

Increases in inequity

Given the above changes it is not surprising to see that income inequalities have persisted: by 1995 the poorest 40 percent of households accounted for only 11 percent of the total income, while the richest 10 percent commanded 40 percent of the total (May, 2000). Perhaps contributing to a greater perception of exclusion among the African majority is that a small African minority is greatly benefiting from the transition period. The proportion of urban Africans in the richest quintile of the South African population increased fivefold from 1990 to 1995, from 2 to 10 percent. This rise may well have been at the expense of the poor as the poorest 40 percent of the population have experienced a drop in their share of income. The level of income disparity between African households (as measured by the Gini coefficient) rose from 0.3 in 1990 to 0.54 in 1998 (almost the same as the national figure of 0.58) (UNDP, 2001).

HEALTH AND MORTALITY

The mortality profile in South Africa partly reflects the protracted-polarized model of diseases with poverty-related diseases, as well as chronic diseases related to an industrialized lifestyle and burdens of morbidity and mortality from trauma and violence (Bradshaw and Laubscher, 2002). It is the poor who are suffering from all patterns of mortality at once. Based on the 1996 South African death registration, infectious diseases together with maternal mortality and malnutrition-related conditions account for 30.6 percent of deaths and chronic diseases account for 31.9 percent. Even before the impact of HIV/AIDS, premature adult mortality in South Africa was high, as a result of the triple burden of poverty-related diseases such as tuberculosis and diarrhoea, injuries and emerging non-communicable diseases (NCDs) such as hypertension and diabetes. This is illustrated in Figure 4, which shows the causes of mortality in the poorest quintile of the population. Even in the poorest quintile, NCDs are responsible for the same proportion of deaths as infectious diseases.

However, this pattern is rapidly being affected by the impact of AIDS. The life expectancy for males is estimated at 59 and for women at 65. It is estimated that premature adult mortality (measured as the probability of a 15-year-old dying before the age of 60) has started increasing and will reach levels close to 80 percent within the next ten years (Dorrington *et al.*, 2001).

FIGURE 4
Male years of life lost in poor areas
N = 446 015

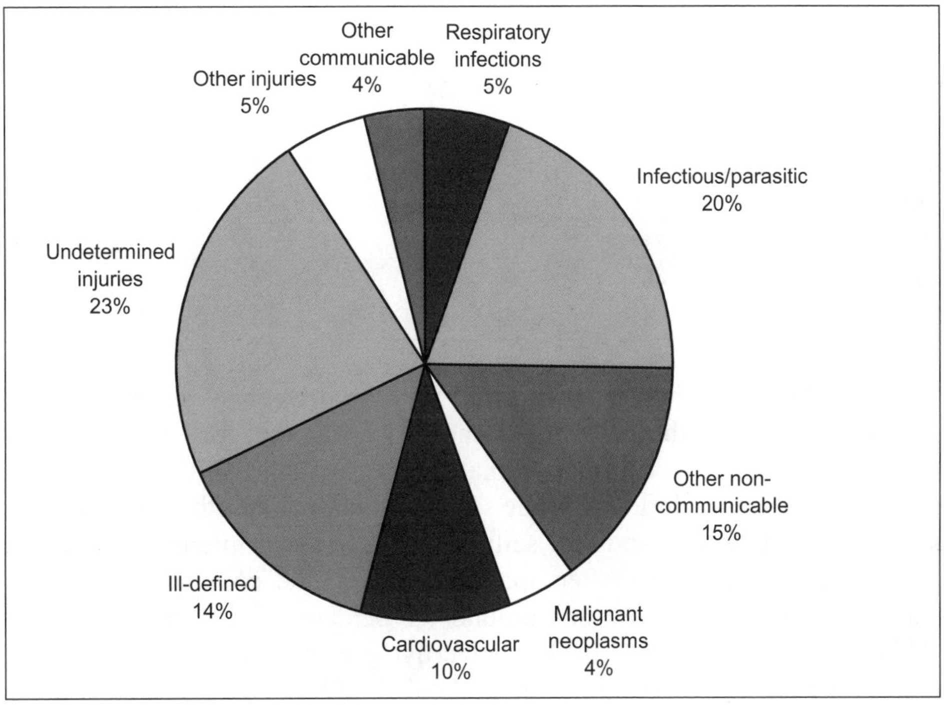

Source: Bradshaw and Laubscher, 2002.

Globalization and urbanization do seem to be changing the exposure to risk factors, especially among the urban poor. For example, a study conducted in the early 1990s found that it was predominantly middle-income men who were most likely to smoke (Steyn *et al.*, 1994). However, by the end of the decade it was poor men in urban settings who were the most likely (Bradshaw and Laubscher, 2002). Local studies have shown the massive increase in cigarette advertising especially in poor urban areas (Benatar, 1999). The 1998 demographic and health survey found that 56 percent of women in South Africa are either overweight or obese (Puoane *et al.*, 2002). Women living in rural areas had a 25 percent less chance of being obese and 37 percent less chance of having hypertension (Bradshaw and Laubscher, 2002).

Changes in diet
A recent review of dietary intake studies concluded that there were some consistent urban/rural differences in food items consumed. Nearly all (98 percent) consumers in the rural areas consumed maize porridge, whereas this decreased to between 27 and 71 percent in urban areas. Portion sizes of maize were substantially higher in rural areas. In urban areas there were more consumers of coffee, carbonated beverages, sugar, meat and offal,

and potatoes. In rural areas there were more consumers of maize, wild leaves and non-dairy creamers. The recent National Food Consumption Survey also reported that children of all age groups living in rural areas had a consistently and significantly lower energy intake than children living in urban areas (Table 1) (Labadarios, 2000).

TABLE 1
Mean energy intakes (sample size = 1 308)

Energy intake	Urban (%)	Rural (%)
Aged one to three		
<50% RDA	20	25
<67% RDA	41	49
>100% RDA	26	18
Aged four to six		
<50% RDA	21	30
<67% RDA	41	53
>100% RDA	21	14
Aged seven to nine		
<50% RDA	21	34
<67% RDA	45	56
>100% RDA	15	12

The post-apartheid era has been marked by the (re)-entry of multinational food companies. South Africa is the most important African market for Coca-Cola, and one of their largest markets in the world (Coca-Cola, 1997). Available in the country for over 60 years, the drink never really left during the sanctions and the apartheid era, simply moving its concentrate plant to Swaziland and selling off its bottling interests, but continuing to sell and advertise its products. After apartheid ended, the company became a leading investor in the country, and now has around 85 percent of the carbonated soft drinks market. This is supported by a $25 million advertising campaign making Coca-Cola one of the top ten advertisers in the country (AdAge Global, 2001). South Africa is the only sub-Saharan African country with multinational fast food chains. Even before international brands entered the market, South Africa had well-established fast food chains, such as Nandos (chicken) and Steers (burgers). South Africa is also one of Kentucky Fried Chicken's largest markets with over 300 outlets (Hawkes, 2002). McDonald's opened its first outlet in 1995 in Johannesburg. Their outlet expansion programme over the following two years was more rapid than any other country. In 26 months, 30 outlets opened; there are now 103 in all parts of the country but nearly always in urban settings (McDonald's, 2000) Though Steers remains more popular, the entry of McDonald's stimulated the fast food market to become more competitive as a whole.

Increased exposure to fast foods, decreases in the relative cost of meat and high fat foods, and reduced time for food preparation are all changing dietary patterns in the urban setting. Until a couple of decades ago the African population consumed a typical traditional diet, where the fat intake was only 16 percent of the total calories. By 1990 the fat intake in an urban African community had increased to 26 percent (Mollentze, Moore and Joubert, 1993). When these data were analysed further, it was shown that those people who had lived in cities for most of their lives already consumed a typical westernized diet with 30 percent of calories from total fat, while those who had spent less than 20 percent of their lives in the city only consumed 22.5 percent of calories from total fat (Bourne, 1996).

Remarkably similar findings have also been recently reported from the Northwest Province. The proportion energy from fat in the diet increased from 22 percent in the rural population to 31 percent in the settled urban population (Bourne and Steyn, 2000). Other studies report fat intakes of 34 percent (Langenhoven, Steyn and van Eck, 1988) and 40 percent (Vorster *et al.*, 1997) among African urban populations.

CAPE TOWN

The urban setting will be examined more closely by using Cape Town as a case study. Cape Town is situated on the southwestern tip of South Africa and is home to about 3.5 million people. It is the third largest city in South Africa after Johannesburg and Durban. Table Mountain and the spectacular Cape Peninsula are central to Cape Town's beauty, which harbours a vibrant cultural mixture of people. A large part of the less affluent population lives on the lower plains, called the Cape Flats, which were relatively unpopulated until the 1960s. Since then two major waves of human settlement took place: after the 1960s forceful resettlement of so-called "coloured" people by the apartheid government; and in the 1980s, when a then illegal process of African migration started en masse from extremely impoverished areas of the Eastern Cape. At present, the area of Khayelitsha and Greater Nyanga accommodates about 750 000 people. In combination, apartheid spatial planning and strong migratory push factors contribute to the continual urban sprawl of Greater Cape Town and the expansion of its highly racialized economic geographies. While it has unique demographic and historical features, the rapid growth, especially in the poor African townships, with the concomitant social, economic and political challenges make the issues facing Cape Town similar to other cities in South Africa.

Economic insecurity

The uniqueness of the Cape Town urban sprawl is not restricted to its recent and very rapid population growth, but also reflects a melting pot of extremes. Cape Town has a strong and relatively varied economy with a monocentric structure, characteristic of South African cities in general. It is also an extremely polarized city where affluent suburbs and economic centres present a stark contrast to the overcrowded, impoverished township communities. A recent survey of over 1 500 households in the townships by the School of Public Health and the Programme for Land and Agrarian Studies at the University of the Western Cape found that two-thirds (67 percent) of wage earners do not earn enough to push their households above the poverty line, making them the "chronic working poor", and more than half of breadwinners (52 percent) receive less than the minimum wage per month (US$120). In addition to earning low wages in general, the income stability of those households with employment is very volatile and precarious. For example, in 32 percent of households the main breadwinner had lost his or her job at some stage during 2002, and 31 percent of households suffered the permanent loss of a full-time job during the last five years.

Not surprisingly, many families are struggling to make ends meet and attain food security. Nearly all the households (83 percent) do not have any savings, while most of the remainder reported savings of less than R1 000. Buying food constituted 40 percent of expenditures of households but a significant minority (38 percent) reported spending more than 75 percent on food. Despite the low income levels, 62 percent of all households invested in burial insurance, and 9 percent of households held life insurances.

Food insecurity

Seventy percent of households reported that they went without sufficient food during the last year. When asked specifically about food security in the previous 12 months, 81 percent of households indicated that there was too little food available. Moreover, an average of 43 percent of households has a food shortage at any given time of the year. The reported coping strategies in times of food shortage are summarized in Table 2.

TABLE 2
Coping strategies during times of hunger

Coping strategy	Percentage
Could not do anything	40
Borrowed/begged for food	33
Borrowed money/asked for credit from food sellers	32
Worked for food	13
Collected from refuse dumps/bins	2
Other	16

Comparing their food security situation to the previous year, 54 percent of households felt that they were worse off now, 27 percent thought that their situation was about the same, and only 18 percent of households believed that their food security situation improved over the last year. Furthermore, 55 percent of all households indicated that the general food consumption had been less this year as compared to last year. Thus, based on the overall subjective perceptions in the survey, the extent of hunger increased over the preceding 12 months.

Lack of infrastructure

Apart from obvious handicaps such as lower education and skill levels (mostly a result of the appalling quality of schooling in rural and poor urban areas), the spatial isolation of most poor African inhabitants is an often forgotten barrier to employment. Forty percent of main breadwinners take more than an hour to get to work. Transport by train is the most common means of accessing work (42 percent), followed by taxi (17 percent) and bus transport (15 percent). For 60 percent of breadwinners, a return journey to work exceeds R20 (US$3) per trip. A recent report found that the poor in Cape Town have to commute 16 km on average to get to work, compared with 12 km for the rich (Cape Town Metropolitan Council [CMC], 2002).

This factor reflects the inability of the city administration to instigate significant changes in the social and economic distribution across the city. Turok (2001) highlights how the pressure to become a global city that attracts foreign investment and tourism has severely limited progress towards urban integration. Despite an extensive and widely publicized process of identifying development nodes that are situated closer to the areas where there are concentrations of the poor, nearly all private investment has continued to flow to the richer suburbs. This is largely because of the reluctance and inability of local government to influence market forces – "the general implication is that income, social class and market forces have replaced race and state control in directing the pattern of urban development" (Turok, 2001, p. 2362). Cape Town has been hit hard by the lowering of tariffs, especially in the textile industry, with significant job losses. This is giving rise to an informal economy. In 1996 35 percent of economically active people were engaged in the sector but this had risen to 45 percent by 2001 (CMC, 2002).

There is at present a backlog of about 220 000 housing units, which is increasing by 30 000-50 000 per annum (Cape Metropolitan Housing Task Team, 1999). Yet at the same time housing resources allocated by the central government to Cape Town are decreasing as it is deemed less needy than other provinces. Furthermore, Jenkins and Wilkinson (2001) show that the ability of public investment to offset this is being compromised by pressure to cut expenditure, especially in human resources. Often this is leading to the building of sports and community centres that remain closed because of a lack of personnel and operating costs. Finally, Smith and Hanson (2003) provide compelling evidence of how the pressure for local government to become more "entrepreneurial" is fostering partnerships with the private sector in the provision of basic services such as water and sanitation, and leading to increased lack of services in the poorer parts of the city because of non-payment.

The constricting ability of the state to respond to these needs is putting increasing pressure on land and social tensions. This is also restricting the ability of households to improve food security through home gardening. In the University of the Western Cape survey only 3 percent of households engage in home food gardening (grains and vegetables), and do so solely for their own use and not for trading or selling. Similarly, livestock ownership is rare among the households, with poultry being the highest percentage (11 percent). In the small number of households engaging in agricultural activities, there was no indication that garden cultivation and the possession of livestock significantly reduced the vulnerability of households to hunger. Most respondents stated that the severely limited spatial constraints, the unfertile soil and the perception that agriculture was an activity for rural and not urban dwellers were the main reasons for not growing food. Fear of crime was one of the most common complaints and with good reason. Cape Town has one of the highest murder rates in the world, nearly all concentrated in the poor townships.

Health patterns across the city

Total mortality varies across the city. The two districts with the highest concentration of poor African populations, Khayelitsha and Nyanga, have the greatest mortality. This difference is accentuated if we focus upon premature mortality as measured by years of life lost (YLL) (Figure 5). This is of particular interest to public health managers who work to avoid premature and preventable mortality. The average YYL in the city are 11 178 if Nyanga and Khayelitsha are excluded. This is almost half the premature mortality experienced by Nyanga (20 502) and Khayelitsha (18 974).

FIGURE 5
Premature mortality in YLL compared with age-standardized mortality rate

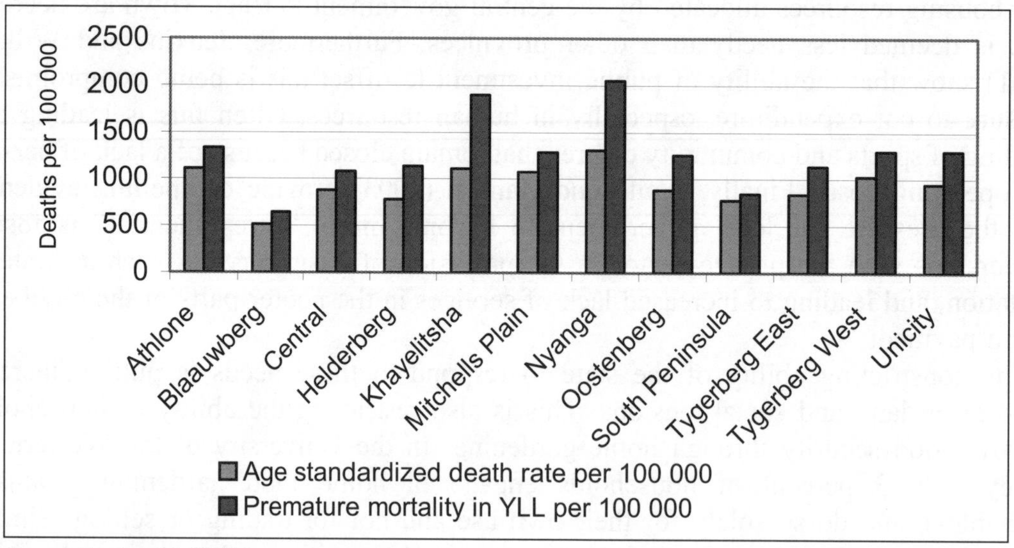

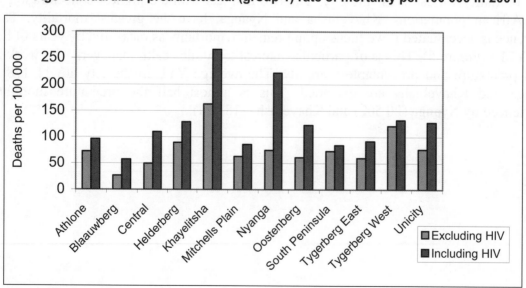

Source: Scott *et al.*, 2001.

To understand the causes of premature mortality better, a review of the distribution of causes of mortality in each subdistrict is helpful. It appears that the disproportionate burden of premature mortality in Nyanga and Khayelitsha is as a result of high levels of infectious disease, injuries, road traffic accidents and homicide (Figure 6). The age-standardized mortality rate (per 100 000) for infectious diseases is highest in Khayelitsha (266) and Nyanga (221) and lowest in Blaauwberg (58), South Peninsula (84) and Tygerberg East (92).

FIGURE 6
Age-standardized pretransitional (group 1) rate of mortality per 100 000 in 2001

Source: Scott *et al.*, 2001.

The responsibility for addressing this inequity must rest firmly with the city, as the provider of basic services: water, sanitation and housing. Inadequate provision of water and sanitation is largely responsible for gastrointestinal infections and overcrowded housing allows the spread of respiratory infections such as tuberculosis. Maternal deaths are preventable if there is access to a good-quality health service. The burden of HIV is once again borne predominantly by Khayelitsha and Nyanga.

A slightly different pattern emerges for mortality from non-communicable diseases (NCDs) (Figure 7). The levels remain high in the poorest districts but are overtaken by districts such as Athlone and Mitchells Plain that rank just above the poorest districts. This reflects the increased prevalence of risk factors such as hypertension, smoking and diabetes in these poor communities compared with wealthier districts.

FIGURE 7
Non-communicable age-standardized deaths per 100 000 persons in 2001

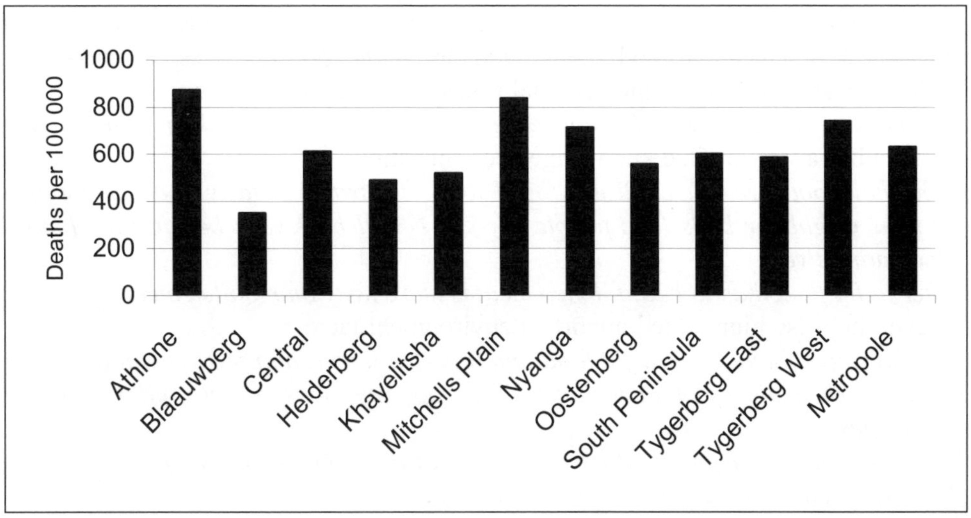

Source: Scott *et al.*, 2001.

Obesity and diet

In the University of the Western Cape survey 70 percent of women are overweight (with 24 percent overweight and 46 percent obese) and only 28 percent fall within the normal weight range. In line with the findings of the Demographic and Health Survey (DHS) (Puoane *et al.*, 2002) only about 20 percent of women actually perceived themselves to be overweight. More in-depth qualitative work with samples of obese women in the Cape Town townships has uncovered a complex array of factors influencing perceptions of body shape (Mvo, Dick and Steyn, 1999). On the one hand some younger women and those with higher levels of education are aware of, and aspire to, a slim body shape. However the majority of African women associate thinness with illness and now with HIV/AIDS. Being large is a sign of wealth and for men a sign that they can look after their families.

Dietary assessments and observations of preparation of food show that women in the townships are very adept at accumulating calories at relatively little financial cost. But their new environments and situations also mean a sharp reduction in physical activity for some. These points are highlighted in the example in Box 1.

BOX 1
Ecology of obesity (taken from Chopra and Puoane, 2003)

Zanempilo is an NGO providing primary health care and rehabilitation services in the urban townships of Cape Town. Community health workers (CHWs) were residents of Khayelitsha and shared the same sociocultural and demographic profiles as ordinary members of this community. As part of an initiative to address the problems of overweight and obesity, a participatory approach of assessment, analysis and action was used to collect baseline data from CHWs on barriers to healthy living, including risk factors, prevention and treatment of diabetes.

Of 44 CHWs measured, two were normal weight, two were overweight, 25 obese and 15 extremely obese. Most perceived moderately overweight women as attractive, associated with dignity, respect and confidence. Negative aspects were continuous body aches and tiredness. Photographs showed unhealthy food preparation and large portion sizes. Barriers to physical activity included fear of losing weight, personal safety and lack of exercising.
"I am scared of exercising because I will lose weight and people may think that I have HIV/AIDS."
They also had a very limited knowledge about nutrition.
"People who boil food are not civilized. Fried food is attractive, tasty such as Kentucky fried chicken. If your neighbour boils food people say she is still backward because the food does not taste nor look attractive."
"It's quicker to fry food than to boil it. Fried meat is more tasty than boiled meat."
However they also highlighted important environment factors.
"There is a shortage of healthy, low-fat food and little fresh fruit and few vegetables are available in the townships. The majority of local shops sell cheap fatty foods. Street vendors' stalls sell fatty meat and sausages."
"To drink low-fat milk is impractical because it is not available in our shops," stated one of the CHWs after she had tried to cut down on the fat in her diet.

The combination of high unemployment and poverty, the continuing influx of rural migrants with low levels of resources and formal skills generate intense pressures for land, shelter and fuel. This in turn breeds rivalry and often conflict between groups and individuals as they attempt to cling on to territory and power (Moosa, 1998). The pervasive climate of fear and violence is another, but under-researched, factor in explaining dietary and lifestyle choices of people. The instant gratification of sweet and fried fatty foods can be succour for the hardships faced. And the legitimate fear of crime and violence restricts recreational opportunities especially after dark.

Responses
Despite the considerable constraints facing the state, there have been a number of interesting responses from the national, provincial and local government. Nationally there is recognition of the need to mitigate some of the "push" factors that are taking people out of the rural areas. A number of the poorest rural districts have been identified as "developmental nodes" that should be receiving extra infrastructural and human resources. To date there has been no evaluation of their success.

More locally, the Provincial Department of Health is working with its municipal counterparts to improve household food security in urban settings. In Cape Town for example, a team of five community nutrition officers dispense grants for totally more than US$50 000 per annum supporting community garden projects (PAWC, 2002). With support, most of these gardens are now cooperating under the umbrella of three consortia, allowing them economies of scale and opportunities to share skills and ideas.

In most urban areas of South Africa there are also active NGOs and in some cases they are very sophisticated. Government is realizing that partnerships with civil society are going to be essential if they are have any hope of addressing the development needs of South Africans. This is becoming especially acute with the increasing impact of HIV/AIDS. Box 2 is an illustration of a partnership between provincial and local government with local NGOs and research institutions.

BOX 2
Combating worm infestation

Khayelitsha is the largest township in the Western Cape with an estimated population of 300 000. It is a mixture of formal and informal squatter communities. The high watertable, poor soil, low incomes and extreme overcrowding make sanitation and hygiene formidable challenges. Diarrhoea is the leading cause of death among young children. Following a request from a local medical officer, a survey to determine the prevalence of intestinal worms in primary schoolchildren was conducted in 1999. All 12 primary schools in Khayelitsha were sampled and over 1 200 children's stools examined. The results are astounding. Prevalence of whipworm (*Trichuris trichiura*) and roundworm (*Ascaris lumbricoides*) was estimated, respectively, as 80.3 percent (SD 9.5, SEM 2.7) and 69.7 percent (SD 9.2, SEM 2.6). In many schools nearly all the children examined were infested.

The initial action was to raise funds and deworm the children with medication. Anthelmintic treatment during 1999 reduced excretion of whipworm and roundworm eggs per gram of stool, respectively, by 85.4 percent (SD 15.7, SEM 4.7) and 98.6 percent (SD 2.4, SEM 0.7). The medical intervention was successful in reducing worm eggs from recycling to the environment in areas without sanitation. The interest generated by the deworming was used to engage parents and teachers in addressing the broader causes of infestation and undernutrition. This was done using techniques involving participatory approaches. A series of educational materials focusing upon hygiene and environmental improvement has been developed and integrated by the Department of Education into the curriculum. It also initiated a broader environmental intervention involving all role players. The Khayelitsha Task Team now comprises teachers, school nurses, city of Tygerberg officials, parents, the local university and NGOs. They are at present engaged in testing various "dry sanitation" options.

CONCLUSION

It should be quite clear that the new dispensation in South Africa has unleashed a number of forces that threaten to overwhelm the capacity of urban governments, services and communities to cope. Local agencies need to establish new ways of operating that are appropriate to addressing the new kinds of problems. A key priority is the formulation of policies that are based upon a more detailed understanding of the reality and dynamics of new urban poverty. What are the factors leading to the apparently contradictory emergence of obesity and poverty? What are the key strategies undertaken by urban households to attain household food security? What is the price paid by the most vulnerable members of the households in the livelihood choices made by households? This paper has attempted to illustrate some of the links between globalization, urbanization, local government capacity and policies, poverty and diet. There still remains much to be done.

Bibliography

AdAge Global. 2001. *Hey, big spenders*. 1 November 2001 (http://www.adageglobal.com). Accessed on 5 May 2002.

Benatar, D. 1999. Beyond the haze of the tobacco bill debate. *S. Afr. Med. J.,* 89(7): 752-4.

Bourne, L.T. 1996. *Dietary intake in an urban African population in South Africa, with special reference to the nutrition transition*. South Africa, University of Cape Town. (Thesis for Doctoral Philosophy)

Bourne, L. & Steyn, K. 2000. Rural/urban nutrition-related differentials among adult population groups in South Africa, with special emphasis on the black population. *S. Afr. J. Clin. Nutr.,* 13: S23-S28.

Bradshaw, D. & Laubscher, R. 2002. Mortality profile of the rich and the poor. *In* D. Bradshaw & K. Steyn, eds. *Poverty and chronic diseases in South Africa*. Cape Town, Medical Research Council.

Cape Metropolitan Housing Task Team. 1999. *Statement of intent with regard to housing in CMA*. Cape Town, CMC.

Cape Town Metropolitan Council (CMC). 2002. *Economic trends and spatial patterns in the Cape Metropolitan area: Update*. CMC, Cape Town

Chopra, M. & Puoane, T. 2003. *Prevention of diabetes throughout an obesegenic world*. (*Diabetes Voice Special Issue*.) Brussels, International Diabetes Federation.

Coca-Cola Company. 1997. *Coca-Cola Company Annual Report* (www.cocacola.com). Accessed on 5 May 2002.

Dorrington, R., Bourne, D., Bradshaw, D., Laubscher, R. & Timaeus, I.M. 2001. *The impact of HIV/AIDS on adult mortality in South Africa*. Technical Report. Burden of Disease Research Unit. Cape Town, Medical Research Council.

Hawkes, C. 2002. Marketing activities of global soft drink and fast food companies in emerging markets: a review. In *Globalisation, diets and non-communicable diseases*. Switzerland, World Health Organization.

Jenkins, P. & Wilkinson, P. 2001. Assessing the increasing impact of global economy on urban development in South African cities. *Cities,* 19(1): 33-47.

Labadarios, D., ed. 2000. *The National Food Consumption Survey (NFCS). Children aged 1-9 years, South Africa, 1999*. Pretoria, Department of Health. (www.sahealthinfo.org/Modules/Nutrition/foodconsumption/foodconsumption.html). Accessed on 4 August 2003.

Langenhoven, M., Steyn, K. & van Eck, M. 1988. Nutrient intakes in the Peninsula coloured population. *Ecol. Food Nutr.,* 22: 97-106.

Marais, H. 1998. *South Africa: limits to change – the political economy of transformation*. Cape Town, UCT Press.

May, J., ed. 2000. *Poverty and inequality in South Africa: meeting the challenge*. Cape Town, David Philip Publishers.

McDonald's. 2000. Annual Report 2000 (www.macdonalds.com). Accessed on 5 May 2002.

McGrath, M. 1990. Economic growth, income distribution and social change. *In* N. Natrass & E. Ardington, eds. The political economy of South Africa. Cape Town, Oxford University Press.

Mollentze, W.F., Moore, A. & Joubert, G. *et al*. 1993. Cardiovascular risk factors in the black population of QwaQwa. *S. Afr. J. Clin. Nutr.,* 6: 50-51.

Moosa, E. (chair) 1998. *Crossroads and Philippi Crisis. Report of a Commission of Enquiry*. Cape Town City Council.

Mvo, Z., Dick, J. & Steyn, K. 1999. Perceptions of overweight African women about acceptable body size of women and children. *Curationis,* 22: 27-31.

Potter, R.B., Binns, T. & Elliot, J. 1999. *Geographies of development*. London, Longmans.

Provincial Administration Western Cape (PAWC). 2002. *Annual Report for Health*. Western Cape, South Africa.

Puoane, T., Steyn, K., Bradshaw, D., Laubscher, R., Fourie, J., Lambert, V. & Mbananga, N. 2002. Obesity in South Africa: the South African demographic and health survey. *Obes. Res.,* (10): 1038-48.

SA Urban Foundation. 1991. *Changes in the social demography of South Africa 1980-1990*. Johannesburg, David Philip Publishers.

Scott, V., Sanders, D., Chopra, M., Groenwald, P., Bradshaw, D. *et al*. 2001. *Cape Town mortality 2001. Equity Issues Technical Report*. Cape Town, Medical Research Council/UWC.

Smith, L. & Hanson, S. 2003. Access to water for the urban poor in Cape Town: where equity meets cost recovery. *Urban Studies,* 40(8): 1517-1548.

Statistics South Africa. 1996. *The People of South Africa Population Census, 1996*. Census in Brief. Report No. 03-01-11. Pretoria.

Statistics South Africa 2001. *Statistics South Africa Census 2001* (www.statssa.gov.za).

Statistics South Africa 2002. *October Household Survey 1999*. Statistical Release P0317 (http://www.statssa.gov.za/Statistical_releases/Statistical_releases.htm).

Statistics South Africa. 2003. *The People of South Africa Population Census, 2000*. Census in Brief. Report. Pretoria, Statistics South Africa.

Steyn, K., Bourne, L.T., Jooste, P.L., Fourie, J.M., Lombard, C.J. & Yach, D. 1994. Smoking in the black community of the Cape Peninsula, South Africa. *East Afr. Med. J.,* 12: 784-9.

Turok, I. 2001. Persistent polarisation post-apartheid? Progress towards urban integration in Cape Town. *Urban Studies,* 38(13): 2349-2377.

United Nations Development Programme (UNDP). 2001. *Human Development Report*. Oxford, Oxford University Press.

Vorster, H., Oosthuizen, N., Jerling, J., Veldman, F. & Burger, H. 1997. *The nutritional status of South Africans. A review of the literature 1975-1996*. Durban, Health Systems Trust.

Impact of globalization on food consumption, health and nutrition in urban areas: a case study of Dar es Salaam, United Republic of Tanzania

Joyce Kinabo [1]

INTRODUCTION

The United Republic of Tanzania, located in eastern Africa, has a total area of 945 087 m^2 (Figure 1). The climate varies from tropical along the coast to temperate in the highlands. Most of the United Republic of Tanzania lies more than 200 m above sea level. Mount Kilimanjaro rises to more than 5 000 m above sea level, the highest point in Africa. The country gained independence from British rule in 1963 and today is a growing multiparty democracy of 35 million citizens (National Bureau of Statistics, 2002).

FIGURE 1
Map of the United Republic of Tanzania

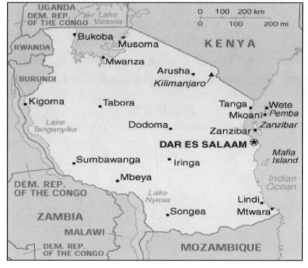

Source: CIA (Central Intelligence Agency) , 2004.

Socio-economic characteristics

The proportion of people living in urban areas has increased from less than 10 percent in 1975 to 33 percent in 2003 (Figure 2). The United Republic of Tanzania's rapid urbanization rate is

[1] Joyce Kinabo (Ph.D.)
Associate Professor of Human Nutrition
Sokoine University of Agriculture
Department of Food Science and Technology
PO Box 3006
Morogoro, United Republic of Tanzania
E-mail: joykinabo@hotmail.com

among the highest in the world. As a result, pressure is placed on the capacity of urban services and on the growth of opportunities for gainful employment in and around the urban centre.

FIGURE 2
Trends of urbanization in the United Republic of Tanzania from 1975 to 2005

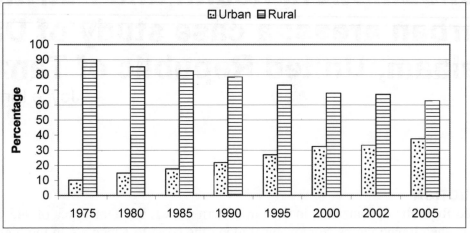

Source: National Bureau of Statistics, 2003.

The population structure of the United Republic of Tanzania shows that the proportion of children under 14 years of age is more than 48 percent and the elderly population (above 60 years) accounts for 6.1 percent. The dependency ratio increased from 98 percent in 1967 to 116 percent in 2002. This is indicative that the economic burden on persons in the reproductive age groups has not changed significantly over the last 30 years. The average life expectancy at birth is 51 years; total fertility rate is 5.2; the infant mortality rate is 104 per 1 000 live births; the under five mortality rate is 165 per 1 000 live births; and the maternal mortality rate is 530 per 100 000 (UNICEF, 2003).

The population structure of Dar es Salaam is shown in Figure 3. The population pyramid shows the age and sex structure of the population in five-year age groups.

FIGURE 3
Dar es Salaam population pyramid, 2001

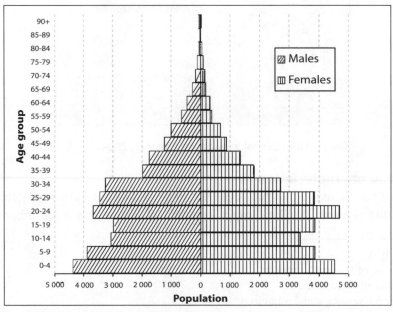

Source: Ministry of Health (the United Republic of Tanzania), 2001.

The United Republic of Tanzania has a mixed economy in which agriculture plays a dominant role. Agriculture contributes the largest share to the gross domestic product (GDP), which has been increasing since the early 1990s. It was 3.4 in 1991 and is currently 5.6. However, the contribution to GDP from agriculture has been declining from 48 percent in 1991 to 44.8 percent in 2002 (Research and Analysis Working Group, 2002). Currently, the urban labour force is 16.8 percent of the total labour force in the country.

Dar es Salaam

Dar es Salaam is located along the Indian Ocean and covers a total area of 139.3 km^2. Administratively, the city is divided into three municipalities – Kinondoni, Temeke and Ilala.

Dar es Salaam is the commercial city of the country and one of the fastest growing cities in Africa. It has a population of 3 497 940 (census, 2002) with an intercensual growth rate of 4.3 percent (1988-2002). The Dar es Salaam population (Figure 4) is fuelled partly by an influx of unemployed youth from the rural areas looking for better opportunities in urban areas. On average, 16 percent of the city population are migrants from other places in the United Republic of Tanzania who have migrated over the last six years.

FIGURE 4
Dar es Salaam population changes from 1967 to 2004

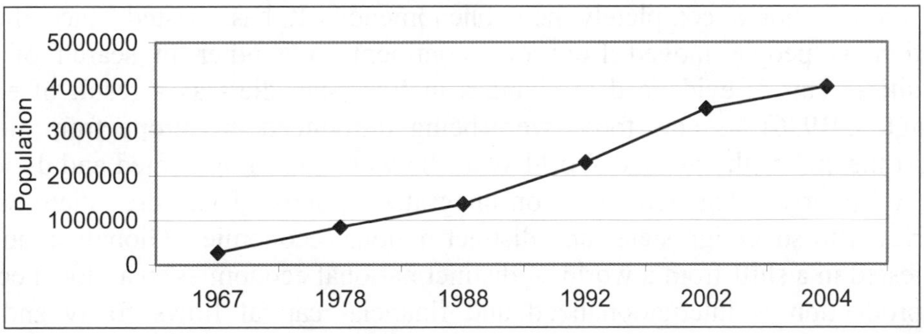

Note: the population figures for 1992 and 2004 are based on estimates.
Source: UNDP, 1998, 2003.

Urban livelihoods

The average income earner in Dar es Salaam is responsible for four people, which is a significant burden given the low level of earnings. Most workers are self-employed rather than wage earners. The majority of the poor are proprietors of small businesses and account for 20 to 40 percent, depending on the area of the city. Petty traders or street vendors are 15 to 20 percent and consist mainly of male youth between 20 and 29 years of age. Skilled workers account for 20 percent of the labour force. Unskilled labourers are 10 to 30 percent (Research and Analysis Working Group, 2002). Seasonal fluctuations in incomes leave many households throughout the city particularly vulnerable when food prices are high. However, the urban poor often maintain a link with their rural background either in the form of a plot or food remittances from time to time. This acts as a coping strategy when the situation gets harsh.

Urban living conditions

Problems facing the urban poor include rudimentary housing, an unhealthy environment and dilapidated physical infrastructure. Few families own houses in the dense areas of the city, where rents can be high. Few homes have indoor bathrooms and instead common pit latrines are used, which are poorly maintained. Hygiene practices are poor among the urban residents, particularly in densely populated areas. Refuse disposal is ineffectual and what is not collected is usually dumped on the street. The situation is likely to worsen as the city becomes more congested.

Public services have deteriorated and private services are emerging but tend to be far less accessible to the poor because of high costs. Poor living conditions (overcrowding, poor housing, health, water facilities and services) leave the population more susceptible to diseases. Adequate health care is becoming increasingly inaccessible to the poor because of budgetary reduction in health services and the introduction of cost-sharing policies in the health sector. In addition, the urban poor tend to have a lower level of education than middle-income urban people; they have a low level of awareness on how to make use of health care facilities. This leads to a high incidences of disease, especially in children. Child malnutrition is a severe problem and about 40 percent of the children in Dar es Salaam are stunted (CARE the United Republic of Tanzania, 1998; IFPRI, 2001). High-income groups, however, tend to have access to all the basic services and facilities. But they suffer more from diseases of affluence.

INDICATORS OF GLOBALIZATION

Globalization is a complex process that involves political, economic and sociocultural changes across the globe (Lubbers and Koorevaar, 1999). It should be noted, however, that globalization is not a completely new phenomenon. It has existed since the time of exploration as people moved from one continent to another in search of land and commodities. This is evidenced in changes in European diets as a result of exploration (Washington, 1996), as new foods were being introduced in Europe from all over the world. At the end of the Second World War, the world was fragmented and divided into a number of poorly integrated and non-integrated groups. Therefore, there were clear boundaries with sovereign states and distinct national economies. Globalization therefore is manifested in a shift from a world of distinct national economies to a global economy in which production is internationalized and financial capital flows freely and instantly between countries (Tobin, 2000; Stiglitz, 2000; Lubbers and Koorevaar, 1999).

Features of globalization include shifts from distinct national economies to a global economy; internationalized production through transnational and worldwide companies; and free and instant financial capital flows between countries, multinational organizations and companies with vast economic power over states, resulting in a relative loss of control and power of the state to manage its national affairs. Improved telecommunications and the development of an electronic communication network such as the Internet have helped to overcome the barriers of physical distances. Indicators that are used to determine the influence of globalization include communication, transportation, banking systems and electronics. Essentially globalization has to do with the evolution of humanity: communication, science, technology and development.

Communications

Communications as used here include telecommunications and electronic communication and are related to information access. Access to information in Africa is scarce – one in every 5 000 people has access in electronic form (Raychaudhuri, 1999). The situation is worse in rural areas where the necessary facilities for accessing information are lacking. Access is increasing in urban areas but at a very slow rate and only for a small proportion of the population. On average, there are 142 radio sets and 23 televisions for 1 000 people (UNESCO and World Bank, 2002).

In the United Republic of Tanzania, a similar trend is observed. Immediately after independence and up to the early 1990s, the United Republic of Tanzania had one state-owned telephone company, one radio station, no television station in the mainland and one television station in Zanzibar. Table 1 gives some statistics regarding communication in the country. It should be noted, however, that most of the facilities are located in urban areas. This is because of the low development of telecommunications infrastructure in rural areas and exorbitant telephone tariffs charged to telephone subscribers.

TABLE 1
Information and communication statistics of the United Republic of Tanzania

Service	1990	1995	2000	2002
Telephone lines/1 000	3	3	5	5.3
Telephone lines in large cities/1 000			23	35
Mobile phones/1 000	0	0	5	8
Internet users/1 000	0	0	115	120
Mobile lines operators	0	0	0	4
Radio /1 000	141	280	290	356
Television/1 000	0	17	20	23
Personal computers	0		2.8	>2.8
Television stations	0	0	3	7
Radio stations	2	2	4	30
Internet service providers	0	0	6	13
Internet cafés	0	0	0	1 000+
Satellites	0	0	0	1

Source: UNESCO, 1996; UNESCO and World Bank, 2002; Mgaya, 2000.

The increasing trend in both the size and quality of services has been a result of investment by private companies in the sector. Trade liberalization policies led to an increase in the number of private companies and service providers (UNESCO, 1998; Mgaya, 2000). These are concentrated mainly in the towns and cities. The shortfall in rural areas is partly offset by the greater use of radio. At the current rate of 356 radios sets per 1 000 people, the use of radios in the United Republic of Tanzania is significantly above the average of 196 for sub-Saharan Africa (UNESCO and World Bank, 2002).

Despite huge improvements in terms of the numbers of various facilities, the infrastructure is still poorly developed. In addition, the cost of the Internet remains a strong deterrent to significant improvement in services. Although there are increased private sector ISPs, service provision has not improved significantly. This is because it is carried out through the government telephone company; its service is inadequate in terms of robustness, combined with low bandwidth, congestion and noisy lines. Consequently, some local service providers use ISPs in the United States and Europe, which makes the service very expensive. In urban areas, accessibility to information is hampered because of frequent electricity interruptions.

Information technology offers an opportunity to disseminate information to a wide population and therefore influence people's behaviour and practices. However, the language barrier prevents many people from understanding what is beamed on the Internet. Information available through information and communication technologies (ICT) is mainly in English, which the majority of rural and urban communities in the United

Republic of Tanzania cannot understand. In addition, there is a lack of local content on the Internet. In 1999, for example, Africa generated only 0.4 percent of global content. There is a marked shortage of relevant materials in local languages on the Internet that respond to the needs of users. In addition, the literacy and basic skills levels of the general population are low, so that accessibility also remains low. There is a clear link between the development of skills and gains in ICT. However, despite tremendous ICT gains, social gender inequality still exists. Already disadvantaged in access to education, credit and land, women are also marginalized in all areas of ICT.

Transportation

The country has a total 88 200 km of roads, from feeder roads to highways. Of these, 3 704 are paved with tarmac and 84 496 are unpaved. Only 12 percent of the roads are passable throughout the year. The rest are passable only during the dry season and partly impassable during the rainy season. This has a significant influence on the movement of people and commodities from one area to another. There are 3 569 km of railway lines running between Dar es Salaam and Kigoma, Dar es Salaam and Moshi and Dar es Salaam and Zambia. In addition, the country has 12 ports and 126 airports and airstrips.

Banking

Before 1991, the financial sector comprised only six state-owned banks, one large government insurance company and three government-owned pension funds. In 1991, parliament passed a new financial institution and banking act, which allowed for the establishment of private commercial banks, financial institutions and foreign bureaus.

Liberalization of the banking sector removed the monopoly of the state-owned banks and financial institutions by allowing participation of the private sector through privatization and/ or the establishment of new banks. This created competition and greater efficiency in the banking sector. Formation of the Dar es Salaam Stock Exchange paved the way for the increased role of the private sector in production as well as mobilization and utilization of domestic resources. Foreign banks led by Barclays, Standard Chartered, South Africa (ABSA and Stanbic) and Citibank now account for a third of the market. Currently, there are 21 commercial banks and 12 financial institutions.

ROLE OF GLOBALIZATION AND URBANIZATION ON DIETARY CHANGE

Globalization is influencing food habits and dietary patterns in many parts of Africa (and the world in general), especially in urban areas. It has increased free movement of processed foods and other commodities such as cooking oil, soft drinks, biscuits, cakes, sweets and chocolates and ready to eat foods. These have become readily available on the market and consumption has increased significantly in urban areas of Africa. The dietary intake pattern is now changing rapidly from a traditional diet of high carbohydrate, high fibre to one containing many manufactured, processed and non-traditional foods. This trend is accelerated by the increased rate of urbanization. Increased urbanization and changing food habits and lifestyles have created an additional burden of nutrition problems in Africa (WHO, 2003). For example, in 1930 there was no incidence of diabetes in Kenya, but by the late 1970s it had become common (Mwaluko *et al.,* 1991). This phenomenon occurs independently from socio-economic change (Popkin, 1994; Drewnowski and Popkin, 1997).

Nutritionists in Africa have to deal with different types of problems. One is undernutrition, most prevalent in rural areas and resulting from dietary deficiencies in energy and micronutrients combined with poor hygiene, poor sanitation and frequent illness. The diets of the middle- and low-income urban populations are changing as they strive to consume more modern imported foods and fewer traditional ones, but they cannot afford an adequate diet because of poor accessibility (low incomes). These populations tend to have a high prevalence of micronutrient deficiency and some energy insufficiency. Other types of nutritional problems are mainly seen in the urban upper class, which has had a dramatic change in lifestyle and food habits. These people have increased their consumption of highly refined energy-dense foods (fats and sugar), meat and alcohol (Garine, 1969; Drewnowski and Popkin, 1997). Nutritional-related problems for this group include obesity, diabetes and cardiovascular diseases. Problems of overnutrition are also increasing in rural communities.

The analysis by Drewnowski and Popkin (1997) shows that there is a major shift in the structure of the global diet. The global availability of cheap vegetable oils and fats has resulted in increased fat consumption among low-income countries. As a result, the problems of dietary-related diseases occur at lower levels of the GNP than hitherto. This is also accelerated by urbanization. Those working to improve the nutritional well-being of the poor in developing countries are now confronted with an additional challenge on how to deal with the emerging crisis of excess nutrition and chronic dietary-related diseases without drawing resources away from the problems of undernutrition and poverty. It should be noted that the ultimate goal is to have adequate nutritional status for all populations irrespective of their economic status (rich or poor).

One of the opportunities of globalization and market liberalization is that it allows diet diversification. The traditional diets of Africa, and the United Republic of Tanzania in particular, are based on a very limited number of foods and often consist of more starchy roots and coarse grains, less fat and high fibre, and offer little in terms of diversity or variety. With the introduction of foods from other regions of the world, there is a shift from high carbohydrate staples to a more diverse diet, ensuring availability of more nutrients, even those that are known to be deficient in foods produced from the local soils. The movement of foods from one region to another allows exchange of nutrients between regions and helps to supplement or complement the missing nutrients in the local diets.

Evolution of urban food supply

Crop production data (Ministry of Agriculture and Food Security, 2003) show that the Dar es Salaam region can only attain 6 percent of its food sufficiency; therefore 94 percent of its food requirements are obtained from other regions and through imports from other countries. Limited production and trade liberalization paved the way for the proliferation of food-based investments such as supermarkets and food merchants, as evidenced by the food supply trend at Kariakoo market (Table 2) and from food imports data recorded by the Ministry of Agriculture and Food Security (2003).

TABLE 2
Food supply trend of fresh foods entering Dar es Salaam (tonnes)

Commodity	1999	2000	2001	2002	2003 (July)
Vegetables	161.8	26 390	32 939	39 645	23 774
Fruit	4 260	8 412	13 283	11 948	9 361
Fish	2 609	2 904	2 030	1 669	1 027
Roots and tubers	11 940	12 203	15 623	18 864	16 259

Note: the leap increase in vegetable supply at Kariakoo market is a result of poor record-keeping of the vegetable supply prior to 2000. In 2000 a private operator took up the market, which made an improvement.
Source: Mjawa, 2003, unpublished.

The supply of fresh foods, especially of fruit and vegetables, has been increasing annually since 1999 as a result of increased production and improved transportation, which have been brought about by globalization. Under globalization, many people are now free to produce and market their products anywhere in the country with minimum restrictions, unlike the period before liberalization. Similarly, imports have been increasing year after year. For example, in 1999/2000 importations of non-cereal products were 21 137 tonnes and increased to 221 258 tonnes in 2001/2002. However, importation of cereal products has been declining with time from 426 253 tonnes in 1999/2000 to 380 548 tonnes in 2001/2002. This could be attributed to higher prices charged on imported cereals compared to local ones. In addition, the taste of imported cereals is quite different from what people are accustomed to and therefore imported cereals serve just a small proportion of the population, mainly those of Asian origin. Total food imports have been increasing from 447 390 in 1999/2000 to 689 187 tonnes in 2002 simply because of the increasing importation of non-cereal food items such as oils, soft drinks, fruit and vegetables.

Street foods
Street foods account for 70 percent of the total calorie intake of the urban low- and middle-income groups. In a survey carried out in Dar es Salaam (Mjawa, 2003, unpublished), it was observed that on average 168 people visit one street food vendor per day. This was not the situation about 20 years ago. Take-away meals from street food vendors are also becoming very popular in urban areas (Nkurlu, 2000). Many households buy food from vendors to save on the cost of food ingredients and cooking fuel, save preparation time and try new foods. Men from low-income groups account for 70 percent of all consumers of street foods. Persons in the higher socio-economic groups tend to eat out in western-type fast food restaurants (such as Steers and Burger King).

The types of foods served by street food vendors include rice, stiff porridge from maize flour, plantains, and maize cooked with beans. Other foods include fried potato, cassava and sweet potato chips; roast and fried chicken; roast pork, beef and goat meat. Foods sold in western-type fast food restaurants include fried chicken, beef burgers, pizzas, potato chips and soft drinks. All these foods have high proportions of oil, salt and sugar and are therefore higher in calories than other foods.

Urbanization, coupled with low wages offered to employees and labourers, has led to a proliferation of street food vendors who offer commercial meals but with high microbial contaminants caused by poor hygiene and handling methods. Vendors' stalls are usually located outdoors or under a roof and are easily accessible from the street. They have low-cost seating facilities, which are sometimes rudimentary. Their marketing success depends exclusively on location and word of mouth promotion. Individuals or families usually operate street food businesses, but benefits from their trade extend throughout the local economy. Vendors buy their fresh food locally, thus linking their enterprise directly with small-scale farms and gardens in the urban areas. These have partly contributed to the expansion of urban agriculture in Dar es Salaam (Christopher, Kinabo and Nyange, 1994).

With urbanization on the increase, street foods will tend to become even more important, hence there is a need for more research in this area in order to identify ways of improving preparation and handling of these foods.

Supermarkets

Supermarket growth in the United Republic of Tanzania took off in the 1990s and early 2000. In the 1980s, the state was in charge of public sector retail operations, regional trading companies and household supply companies. These were privatized in the 1990s when trade liberalization was taking place and were rapidly replaced by a proliferation of private minimarkets and small grocers in the mid-1990s. Currently, there are 11 supermarkets in Dar es Salaam, and these include two domestic chain supermarkets: Imalaseko and Shoppers' Plaza. About 80 percent of foods sold in supermarkets are imported, and only 20 percent originate from the United Republic of Tanzania. This small proportion is actually achieved through a regulation, which requires supermarkets to include local foodstuffs on their shelves. However, access by farmers to these supermarkets (either to sell or buy) is very limited.

Fast food chains

Up until the mid-1990s, multinational fast food chains had more or less ignored the East African market, especially the United Republic of Tanzania and Uganda, where the middle class, the target group, only recently began to develop a liking for fast food (Kaiza, 1999). The entry of fast food chains has stimulated a lot of business in urban areas, especially in Dar es Salaam. Currently, there is tremendous expansion of the major fast food companies in Africa such as Steers, Nandos and Innscor. In a period of four years, the food licensing board issued 35 new licences and 23 in 2002/2003 (Mjawa, 2003, unpublished). Fast food outlets serve only a few types of food, usually prepared by frying, e.g. hamburgers, chicken, potato chips and pizzas (Pan African News Agency, 2002). Some of these food items are imported. Owners, who in most cases are foreign investors, usually have a franchise arrangement with a transnational company, which also controls the provision of raw materials, the menu and mode of preparation, thus decreasing potential stimulation of local producers. The fast food chains do not offer much in terms of generating local production of the food items that are used in their recipes.

Increased consumption of fast foods especially among the young population is linked to increased marketing activity. Advertisements and sales promotions are playing a key role in expanding and stimulating demand among the younger generation. Such promotions increase purchase frequency by giving consumers an incentive, a gift or a prize, encouraging them to drink or eat more. Sales promotions drive frequent purchasing particularly among children. Promotions are carried out even in rural areas. It is common to find an advertisement for Coca-Cola in remote villages of the United Republic of Tanzania. This is a clear indication that the multinational corporations have penetrated the country so deeply that they have also influenced the pattern of consumption. Instead of drinking fruit juice or any other locally available natural beverage, many people have switched to drinking Coca-Cola and other soft drinks.

IMPACT OF GLOBALIZATION ON LIFESTYLE IN URBAN AREAS

Walking to and from work was commonplace in the 1980s and early 1990s when the importation of cars was restricted. In addition to less active commuting, there has been a significant reduction in physical activity at work and at home because of availability and ability to buy household labour-saving devices such as dishwashers, washing machines and vacuum cleaners, particularly for the high-income group. Women's workload in this group has diminished significantly. Even without these labour-saving appliances, high-income families can afford to hire several workers to help with the household chores, their leisure time has increased and this time is usually spent watching television, talking or reading but not engaging in demanding physical activity. The level of activity in other income and age groups is also low compared to that in rural areas. Consequently, obesity and cardiovascular diseases are on the increase. To alleviate this problem, people have been encouraged to incorporate physical exercise in their lifestyles. This has led to a proliferation of gyms and health or fitness clubs in Dar es Salaam. These facilities are not free, and serve only those who can afford access. Low-income groups, who also tend to be obese, cannot afford to use them.

Transportation systems

Increased importation of cars has improved the transport system in Dar es Salaam and in other urban areas of the country. In the early 1980s, the transport system was virtually collapsing. Movement of people and commodities was difficult and prices were high because of high transportation costs. Immediately after trade liberalization there was a huge influx of cars, mainly reconditioned ones from Japan and the Republic of Korea. Currently, most urban areas have public transport run by private individuals. The private transportation industry is something like the informal street food industry; even unskilled illiterate persons operate taxis or minibuses. The urban "public" transportation system is a collection of privately owned cars operating as buses and taxis. There is a state-owned company, but it is on the verge of collapse. Traffic is worsening in cities, particularly in Dar es Salaam. The increased number of cars has also contributed to environmental pollution.

Crime

Crime rates have increased significantly over the past 20 years. The most prevalent crime is burglary with about 43 percent of households reporting being burgled over the last five years. Simple theft is the second most frequent crime. Theft of livestock and crops is common in the rural areas of the city. Hijacking and vehicle theft rates are very low, but theft of external motor vehicle fittings is common. This has been experienced by 19 percent of the people surveyed. There are also high (16 percent) levels of assault. The rates of violent crime in Dar es Salaam and other urban areas of the country are lower than those found in other cities such as Durban where similar studies have been carried out (Robertshaw, Louw and Matni, 2000). Increased crime rates are a result of unemployment and lack of alternative income-generating activities in both rural and urban areas. Because of the increased cost of living and changing lifestyles, those without employment resort to burglary as a means of raising income.

Alcohol and smoking consumption

Alcohol consumption

Production of bottled beer has gone up greatly in the last few years. Beer is much more available now than it was in the early 1990s, with production increases from 529 955 hectolitres in 1988 to 1 221 307 hectolitres in 1996, 1 865 000 in 2001 and a slight decline to 1 804 000 in 2002 (Barth and Sohn, 2003). However, because the cost of living has been increasing, people buy less beer now than before although they have more varieties from which to choose. The average per capita consumption is 0.6 litres – about 10 percent of that in Europe – and accounts for 20 percent of total beer production in the country. However, this does not mean that people in the United Republic of Tanzania do not drink. Small local producers produce 80 percent of the alcohol consumed in the country (Alcohol in East Africa, 2000). In Dar es Salaam, the common local brew is made from palm sap and is very popular during traditional ceremonies.

Drinking patterns have changed significantly. Most of the alcohol made in the past was not for sale. People drank for rituals and in social settings (ceremonial), and only elderly men were allowed to drink, not women and younger men. Today, drinking has become commercialized and people drink without a purpose.

This change in the pattern of alcohol consumption has had both positive and negative consequences. On the one hand, it has opened up an avenue for women to generate income. As a result, most producers of local brews are women. This is an example of a self-driven, sustainable and community-based enterprise which, if improved, could benefit women and their families.

However, on the negative side, alcohol consumption is depleting the meagre resources of the household. Women and children become the victims when household resources cannot cover their general health or schooling expenses. There is a need to conduct a study to establish the proportion of household income spent on alcohol and how this affects the well-being of household members.

Smoking

There are no validated comparable population-based data available to indicate the trend of smoking in the United Republic of Tanzania (Jagoe *et al.,* 2002). Information about smoking or tobacco use in the United Republic of Tanzania is sparse and is based on scattered surveys mainly carried out in urban areas. In addition, most of the studies on smoking or tobacco use have focused on occupational or other selected groups such as hospital patients.

In Dar es Salaam, the prevalence of smoking is 27 percent for men and 5 percent for women (Jagoe *et al.,* 2002). The prevalence of smoking in adolescent males is 12.6 percent, but they have higher rates of inhalation of solvents (17.5 percent) compared to their counterparts in Harare (8.5 percent) and Cape Town (5.9 percent). The main reason is that the United Republic of Tanzanian youth have less income at their disposal and therefore cannot afford to buy alcohol. Consequently they resort to alternatives. Smoking is more common in males than in females. However, increased marketing activities of tobacco companies are targeting females, especially in urban areas. As many cultural prohibitions on women are easing with the effects of globalization, women are at high risk as regards increases in smoking.

Figure 5 shows that overall per capita cigarette consumption has been declining since 1970. It is currently at 170 sticks per annum despite increased production and the availability of cigarettes. The reason for the decrease is not clear but could be related to health campaigns that have been going on over the last two decades.

FIGURE 5
Annual per capita cigarette consumption in the United Republic of Tanzania, 1970-1999

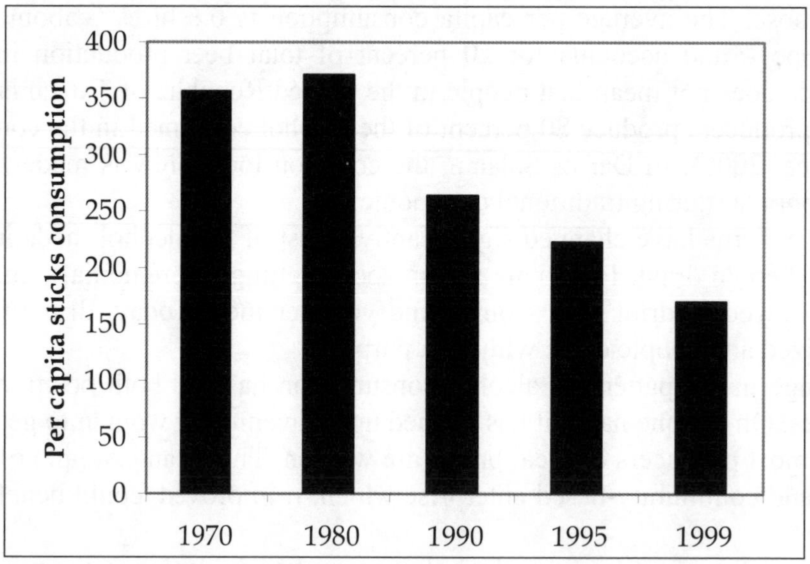

Source: Jagoe *et al.*, 2002.

The changing role of women and impact on child care and feeding

Since the late 1970s, there has been a rapid rise in the number of female employees. Between 1977 and 1984 the number in the public sector rose by 200 percent (Tripp, 1992). Self-employment has been a more important type of income-earning activity for women than wage employment. Since the 1990s even more women have joined the informal sector. This is also observed in rural areas where non-farming activities have become important elements of the household survival strategy. Participation of women in the informal sector has given them more independence but has also increased their responsibilities for providing a cash income while maintaining their traditional role in the family.

Both the prevalence and duration of breastfeeding have declined in most urban areas (National Bureau of Statistics, 2000; Popkin and Bisgrove, 1998). Less breastfeeding and earlier weaning in urban populations contribute to earlier faltering of growth (Atkinson, 1992). Other influences in urban areas that contribute to breastfeeding decisions are the increased promotion and availability of infant formulas. Globalization has caused an increase in the importation of foods, including breastmilk substitutes. In addition, the presence of marketing activities may have caused a switch from breastfeeding to formula feeding by the educated and a switch from breastfeeding to feeding other commercial breastmilk substitutes by uneducated mothers. Such behaviour is considered trendy and prestigious.

PREVALENCE OF MALNUTRITION IN URBAN AREAS
Trends for children

Based on the Health Statistics Report (1995), the 1991/92 and 1996 the United Republic of Tanzania Demographic and Health Surveys, and the 1999 the United Republic of Tanzania Reproductive and Child Health survey data, the trend of malnutrition as indicated by underweight, and acute and chronic malnutrition has been increasing in Dar es Salaam and other urban areas of the United Republic of Tanzania. Underweight increased from 23 percent in 1991/92 to 26 percent in 1996 and 28.7 percent in 1999 (Figure 6).

FIGURE 6
Trend of nutritional status of children in Dar es Salaam

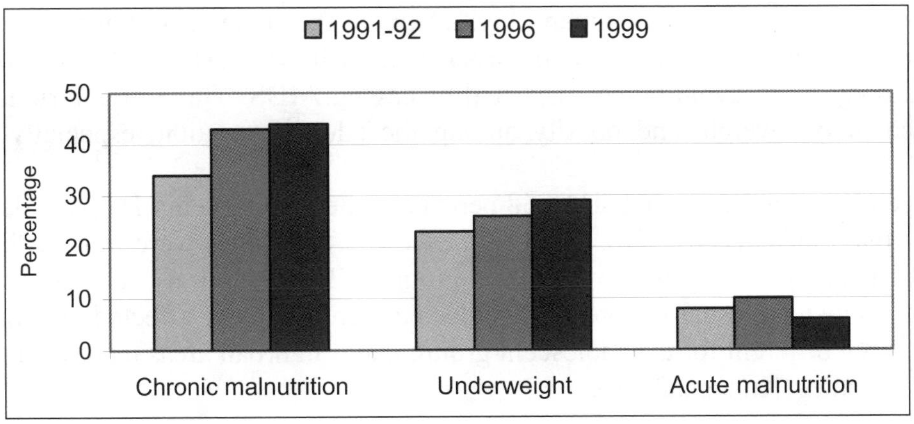

Source: National Bureau of Statistics, 1997b and 2000.

The proportion of children with chronic malnutrition increased from 34.4 percent in 1991/92 to 43.8 percent in 1999. In a recent study conducted in Dar es Salaam, it was observed that the rate of chronic malnutrition increased to 47.6 percent (Rashid, 2003, unpublished). The prevalence of wasting declined from 9.6 in 1996 to 5.9 percent in 1999.

These results indicate that stunting and underweight are major nutritional problems in Dar es Salaam. This, however, does not reflect the trend of GDP, one of the indicators of the performance of the economy, which has been increasing during the same period. GDP was US$5.0 billion in 1991 and increased to $9.1 billion in 2000. GDP per capita has also been increasing from 0.6 in 1991 to 3.0 in 2000. Per capita income is often used as a proxy indicator of nutritional status. Countries with high GDP also tend to have fewer problems with undernutrition, suggesting a strong link between the strength of the economy and the well-being of the people. However, this is not the case for Dar es Salaam, because indicators of nutritional status in children have been worsening despite increased per capita GDP. This suggests two things: increased income inequality among Dar es Salaam residents and increased unemployment, poor living conditions and inaccessibility to health and water facilities and services. Reduced budgets on health, water and education – typical features of globalization – coupled with increased population may explain the deteriorating trend in the city. The deteriorating nutritional status could also be a result of the high prevalence of HIV/AIDS and other infectious diseases such as malaria and diarrhoeal diseases. It could also be because of reduced time for child care as more parents engage in income-generating activities to raise household incomes.

Trends for adults

There has never been any systematic assessment of the nutritional status of adults in the United Republic of Tanzania. However, results from various studies (Rweyendera, 1993, unpublished; Kitange, 2000; Rashid, 2003, unpublished) have shown that overweight and obesity are increasing among the urban population. Females in the low-income group are more affected than males, while in the higher-income groups males are more affected than females. In Dar es Salaam overweight and obesity were observed mainly in low-income group women above 40 years of age (Rashid, 2003, unpublished). Women in this age category tend to perform fewer physical activities; they are engaged in light activities such as weaving, fishmongering and street food vending.

In the United Republic of Tanzania, overweight and obesity among women are considered attractive. In the past, the man with the fattest wife was highly respected because he had the most beautiful wife (Maletnlema, 2002). Overweight and obesity in men are signs of wealth and command high status in the society. Slimness among adults was never admired and it is currently associated with HIV/AIDS. People now prefer increased body fat to avoid being suspected of having AIDS. This has contributed to the prevalence of overweight and obesity among the adult population, especially in urban areas.

Kitange (2000) observed that about 58 percent of the population in Dar es Salaam had a low body mass index (BMI ≤20). The results showed that males were more affected than females, especially among the low-income groups. This is contrary to the conventional belief that women are usually more vulnerable and therefore more affected than males. The situation is not different for the adolescent group; males in urban areas tend to have a lower BMI than females (Kitange, 2000).

Micronutrient deficiencies

The common micronutrient deficiencies of public health significance in the United Republic of Tanzania are vitamin A, iron and iodine. Iodine deficiency is not very common in Dar es Salaam since most people consume seafood, which contains significant amounts of iodine. The most widespread micronutrient problem is iron deficiency anaemia. Prevalence of anaemia in Dar es Salaam is 80 percent in males and 74 percent in females (Rashid, 2003, unpublished). Causes of anaemia in Dar es Salaam include the high prevalence of malaria, hookworms (Mwaluko, *et al.*, 1991) and a low intake of foods rich in iron, such as green leafy vegetables and animal source foods.

TRENDS IN HEALTH STATUS IN URBAN AREAS/ENVIRONMENT
Infectious diseases – HIV/AIDS and tuberculosis

In the United Republic of Tanzania, the HIV epidemic began in the early 1980s. A steady increase in infection levels among pregnant women occurred up through the mid-1990s. There is some evidence of a decline in recent years (UNAIDS, 2000), although the epidemic remains a serious problem. Females are infected at younger ages than males and rural areas are less affected than urban areas. Since the mid-1990s, HIV seroprevalence among pregnant women in Dar es Salaam has remained at around 14 percent. In 1998, prevalence levels among female blood donors in Dar es Salaam were 32 percent. Female clinic patients suffering from sexually transmitted diseases (STDs) in Dar es Salaam had generally higher HIV seroprevalence levels than male patients. HIV-1 seroprevalence among female STD patients in Dar es Salaam has been fluctuating between 20 and 40 percent from 1988 to 1997. The Republic of Tanzania has a cumulative total of 660 000 AIDS cases and a prevalence of 7.8 percent since 1983 when the first AIDS cases were diagnosed in the country. Male and females are equally affected but the peak number of AIDS cases in females is at the age of 25 to 29 years, while most affected males are aged 30 to 34.

Non-communicable diseases (NCDs)

NCDs are already a major health problem for adults in the poorest countries of the world. Demographic data show that age-specific death rates from NCDs in the United Republic of Tanzania are higher than in wealthier countries (Kitange *et al.*, 1993). Mortality rates for some NCDs, such as strokes, are particularly high. However, while NCDs account for 80 percent of adult deaths in developed regions, the figure is less than 30 percent in the United

Republic of Tanzania, reflecting the continuing burden of infectious diseases. Thus, the United Republic of Tanzania suffers the "worst of both worlds" (World Bank, 2002). The prevalence of some NCDs and their associated risk factors in the United Republic of Tanzania are shown in Table 3.

TABLE 3
Prevalence of some NCDs and their associated risk factors

Disease	Prevalence (percentage)		
	Male	Female	All
Hypertension	2.6-10.5	3.4-14.6	3.0-12.8
Diabetes mellitus	0.6-1.7	0.5-0.8	0.6-1.1
Obesity	0.1-2.1	0.8-10.6	0.7-6.6
Cigarette smoking	8.6-42.0	1.3-3.9	5.4-16.9
Alcohol drinking	12.2-77.8	4.1-75.6	7.8-76.1
High cholesterol	0.4-7.1	0.8-8.2	0.6-7.8
High triglycerides	8.1-16.4	7.7-11.8	7.9-13.2

Source: Kitange, 2000.

Diabetes places a severe strain on the limited resources of developing countries. In the United Republic of Tanzania, the average annual direct cost of diabetes care in 1990 was $280 per patient requiring insulin and $130 for a patient not requiring it. However, with implementation of the cost-sharing policy on health services, diabetic patients now have to bear an increasingly large share of the cost of treatment. It is likely that this will be reflected in a higher level of morbidity and mortality in the diabetic population. The increase in NCDs creates an enormous strain on the health budget.

FIGURE 7
Trends of common NCDs in Dar es Salaam over the past five years

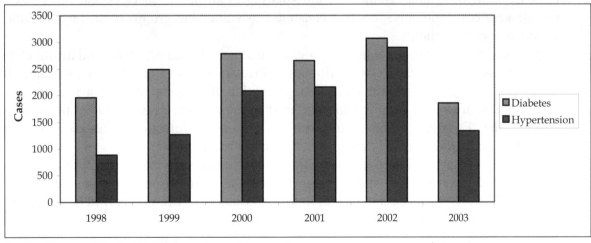

Source: Kitange, 2000; Rashid, 2003, unpublished.

PROGRAMMES THAT HAVE TRIED TO ADDRESS FOOD AND NUTRITION ISSUES
Broad programmes
Reduction of economic inequalities

Reduction of economic inequalities was implemented through regulating wages by a progressive taxation system, the introduction of subsidies for production inputs for farmers, some basic food subsidies and price control. However, the situation changed after the introduction of economic reform programmes in the early 1980s. Subsidies have been removed, and liberalization of the economy has resulted in cessation of control over prices. The market forces now determine prices. Downsizing of the civil service and the public sectors has reduced considerably the purchasing power of most people. This may have a significant influence on their nutritional status. An analysis is needed to establish the extent of the influence of these reforms.

Food security for all

In the 1970s food security for all meant food sufficiency. Relevant programmes included the National Strategic Food Reserve, Early Warning System, the National Maize and National Food Strategy and Comprehensive Food Security. The impact of the programmes was reflected in increased food production. However, this did not correspond with improvements in health or nutrition. The infant mortality rate remained high even in regions with good food supplies. This suggested that apart from food supply alone, there could be other factors responsible for the nutritional status of the people. In this regard, food supply alone was seen to be insufficient to ensure good nutrition.

Provision of social services

the United Republic of Tanzania adopted a policy of providing free social services to all as a right. The provision of clean water, and health, sanitation and education services was free for all citizens. Among other things, this policy contributed to improved nutrition during the late 1970s and 1980s. However, economic strategies have changed and so have the policies. Now there is an element of cost-sharing in all public services and full costs for private services. Evidently, this is a constraint to vulnerable groups of society, including resource-poor households.

Free services are still provided for programmes such as maternal and child health clinics and childhood immunization. In addition, the Primary Health Care Programme under the health sector emphasizes health education, promotion of food supply and basic sanitation – elements that are key to the prevention of most communicable diseases. Other programmes include the Essential Drugs Programme, Control of Infectious Diseases, Hygiene Education and Sanitation and School Health and Nutrition.

Despite all efforts to improve the situation, achievements have been limited because of a number of factors. One of these is the perception of nutrition issues at national and individual levels. At the national level, nutrition issues have been perceived to belong only to the health and agriculture sectors – the health sector, because of the diseases that arise through undernutrition, and the agricultural sector because it deals with food production. At the individual level, people do not appreciate the link between food and disease and perceive illness as a purely medical problem. The current climate of misperception calls for advocacy and lobbying to change the awareness of individuals and that of decision-makers at the national level with regard to nutrition issues. To ensure success in nutrition improvement there is a need for solid multisector collaboration and articulation of broad-based policies, since it is now recognized that nutrition issues cannot be addressed by the health and agriculture sectors alone. This will also ensure inclusion of nutrition considerations in other sectors of the economy.

Specific nutrition intervention programmes

Specific interventions to reduce malnutrition have included both supplementation and food fortification programmes. Dietary supplements of vitamin A and iodine have been provided and salt has been used as a food vehicle for iodine.

One of the contributing factors to poor nutrition in the United Republic of Tanzania is lack of dietary diversification. Diets are monotonous and consist of very few items. They are composed of one staple and one type of relish – legumes, meat, fish or vegetables. A typical meal consists of only two dishes. Fruit is not consumed during meal times. It is considered to be a snack and therefore not very important. This is unfortunate because it is well known that there are complementarities in the supply and utilization of nutrients.

Thus, it is imperative that efforts be made as follows.

- Encourage diet diversification to increase the amount and variety of nutrients. This is necessary because nutrients tend to interact in function and utilization in the body.
- Develop food and nutrition guidelines based on the types of foods available in the country (if possible local areas) and provide information regarding the nutrient content of the different foods to allow people to make informed decisions on food choices.
- Develop recipes that are simple to prepare, using indigenous foods. This is crucial because sometimes people fail to use certain foods, which are not familiar, simply because they do not know how to prepare or cook them. Development of recipes would enhance and probably help to increase diet diversification.
- Provide nutrition education as an important tool in giving people access to knowledge and information to help improve their nutritional status and health. Nutrition education, particularly for girls and women, on food preparation, proper hygienic practices and nutrient requirements of different age groups would build up their capacity as mothers and caretakers of large families.

Sectors that need to come together to address the problems effectively
Local government authorities at the level of individual, family and community
- Provide nutritional education, particularly for women and girls.
- Provide adequate knowledge on the HIV/AIDS pandemic and encourage HIV-positive individuals to eat well.
- Encourage individuals to reduce the use of tobacco and introduce community-based interventions that discourage its use.

At the level of the Ministry of Health and health research institutions
- Initiate educational and research programmes on nutrition in primary and secondary schools.
- Determine the magnitude of the burden of poor nutrition and all possible risk factors.
- Carry out controlled studies to develop targeted and effective prevention methods.

At the level of sectors other than that of health
- Develop policies that will improve the agricultural sector, the roads sector and the food processing industry.
- Create an environment conducive to investment in the agro-based and food processing industry.

At the level of government, i.e. macroeconomic policies
- Strengthen the capacity of relevant research and development institutions and universities so that they can generate and package information regarding food and nutrition in the country for the purpose of improving the nutritional status of the people. Much-needed information includes the nutrient composition of foods and nutritional requirements of people living in disease-prone areas.

CONCLUSION

Poverty and food and nutrition insecurity are increasing in urban areas, partly as a result of global policies, which seem to affect people's behaviour and practices with regard to access to food and food choices. Globalization is influencing people's incomes and livelihoods and consequently their access to the necessary public services. It also influences diets and disease patterns. Problems arising through undernutrition and overnutrition are increasing. This has created an additional burden on the health systems of Africa.

Bibliography

Atkinson, S. 1992. *Food for cities, urban nutrition policy in developing countries.* Urban Health Programme, Health Policy Unit, Department of Public Health and Policy. London School of Hygiene and Tropical Medicine.

Barth, Joh. & Sohn. 2003. *The Barth Report 2002/2003.* Joh. Barth & Sohn GmbH & Co. KG. Nuremberg, Germany. July (www.johbarth.com/report02/Barth_2003_English.pdf).

CARE Tanzania. 1998. Dar es Salaam urban livelihood security assessment in Tanzania. In *Urban challenges to food and nutrition security.* International Food Policy Research Institute.

Christopher, S., Kinabo, J. & Nyange, D. 1994. *Urban horticulture in Tanzania: a situation analysis of production, marketing and consumption in Dar es Salaam, Dodoma and Arusha.* Dar es Salaam, German Agency for Technical Cooperation (GTZ).

CIA. 2004. *The Worldfact book – Tanzania.* Washington, DC, Central Intelligence Agency (www.cia.gov/cia/publications/factbook/geos/tz.html).

Drewnowski, A. & Popkin, B.M. 1997. The nutrition transition: new trends in the global diet. *Nutr. Rev.,* 55(2): 31-43.

Garine, J. 1969. Food, nutrition and urbanisation. *Nutrition Newsletter,* 7(1): 1-19.

Health Statistics Report. 1995. *Tanzania Country Health Statistics Profile* (www.usaid.gov/countries/tz/tanzan).

IFPRI. 2001. *Rapid assessment in urban areas: lessons from Bangladesh and Tanzania.* FNCD Discussion Paper No. 107. Washington, DC, International Food Policy Research Institute.

Jagoe, K., Edwards, R., Mugusi, F., Whiting, D. & Unwin, N. 2002. Tobacco smoking in Tanzania, East Africa: population-based smoking prevalence using expired alveolar carbon monoxide as a validation tool. *Tobacco Control,* 11(3): 210-214.

Kaiza, D. 1999. Steers, Nandos fast-food chains enter Dar, Kampala. *The East African,* 17-23 November. Published weekly by the Nation Group.

Kitange, H.M. 2000. *Recent development of non-communicable diseases in Tanzania.* Seventeenth NIMR Annual Joint Research Conference and Symposium on Changes in Disease Patterns and Health Systems: Which Way Africa. Arusha, United Republic of Tanzania.

Kitange, H.M., Swai, A.B.M., Masuki, G., Kilima, P.M., Alberti, K.G. & McLarty, D.G. 1993. Coronary heart disease risk factors in sub-Saharan Africa: studies in Tanzanian adolescents. *Int. J. Epidemiol. Community Health,* 21: 303-307.

Lubbers, R. & Koorevaar, J. 1999. *Primary globalisation, secondary globalisation and the sustainable development paradigm-opposing forces in the 21st century.* Paper presented at Expo 2000. Organisation for Economic Co-operation and Development (OECD) Forum for the Future, Conference on 21st Century Social Dynamic: Towards the Creative Society, 6-7 December 1999. Berlin.

Maletnlema, T.N. 2002. A Tanzanian perspective on the nutrition transition and its implications for health. *Public Health Nutrition,* 5(1A): 163-168.

Mgaya, K. 2000. Development of information technology in Tanzania. United Nations University Press (www.unu.edu/unupress/). 12 pp.

Ministry of Agriculture and Food Security. 2003. *Food production data for Tanzania for the period 2001/2002.* United Republic of Tanzania.

Ministry of Health, Tanzania. 2001. *Burden of disease profile.* Data from Ministry of Health National Sentinel System/Local Council/AMMP-supported Demographic Surveillance adapted from a format developed by the Ministry of Health's Tanzania Essential Health Interventions Project (TEHIP).

Mjawa, A. 2003. *Globalisation and food consumption pattern in Dar es Salaam.* A special project report submitted to the Open University of Tanzania (OUT) in partial fulfilment of a B.Sc. in home economics. (unpublished)

Mwaluko, G.M.P., Kilama, W.L., Mandera, P.M., Murru, M. & MacPherson, C.N.L. 1991. *Health and diseases in Tanzania.* Harper Collins Publishers.

National Bureau of Statistics (Tanzania). 1997a. *Trends in demographic, family planning and health indicators in Tanzania 1997.* Calverton, Maryland, United States, Macro International Inc.

National Bureau of Statistics (Tanzania). 1997b. *Tanzania Demographic and Health Survey 1996.* Calverton, Maryland, United States, Macro International Inc.

National Bureau of Statistics (Tanzania). 2000. *Tanzania Reproductive and Child Health Survey 1999.* Calverton, Maryland, United States, Macro International Inc.

National Bureau of Statistics (Tanzania). 2002. *Household Budget Survey 2000/2001.* Dar es Salaam.

National Bureau of Statistics (Tanzania). 2003. *National Population Census 1967-2002. Population Census, Basic Demographic and Socio-economic Characteristics.* Dar es Salaam.

Nkurlu, R.L. 2000. *The role of women's income-generating activities in household food security in the urban poor: the case of Temeke district, Dar es Salaam.* Morogoro, United Republic of Tanzania, Sokoine University of Agriculture. (M.Sc. thesis)

Pan African News Agency. 2002. "UNICEF MULLS OVER DUMPING MCDONALD'S DEAL." 8 October.

Popkin, B.M. 1994. The nutrition transition in low-income countries. An emerging crisis. *Nutr. Rev.*, 52(9): 285-298.

Popkin, B.M. & Bisgrove, E.Z. 1988. Urbanization and nutrition in low-income countries. UNU Press. *Food and Nutrition Bulletin*, 10(1).

Rashid, S. 2003. *Effect of globalisation on nutritional status and prevalence of NCD in children and adults in Dar es Salaam.* A special project report submitted to the Open University of Tanzania (OUT) in partial fulfilment of a B.Sc. in home economics. (unpublished)

Raychaudhuri, S. 1999. *Is globalisation by-passing Africa?* UNDP Human Development Report (www.igc.apc./global policy/socecon/inequal/africa.liter).

Research and Analysis Working Group. 2002. *Poverty and Human Development Report 2000.* United Republic of Tanzania.

Robertshaw, R., Louw, A. & Matni, A. 2000. *The city victim survey* (www.iss.co.za/pubs/other/daresSalaam).

Rweyendera, B. 1993. *Prevalence of obesity among executives in Dar es Salaam.* A special project report submitted to Sokoine University of Agriculture in partial fulfilment of a B.Sc. in home economics and human nutrition. (unpublished)

Stiglitz, J.E. 2000. Capital market liberalisation, economic growth and instability. *World Development,* 28(6): 1075-1086.

Tobin, J. 2000. Financial globalisation. *World Development,* 28(6): 1101-1104.

Tripp, A.M. 1992. The impact of crisis and economic reform on women in urban Tanzania. In *Unequal burden: economic crisis, persistent poverty and women's work,* p. 46-87. Boulder, Colorado, United States, Westview Press.

UNAIDS. 2000. *UNAIDS Report on the Global HIV/AIDS Epidemic.* June. Geneva. Joint UN Programme on HIV/AIDS.

UNESCO. 1996. *Statistical Yearbook.* UNESCO Publications/Berna Press.

UNESCO. 1998. *World Education Report. Teachers and teaching in a changing world.* UNESCO Publications.

UNESCO & World Bank. 2002. *ICT infrastructure and access.* World Economic Forums Global Competitiveness Report 2001-2002.

UNICEF. 2003. *State of the World's Children.* New York, USA. United Nations Children's Fund (www.unicef.org/sowc03).

United Nations DELSA. 1995. *World urbanization prospects, 1994 revisions.* ST/ESA/SERA/150. New York. USA.

United Nations Development Programme (UNDP). 1998. *Human Development Report 1998.*

United Nations Development Programme (UNDP). 2003. *Human Development Report 2000* (www.undp.org/hdr 2003/indicators/cty).

University of Durham (UK). 2000. Alcohol in East Africa 1850-1999. Research project supported by the Economic and Social Research Council and the British Institute in Eastern Africa (www.dur.ac.uk).

Washington, S. 1996. *Globalisation: what challenges and opportunities for governments?* (www.oecd.org/gumance).

Weatherspoon, D.D. & Reardon, T. 2003. The rise of supermarkets in Africa: implications for agrifood systems and the rural poor. *Dev. Policy Review,* 21(3): 1-17 May.

World Bank Group. 2002. *Taking poverty to heart. Non-communicable diseases and the poor Tanzania at a glance.* World Bank Report.

World Health Organization (WHO). 2003. *Diet, nutrition and prevention of chronic diseases.* Report of a WHO Study Group. WHO Technical Report Series No. 797. Geneva.

Trends in health and nutrition indicators in the urban slums of three cities in Bangladesh, compared to its rural areas

Martin W. Bloem[1], Regina Moench-Pfanner, Federico Graciano, Gudrun Stallkamp and Saskia De Pee

INTRODUCTION [2]

Since independence in 1971, Bangladesh has made considerable economic and social progress. Economic growth has accelerated, life expectancy has risen, the fertility rate has fallen, school enrolment has increased and child mortality and undernutrition have declined (BIDS/UNDP, 2001; Helen Keller International [HKI]/Institute of Public Health Nutrition [IPHN, 2001]). But despite these encouraging trends, about half of the people in Bangladesh continue to live in poverty and many millions of children are malnourished (HKI/IPHN, 2002) – clear signs that the country still faces great challenges in development.

As many countries experience similar problems, in September 2000 world leaders adopted the United Nations Millennium Declaration, committing their nations to stronger global efforts to reduce poverty, improve health and promote peace, human rights and environmental sustainability (UNDP, 2003). Enshrined in the Declaration were eight specific goals, referred to as the Millennium Development Goals (MDGs). These were: i) eradicate extreme poverty and hunger; ii) achieve universal primary education; iii) promote gender equality and empower women; iv) reduce child mortality; v) improve maternal health; vi) combat HIV/AIDS, malaria and other diseases; vii) ensure environmental sustainability; and viii) develop a global partnership for development. These goals reflect the international community's recognition of and commitment to a broader development agenda that encompasses economics, food security, education, health, the environment and global cooperation.

However, it must be recognized that development is contextual and what may work in one setting may not work in another. The recognition that each country must pursue a development strategy that meets its specific needs should be the starting-point of any attempt to attain the MDGs. For example, the transfer of people and economic activity from rural to urban areas is the most remarkable difference between Asia today and three decades ago (Ruel and Haddad, 2001) and urbanization will continue to change the face of

---

[1] Martin W. Bloem, MD, Ph.D.
Helen Keller International
02-13 China Court 20 Cross Street
Singapore 048422
E-mail: mwbloem@singnet.com.sg
[2] Acknowledgements
The authors would like to acknowledge the hard work and dedication of the Helen Keller International Bangladesh office of the Nutrition Surveillance Project, particularly Nasima Akhter, Taskeen Chowdhury, Quazi Imad U. Ibrahim and Nahid Sultana Sharif for their valuable work on this paper.

the Asia-Pacific Region, along with its benefits and its ills. According to the United Nations Development Programme (UNDP), by 2015 half of Asia's population will live in cities and will number over a billion (Asian Development Bank, 2001). The region's megacities are becoming larger and there will be a tremendous increase in the urban poor population. The challenges in achieving the MDGs in urban areas are even more complicated as there is very little experience with this phenomenon.

In the case of Bangladesh, 30 million people, over 20 percent of its population, live in urban areas. The capital, Dhaka, has a population of more than 9 million people and the Asian Development Bank reports that Dhaka is one of the fastest growing urban areas in Asia, with an estimated population of 20 million by 2015. This rapid growth of the urban population in Bangladesh is accompanied by increasing poverty, food insecurity and malnutrition, and has serious implications for the welfare and well-being of the country's urban population. Increasing numbers of people living in urban areas put high pressure on development activities in urban slum areas that are home for millions of people in Bangladesh. Appalling living conditions created by poverty, an unsafe environment and poor hygienic conditions combined with a poor-quality diet aggravate the nutrition and health status of the urban poor population.

Country strategies need to be based on timely data from proper monitoring and evaluation systems that can capture as accurate a picture of the country's situation as possible. Helen Keller International has always placed great emphasis on monitoring and evaluation; since 1990, the agency has developed nutritional surveillance and data collection systems in Bangladesh, Viet Nam, Cambodia and Indonesia (HKI, 2001; HKI/Indonesia, 2000). These surveillance systems have led to a much greater understanding of the interdependence of the various causes of undernutrition.

To gain a better insight into the problems of urbanization in Bangladesh, this paper will look at differences in trends of health and nutrition indicators between the urban and rural populations of Bangladesh from 1990 to 2000. The data were collected through the Nutritional Surveillance Project (NSP), jointly implemented by HKI and IPHN in Bangladesh.

STUDY AREA

Bangladesh, a country with a predominantly Muslim population, lies in the tropical region, in the southern part of Asia. With a geographic area of 147 570 km^2, and an estimated population of 131 270 000 in 2001, Bangladesh is one of the most densely populated countries in the world.

The latest published data from the Bangladesh census (1991) indicate that 79.9 percent of the population reside in rural areas, while the remaining one-fifth live in urban areas (Bangladesh Bureau of Statistics, 1994). Data from the 2001 census have not been released yet, but the urban population will probably account for 26 percent of the total population and this figure will increase to 37 percent by the year 2015 (World Bank, 1985).

METHODS

The data used in this analysis were collected by the NSP to guide policies and programmes to improve health and nutrition in Bangladesh and contribute to a greater understanding of related factors, which could also be useful for other developing countries. The NSP was established in 1990 by HKI and IPHN, and between 1990 and 2000 it was implemented in collaboration with 34 non-governmental organizations (NGOs) (Bloem *et al.*, 1994). Data were collected every two months by IPHN and partner NGOs, with training, field supervision, quality control, and data management and analyses conducted by HKI.

Between 1990 and 1997 a multistage random cluster sampling design was used to choose 240-260 children every two months from each purposively selected rural subdistrict (n=30-40) that was either vulnerable to natural disasters or representative of one of the six divisions of Bangladesh (total number of households sampled per round was 6 200 to 14 700). No data were collected between August and January 1997 because the NSP conducted a national vitamin A survey during this period. In February 1998, a stratified multistage cluster sampling design was introduced to provide data that were statistically representative at divisional and national levels. In each round, data were collected from 300 households in four subdistricts in each of the six divisions of the country. In 2000, the sample size in the subdistricts was increased to 375 households. In this way, the total sample size in each round of data collection was increased from 7 400 to 9 000 households.

Since 1990, the NSP has also collected data from four urban poor sites every two months. Of these four sites, two were in Dhaka, one in Chittagong and one in Khulna. In urban areas, households were selected from NGO working areas in the urban slums. Using a convenience sampling procedure, 700 households were selected from the Dhaka slum sites and at least 350 households from the Chittagong slum site. A systematic procedure was used to select at least 350 households from the Khulna slum site. Although urban sampling varied between sites, it was consistent over rounds.

A household was eligible for inclusion if it had at least one physically able child under five years of age and if the mother was present. A structured questionnaire was applied to collect data on children's and mothers' nutrition and health status, health and dietary practices and household demography, socio-economic status and distress, agricultural practices and food prices at village level; anthropometric measurements were taken from children under five years and from their mothers. About 10 percent of the households were revisited on the following day for quality control on selected indicators.

Data cleaning and analysis were carried out by HKI and for this paper data were analysed using SPSS version 11.0.

A more detailed description of the methods applied by the NSP can be found in Bloem, Moench-Pfanner and Panagides, 2003.

CHILD HEALTH AND NUTRITIONAL STATUS

Stunting (low height-for-age) is considered a good indicator of poverty since it reflects the health and nutritional status of the child over a longer period of time, and even of the mother during pregnancy. Figure 1 shows that the prevalence of stunting ranged from 68 to 76 percent during the early 1990s and decreased to 49-58 percent in 2000. It also shows that stunting has always been more prevalent among urban poor children, compared to rural children, and that the difference in stunting levels between the two groups of children has increased over time. This may be related to migration of the poorer families from rural to urban areas.

Figure 2 shows that the consumption of grain (largely rice) decreased between 1990 and 2000, which most likely indicates that the diet has become more diversified, because nutritional status did not worsen during this period (see Figure 1). Among the rural population, grain intake is approximately 20 percent higher than among the urban poor (3.0 kg/per capita/seven days as against 2.4 kg/per capita/seven days in 2000). While this may indicate that the diet of the urban poor is more diversified than that of the rural population, it may also partly reflect a higher energy intake among the rural population. The decline from 1990 to 2000 was greater in rural sites, so diets appear to have diversified relatively more in the rural than in the urban poor areas.

While the prevalence of stunting has clearly declined, both among rural as well as urban poor children (Figure 1), the prevalence of wasting (low weight-for-height) among urban poor children in the three cities did not change much during the period 1990-2000 (Figure 3). There was a seasonal fluctuation for wasting, and the prevalence in Dhaka was somewhat lower than in Khulna and Chittagong. Wasting among Bangladeshi children fluctuates in relation to the different seasons in Bangladesh. From November to February, there are many cereals and vegetables available from production, a time that coincides with a low prevalence of child wasting. From the onset of the dry season in March up to the beginning of the main harvest (October) the prevalence of child wasting is higher. For diarrhoea however, the prevalence gradually declined during the period 1990-2000, especially in Khulna and Chittagong (Figure 4). This may largely be attributed to improvements in sanitation facilities.

FIGURE 1

**The prevalence of stunting (height-for-age Z-score <-2 SD) among 6-59 months old children in urban poor and rural areas during the period 1990-2000
(urban n=107 568, rural n=562 489)**

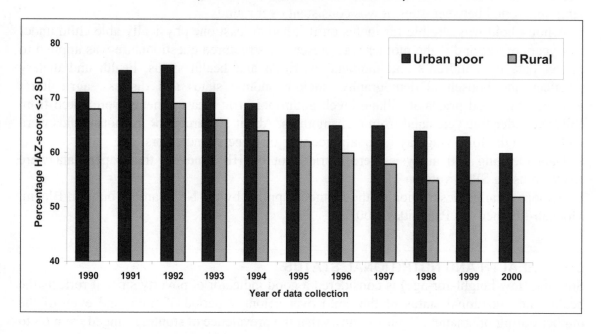

FIGURE 2

Intake of grain (rice, wheat, etc.) per household member during the previous seven days (kg) in urban poor and rural populations during the period 1990-2000 (urban n=77 521, rural n=418 311)

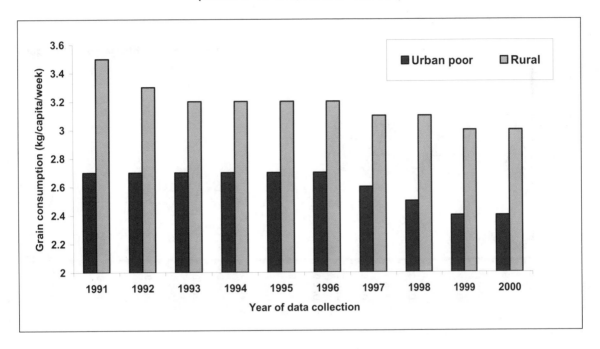

FIGURE 3

Prevalence of wasting (weight-for-height Z-score <-2 SD) among 6-59 months old children in urban poor areas of Dhaka, Khulna and Chittagong between 1990 and 2000 (n=108 215)

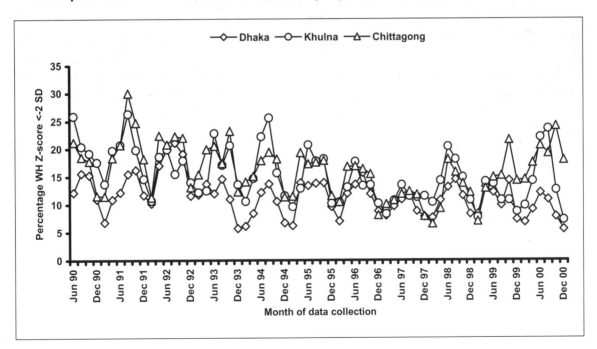

FIGURE 4
Prevalence of diarrhoea on the day before the interview among children aged 6-59 months old in urban poor areas of Dhaka, Khulna and Chittagong between 1990 and 2000 (n=108 441)

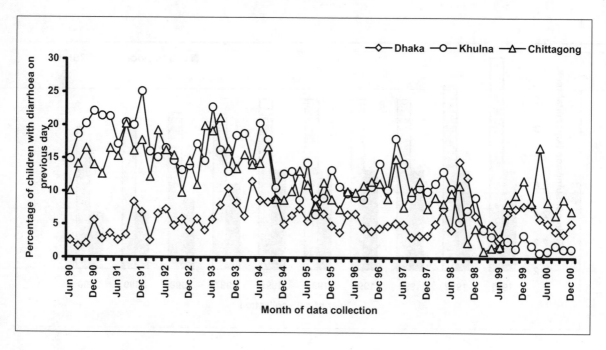

HOUSEHOLD SIZE

Figure 5 shows a gradual decline in the number of children under five years old in households during the period 1990-2000, in urban poor areas as well as in rural Bangladesh. This reflects child spacing that, in fact, results in smaller families, as can be concluded from Figure 6. Families in urban areas are smaller, which may be mainly related to having fewer extended families, since the number of children under five per household is similar in both urban and rural areas. In concurrence with the gradual decline of household size, the crowding at household level among the urban poor also shows a decline from 1991 to 2000. The density of people in a household, expressed as the number of household members per 100 ft^2 (929.03 cm^2) (obtained by dividing number of household members by area of the house), has declined in all slum areas from which households were sampled. In Dhaka, household density has fluctuated between 5.3 (1999) and 7.3 (1994), in Khulna it decreased from 5.9 to 5.1 and in Chittagong from 8.2 to 7.0. Further analysis should provide more in-depth understanding of how this relates to the increase of the urban population.

FIGURE 5
Number of children under five years old per household in urban poor areas of Dhaka, Khulna and Chittagong and in rural Bangladesh between 1990 and 2000 (urban n=86 183, rural n=446 559

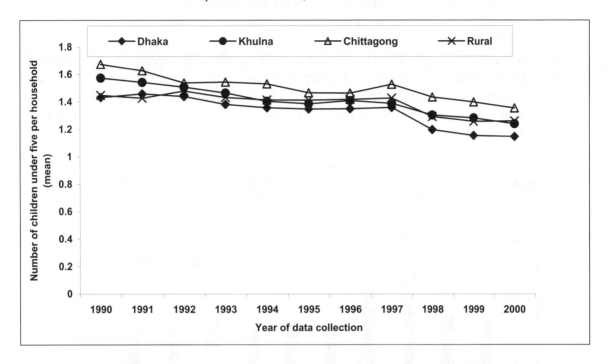

FIGURE 6
Number of household members (people eating from the same pot) in urban poor and rural areas of Bangladesh between 1990 and 2000 (urban n=86 182, rural n=446 544)

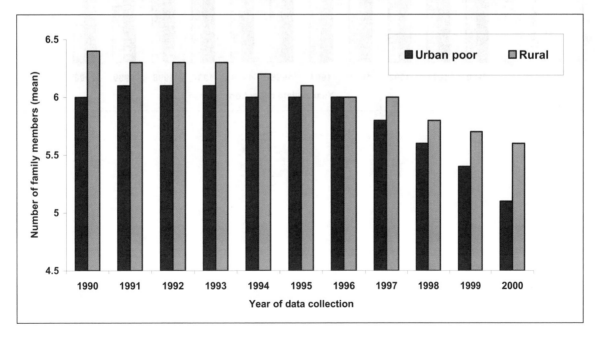

EDUCATION

Figure 7 shows that the percentage of women with no formal education declined between 1990 and 2000, particularly in rural areas. Because most women had their education during their childhood and early adolescence, the figure reflects the trend in education during the 1980s and early 1990s. The fact that the percentage of women without formal education was higher in the urban areas may reflect both poorer schooling facilities for the urban poor as well as migration of poorer women (and men) to urban slums. It should also be noted that by 2000, 56-69 percent of mothers of children under five had not received any formal education.

Figure 8 shows the height-for-age Z-score of 6-59 months old children by the number of years of formal education that their mother had undergone. Z-scores were lowest, and therefore prevalence of stunting highest, among children of mothers who had not had any formal education and Z-scores were better with every extra year of education the mother had obtained.

FIGURE 7

Percentage of mothers without formal education among urban poor and rural population of Bangladesh between 1990 and 2000 (urban n=85 481, rural n=455 322)

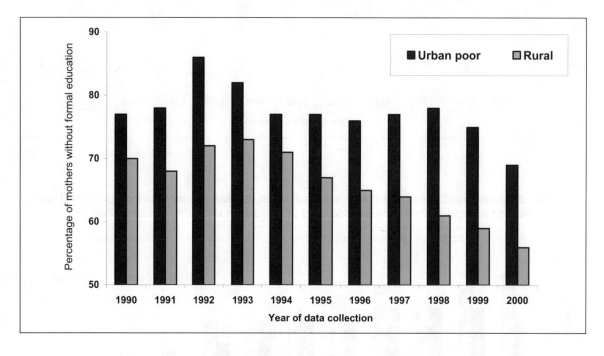

FIGURE 8

Average height-for-age Z-score for children aged 6-59 months by mother's number of years of formal education, rural Bangladesh, 1990-2000 (n=547 327). Bars indicate 95 percent confidence intervals

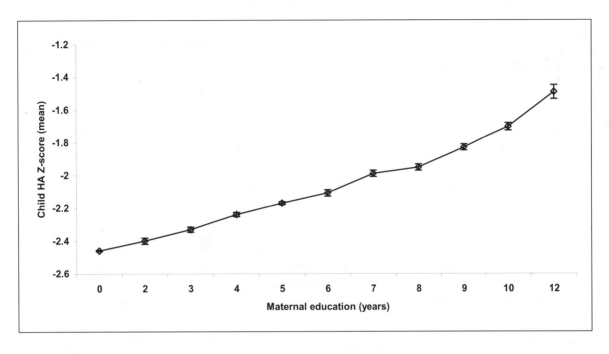

MATERNAL HEALTH

Figure 9 shows that among mothers the prevalence of night blindness, the first clinical sign of vitamin A deficiency, has always been lower in urban than in rural areas and that it might be declining in rural areas.[3]

Figure 10 shows a slight decline in the percentage of mothers who are chronically energy deficient (BMI<18.5 kg/m²) from the beginning of 2000 to the end of 2002.[4] The largest improvement was found in the urban poor areas of Chittagong where the prevalence decreased from 48 to 37 percent. In Khulna's urban poor areas it declined from 43 to 35 percent and in Dhaka from 24 to 21 percent. There is considerable seasonal variation in the urban poor areas of Chittagong and some in the urban poor sites of Dhaka, whereas in the urban poor areas of Khulna the declining curve hardly showed any seasonal patterns.

---

[3] Prior to 1992, the NSP did not collect data on night blindness among mothers.

[4] Weight and height of mothers were not collected until 2000, so that data are shown for 2000-2002 instead of for an earlier period.

FIGURE 9

Prevalence of night blindness among mothers in urban poor and rural areas in Bangladesh between 1992 and 2000 (urban n=68 020, rural n=387 119)

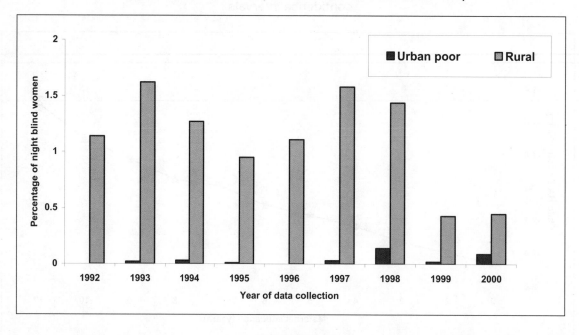

FIGURE 10

Percentage of non-pregnant mothers with chronic energy deficiency (BMI <18.5 kg/m²) in urban poor areas of Dhaka, Khulna and Chittagong between 2000 and 2002 (n=22 997)

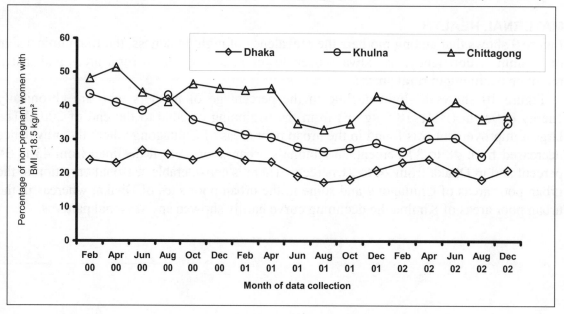

DISCUSSION

Bangladesh is still predominantly a rural country and one of the poorest countries in the world, where an estimated 36 percent of the population live on less than US$1 a day (UNDP, 2003). However, since the country's independence in 1971, there has been an increase in urbanization, and the predictions are that Dhaka will become one of the largest urban centres, with about 20 million inhabitants, by the year 2015 (Asian Development Bank, 2001). This will have dramatic consequences for the country and specifically for reaching the various MDGs by the year 2020. The Government of Bangladesh has an enormous task to improve the infrastructure of Dhaka and its other major cities. The majority of the urban poor are migrants from the rural areas seeking employment. There is a lot of pressure on the land in rural Bangladesh. Only 15 percent of rural farmers are net producers of rice, the main crop in the country. Most of the virtually landless sell their daily labour to the relatively richer farmers (Bloem *et al.*, 1994).

Short introduced the concept of "black holes and loose connections" in the global urban hierarchy by using two data sets: the principal agglomerations of the world by Brinkhoff and the "Globalization and World Cities Group and Network" (GAWC) (Brinkhoff, 2001; GAWC, 2002; Short, 2002). These concepts allude to cities with large populations that are not considered to be connected to the flow of global capital – intellectual, material and financial – and therefore losing out on the benefits of globalization. Both Dhaka and Chittagong are cities with a population of over three million people, but they lack the connectivity which is so typical for world cities such as Tokyo, New York and Seoul. Short argues that these cities do not have the capacity to use the process of globalization in an optimal way, and defines Dhaka and Chittagong as large "non-world cities".

Countries such as Bangladesh are, in a way, trapped in a vicious cycle of poverty, under-education and undernutrition. The only way for development to be sustainable in such a context is to stimulate the growth of a sizeable middle class to spur economic growth and participation in globalization. To breed such a consumer middle class is by producing a workforce with adequate health and education to attract the relocation of industrial bases (e.g. manufacturing) to these countries, and to ensure that wage levels are adequate to generate disposable income. Therefore it is necessary to achieve the second MDG of achieving universal primary education to bring the educational level of the population and its potential workforce to the basic minimum. The NSP data showed that some progress has been made in the country's rural areas, which reflects the national data presented in the latest human development report, but there has hardly been any progress among women in the urban slums over the past ten years. This could be because women in the urban slums are largely the illiterate women who migrated from rural Bangladesh. More data collection is necessary to explore the enrolment rates among children (boys and girls) aged six to 15 years coming from slum areas monitored by the NSP.

It is also necessary for progress in the first MDG – to eradicate extreme poverty and hunger – to be achieved to reduce the number of people living below the poverty threshold and stimulate the growth of the middle class. Stunting or a low height-for age is an indicator that expresses a lack of linear growth. Several publications have shown that stunting is a very good proxy for poverty since the main cause of the growth problem is a lack of both energy and quality of diet. However, a paper by Frongillo, de Onis and Hanson (1997) argued that because the prevalence of stunting and wasting varied most among nations and among provinces within nations, that not only interventions at household level, but also at subnational and national level are clearly important (Frongillo, de Onis and Hanson, 1997). Their paper, using the same data set, showed that trends in malnutrition (measured by underweight) were highly associated with the food expenditure of non-grain products (Torlesse, Bloem and Kiess, 2003). Similar results were observed in Indonesia using data from a health and nutritional surveillance system to monitor the effects of the Asian economic crisis in Indonesia (Bloem and Darnton-Hill, 2000).

Proper health and nutrition are cornerstones of a competitive workforce, particularly in the context of a global economy. The interrelationships between adequate nutrition and good physical and cognitive development necessitate interventions and policy measures to ensure that the nutritional needs of the population, especially in young children, are sufficiently met. In particular, there is growing recognition that a deficiency of iron, which leads to anaemia among children between the ages of six months and two years, can have a permanent impact on cognitive development, limiting the intellectual capacity of affected children. Productivity studies have also shown that iron-deficiency anaemia within an adult workforce can reduce physical capacity, and therefore productivity.

Environmental sustainability is also crucial to the well-being of the population in working its way out of poverty. Smith and Jalal documented a strong association between income levels and environmental problems related to pollution, water and sanitation, solid waste and the risk of disasters, such as floods (Smith and Jalal, 2000). Sewer systems are inadequate to support the high-density urban slums in Dhaka, Chittagong and Khulna. The ubiquity of two-stroke engine vehicles that emit more pollutants than other types of vehicles in cities such as Dhaka have resulted in poor air quality, with high levels of lead. In fact, these vehicles were banned in Dhaka from early 2003. Because anaemia leads to an increased risk of lead toxicity, since iron and lead are competing for the same receptors, environmental pollution in the form of high lead concentrations in the air will lead to even more negative health outcomes, particularly among children.

The development of cities has always been linked with processes at the global level and these processes have influenced the development of urban centres (Smith and Timberlake, 2002). Urbanization that is not managed properly can result in the failure of services, such as education and public health, in reaching the urban underclass that live in the slum areas of these large cities. Most of the cities in the region have many environmental problems: depletion and contamination of water resources, land contamination, air pollution and the loss of valuable natural resources. The economic impacts of pollution in urban areas in terms of loss of productivity and health costs have been estimated to exceed 10 percent of the GDP in some countries. This situation already exists in today's Bangladeshi cities, such as Dhaka, and other similar cities with large populations mired in poverty and a dysfunctional infrastructure. By 2015, with the population explosion in megacities such as Dhaka as projected, these problems will have been exacerbated to a point at which any intervention to address them will be exceedingly expensive. The window of opportunity to address these problems before they reach unmanageable scales becomes smaller every day and we cannot make real progress in meeting the MDGs.

The data of the NSP have been widely used to initiate, improve, or monitor programmes; shape policies; improve targeting for food aid and relief activities; and provide donors and interested agencies with specific information gained. Some specific findings and results of advocacy include the following.

- Some NGOs have been using the NSP data, rather than having to collect their own. For example, Concern has used the urban NSP data as a baseline for their own Urban Nutrition and Household Food Security Programme that is being conducted in Dhaka, Khulna and Chittagong.

- The NSP, as an independent data source, currently monitors the Bangladesh Integrated Nutrition Programme as well as progress towards reaching the MDGs.

- Data of the NSP are also being incorporated into the WHO global database on child growth and malnutrition.

- Information on the coverage of vitamin A capsule distribution among children of 12-59 months old in 1997-98 revealed pockets of consistent low coverage. A special module added to the routine NSP explored possible reasons and strategies in depth, revealing that passing through villages with a microphone to announce the capsule distribution and soliciting the help of imams at mosques were useful to raise awareness about the distribution date among people. Results were shared at national and subnational planning meetings and in 1999 the capsule coverage had improved in all low-coverage areas (Chittagong, Barisal and Sylhet). Similarly, the data that revealed a very low coverage of postpartum distribution of vitamin A capsules among mothers have initiated the process that led to a policy change, increasing the period during which the capsule should be distributed.

In the same way, the NSP will continue to collect and share information about the specific situation and problems facing the urban poor in Bangladesh and contribute to understanding and limiting the scope of the problems.

Bibliography

Asian Development Bank. 2001. *Asian Environment Outlook 2001.* Manila, Philippines.

Bangladesh Bureau of Statistics (BBS). 1994. *Bangladesh Population Census 1991.* Vol.1. Dhaka, Statistics Division, Ministry of Planning, Government of Bangladesh.

BIDS/UNDP. 2001. *Fighting human poverty: Bangladesh human development report 2000.* Dhaka, Bangladesh, Bangladesh Institute of Development Studies (BIDS), United Nations Development Programme.

Bloem, M.W. & Darnton-Hill, I. 2000. Micronutrient deficiencies. First link in a chain of nutritional and health events in economic crises. *In* A. Bendrich & R.J. Deckelbaum, eds. *Primary and secondary preventive nutrition*, p. 357-373. Totowa, New Jersey, United States, Humana Press Inc.

Bloem, M.W., Hye, A., Gorstein, J., Wijnroks, M., Hall, G., Matzger, H. & Sommer, A. 1994. Nutrition surveillance in Bangladesh: a useful tool for policy planning at local and national levels. *Food Nutr. Bull.,* 16: 131-138.

Bloem, M.W., Moench-Pfanner, R., & Panagides, D. eds. 2003. *Health and nutritional surveillance for development.* Singapore, Helen Keller Worldwide.

Brinkhoff, T. 2001. *The principal agglomerations of the world* (www.citypopulation.de/).

Frongillo, E.A., de Onis, M. & Hanson, K.M.P. 1997. Socio-economic and demographic factors are associated with worldwide patterns of stunting and wasting of children. *J. Nutr.,* 127: 2302-2309.

GAWC (Globalization and World Cities Group and Network) 2002. (www.lboro.ac.uk/gawc/publicat.html)

HKI. 2001. *The nutritional surveillance project in Bangladesh in 1999. Towards the goals of the 1990 World Summit for Children.* Dhaka, Helen Keller International.

HKI/Indonesia. 2000. *Monitoring the economic crisis: impact and transition 1998-2000, 11 January 2000.* Nutrition and Health Surveillance System 2000. Jakarta, Indonesia, Helen Keller International.

HKI/Institute of Public Health Nutrition (IPHN). 2001. *Progress in Bangladesh towards the goals of the 1990 World Summit for Children.* Nutritional surveillance, Bulletin No. 3. Bangladesh, Helen Keller International.

HKI/IPHN. 2002. *Nutrition, health and poverty in Bangladesh in 2001. Facilitating action through data sharing.* Bangladesh, Helen Keller International.

Ruel, M. & Haddad, L. 2001. Rapid urbanization and the challenges of obtaining food and nutrition security. In *Nutrition and health in developing countries*, eds. R.D. Semba & M.W. Bloem. Totowa, New Jersey, United States, Humana Press.

Short, J.R. 2002. *Black holes and loose connections in the global urban network.* Globalization and World Cities Study Group and Network. (http://www.mi.vt.edu/Research/WorldCities/Analyses/Mega.pdf)

Smith, D.F. & Jalal, K.F. 2000. *Sustainable development in Asia.* Manila, Asian Development Bank.

Smith, D. & Timberlake, M. 2002. "Global cities" and "globalization" in East Asia: empirical realities and conceptual questions. University of California. Paper 02-09 (http://repositories.cdlib.org/csd/02-09).

Torlesse, H., Bloem, M. W. & Kiess, L. 2003. Association of household rice expenditure with child nutritional status indicates a role for macroeconomic food policy in combating malnutrition. *J. Nutr.,* 133: 1320-1325.

UNDP. 2003. *Human development 2003: Millennium Goals: a compact among nations to end human poverty.* United Nations Development Programme. New York, Oxford, Oxford University Press.

World Bank. 1985. *Bangladesh: economic and social development prospects.* Vol. III. Washington DC, World Bank.

Urbanization, income and the nutrition transition in China: a case study

Michelle A. Mendez, Shufa Du and Barry M. Popkin[1]

INTRODUCTION AND BACKGROUND

China has experienced extremely rapid urbanization in the past 20 years. Like many Asian countries, the proportion of the population in urban areas was relatively low in the 1980s. The urban population is projected to increase from 23 percent in 1985 to an estimated 41 percent by 2005 (see Table 1). There has been growth in urban agglomerations of all sizes. Between 1985 and 1997, the number of cities with over one million residents increased from 22 to 37, with similarly large increases in cities of 500 000 to one million (30 to 49), 200 000-500 000 (94 to 216) and <200 000 residents (178 to 365). The dynamic pace of urbanization is linked to rapid globalization and economic growth. China's average annual gross domestic product (GDP) growth of 11.2 percent between 1990 and 1998 was nearly triple the rate of 3.7 percent in other developing countries, excluding India (World Bank, 2001). This economic growth has been fuelled at least in part by expanding global linkages. Trade has doubled as a proportion of the goods GDP (18.4 percent in 1985, 27.8 percent in 1990 and 42.2 percent in 2000), and there has been a dramatic increase in foreign direct investment (0.9 percent of gross capital formation in 1985, 2.5 percent in 1990 and 11.5 percent in 2000 (World Bank, 2001).

These rapid socio-economic changes have had important effects on China's population. Economic growth has contributed to striking decreases in poverty: the rural population earning <US$1/day fell from 42.5 percent to 24.0 percent between 1991 and 1997, while urban poverty fell from 1.0 to 0.5 percent (Chen and Wang, 2001). Globalization has led to greater availability of non-traditional foods, as more open markets have facilitated rising food imports. For example, imports accounted for 24.5 percent of vegetable oil in 2000, against 9.5 percent in 1980, during which time the per capita supply doubled (from 76.7 to 182.6 kcals/capita) (Food and Agriculture Organization of the United Nations [FAO], 2003). The changing investment climate has also facilitated the evolution of western-style supermarkets and fast food chains with foreign ownership (Reardon, Timmer and Berdeque, 2003; Bolling and Somwaru, 2001; Marr and Hatfield, 1997). In 2001, for example, supermarkets accounted for 48 percent of urban food markets in China, an increase beyond the 30 percent level in 1999 (Reardon, Timmer and Berdeque, 2003). Supermarkets have also begun to spread from big cities into smaller towns, including poorer areas in the interior (Reardon, Timmer and Berdeque, 2003). Meanwhile, direct

[1] Barry M. Popkin, Ph.D.
Carolina Population Center
CB # 8120 University Square
University of North Carolina at Chapel Hill
Chapel Hill, NC 27516-3997
Tel.: (919) 966-1732
Fax: 919-966-9159
E-mail: popkin@unc.edu

imports of French fries from the United States increased tenfold between 1995 and 1999, and the number of Kentucky Fried Chicken outlets – the largest western fast food chain – increased to 600, up from about 250 in 1999 (Cee and Theiler, 1999; Rosenthal, 2002). In summary, China has experienced impressive socio-economic and cultural changes in a short time frame. The implications of these changes for population health and nutrition are, at present, not fully understood.

TABLE1
Urbanization trends in China

	1985	**1990**	**1995**	**2000**	**2005** (est)
CHINA					
Overall urban percentage	23.0	27.4	31.4	35.8	40.6
Average five-year Δ, urban percentage	3.15	3.51	2.70	2.64	2.50
Urban population (N)	246 089	316 563	382 334	456 340	535 958
Average five-year Δ, urban population	4.53	5.04	3.78	3.54	3.22
Rural population	824 086	838 737	837 015	818 793	785 406
Average five-year Δ, rural population	0.53	0.35	-0.04	-0.44	-0.83
WORLD					
World urban percentage	41.5	43.5	45.3	47.2	49.3
Least developed country urban percentage	32.1	35.0	37.7	40.4	43.1

Source: United Nations Population Division, 2002.

Urbanization and development are thought to play a role in the growing global epidemic of obesity, as these processes are often accompanied by lifestyle shifts such as sedentarism and increased consumption of fats and refined carbohydrates (Drewnoski and Popkin, 1997; Gittelsohn *et al.*, 2003). These shifts in diet and activity are characterized as part of the nutrition transition (Popkin, 2003). Indeed, China and other developing countries undergoing rapid growth have experienced considerable increases in the prevalence of overweight and obesity in the past ten years, coexisting with persistent undernutrition (Wang, Monteiro and Popkin, 2002; Du *et al.*, 2002; Doak *et al.*, 2000). Living in urban areas implies greater access to resources such as food markets, motorized transportation and health care services than living in rural areas – factors that may well contribute to obesity risk. While higher levels of obesity have been reported in urban areas than in rural areas of developing countries, little is known about how the process of urbanization may contribute to increasing obesity.

Traditional measures of urbanization include simple urban/rural dichotomies and changes in urban population size, which do not capture heterogeneity in infrastructure and resources within or across cities and urban towns. Consequently, the contribution of more urbanized ecology to obesity risk is unclear. Perhaps more important, such measures do not reflect urbanicity in areas designated as rural towns, many of which increasingly resemble urban areas. The growth of cities often stimulates development in rural areas to provide food and natural resource inputs for urban centres. Changes in resources and infrastructure may contribute to risk in urbanized rural areas, as well as in urban areas. Although China has the world's largest urban population, more than half the population lives in rural areas, and understanding health effects of "urbanization" in rural settings is crucial. Standard measures of urbanization also fail to capture the dynamic environmental changes taking place over time within cities, towns and villages, as infrastructure and resources are put in place. More nuanced, dynamic measures of urbanicity may contribute to better insights into the impact of ecological changes on lifestyle shifts that may affect health or nutritional status.

In addition to increases in overall levels of obesity, a more recent phenomenon reported in some developing countries is rising obesity in low-income groups, suggesting obesogenic lifestyles are increasingly being adopted at all income levels (Monteiro, Wolney and Popkin, 2002; Monteiro *et al.*, 2000; Martorell *et al.*, 1998). Earlier studies found obesity and overweight predominantly in socio-economically advantaged groups. At present, little is known about whether and how urbanization may contribute to this phenomenon. Interestingly, such increases in low-income overweight have been reported only in more industrialized, or middle-income, countries (or regions within countries) (Martorell *et al.*, 1998; Monteiro, Wolney and Popkin, 2002; Monteiro *et al.*, 2003). This suggests that environmental factors play a role. Data are needed to assess the extent to which low-income overweight is limited to urban areas, and whether risk is increasing in "rural" areas with more urbanized environments. In addition, the types of diet and activity shifts that underlie this emerging overweight in low-income populations must be characterized to evaluate similarities and differences versus factors that contribute to obesity risk in high-income groups.

This case study on the nutrition transition in China has three objectives. First, we use an index of urbanicity, rather than simple urban/rural dichotomies, to describe trends in overweight/obesity across areas with different levels of infrastructure and resources. We also assess the extent to which overweight appears to be emerging within low- versus high-income groups in these areas. Next, in order to identify factors that may contribute to obesity risk, we assess the extent to which more diets in more urbanized areas differ from the traditional Chinese diet, which has low intakes of animal foods and edible oils and a large proportion of cereals (rice or wheat) eaten with vegetables. Dietary trends in different urban ecologies are examined by income level to understand better the extent to which urbanicity may promote potentially obesogenic dietary shifts in low-income groups. Finally, we describe changes in food prices in urban and rural areas to assess whether dietary shifts reflect changing prices.

METHODS
China Health and Nutrition Surveys (CHNS)
Data come from ongoing CHNS. These are household surveys in nine provinces that vary substantially in economic, health and demographic factors. Eight provinces (Guangxi, Guizhou, Henan, Hubei, Hunan, Jiangsu, Liaoning and Shandong) were included in 1991 and 1993; a ninth province (Heilongjiang) was added in 1997 when Liaoning did not participate. Households were selected using a multistage random cluster design. Samples in each province were drawn from the capital city and one lower-income city, as well as four rural counties selected at random (one low-, two middle- and one high-income). Neighbourhoods were selected at random from urban and suburban areas in each city, as well as the capital town, plus three villages from each county. Using official criteria of the Chinese Government, city and county capital towns were designated as urban and suburban areas and villages were designated as rural. A total of 190 communities was sampled and, within each community, all individuals in 20 households selected at random were interviewed. The analysis sample included all adults from 20 to 45 years old in 1991 (n=7 026), of which 95 percent participated in 1993 (n=6 662), and 75 percent (after excluding provinces not present in both rounds) in 1997 (4 470 of 6 220). Sixty-three percent of participants in 1991 were present in all three rounds. Data for 1993 (n=6 703) and 1997 (n=6 259) also included additional household members in the eligible age range

present in both follow-up rounds (n=41). The 1997 data also include households from Heilongjiang province, which was added in 1997 (n=709), and new households recruited to replace non-participants in 1997 (n=1 039).

Community surveys were administered to key informants to collect information on factors including infrastructure (such as water, transport systems and electricity); services (family planning, health facilities and retail outlets); economic factors (prevailing wage rates); food prices; and population size and area. These data were used to develop an index of urbanization (Mendez *et al.*, 2003). The urbanization index (range 0-100) sums scores for ten dimensions of urbanicity: population size, population density, access to markets, transportation, communications/media, economic factors, environment/sanitation, health, education and housing quality. Household data were used for the housing quality component. Variability in the index reflects heterogeneity within and between environments designated as urban as well as rural. As indicated by the range of scores, some rural towns have similar or higher levels of infrastructure and resources than some urban communities. Changes in index scores over time reflect developments taking place within communities: mean scores increase in both urban and rural communities, with faster rates of growth in rural areas. Community data on food prices were standardized to reflect prices for the same units at each point in time.

Trained interviewers collected anthropometric data (height and weight) on each individual in the household, used to calculate body mass index (BMI; weight in kg/height in m^2). Data were available on 72-77 percent of individuals in each round of the analysis sample. World Health Organization criteria (BMI$\geq$25.0) were used to classify adults as overweight/obese (hereafter "overweight"). For each round, there was no difference in overweight prevalence in the overall sample from that found among adults who had anthropometric data in all three rounds (60 percent).

Three consecutive days selected at random of 24-hour dietary recalls were collected from each individual within each household (data available on 75-81 percent of individuals in each round). Food models and picture aids were used. Recalls were supplemented by a household food inventory, in which foods were weighed and measured before and after use. These data were used to provide validity checks on reported intakes, and to estimate more accurately added oils used in meat and vegetable dishes (Popkin, Lu and Zhai, 2003, in press). Chinese food composition tables were used to estimate intakes of energy and nutrients. High-fat diets were defined as diets with >30 percent of energy from fats. This analysis focuses on trends in intakes of energy, dietary fats and four key food groups: animal foods (which combine meat, poultry, fish and eggs), edible oils, vegetables and cereals (wheat, rice, other grains and grain products). Income was estimated from household data on earnings from market and non-market activities as well as subsidies (available on 99-100 percent of the sample). Per capita income was estimated using a household roster; income was deflated to 1988 yuan.

Methods
Because residents of urbanized areas have access to resources and infrastructure that may facilitate the diet and activity changes that promote energy imbalance, we hypothesized that in rural areas, greater urbanicity would be associated with higher levels of overweight, as well as
with rapid increases in overweight over time. Within urban areas, we also hypothesized that rapid increases in overweight may be taking place in less as well as more urbanized areas, where residents may be increasingly gaining access to resources and infrastructure once limited to the most urbanized areas. A further hypothesis was that in urbanized areas

FIGURE 1

The China urbanization index reveals variation within urban and rural communities

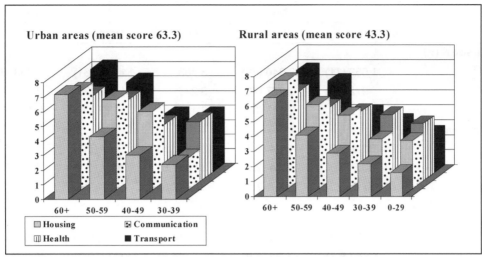

* Charts show mean scores for selected components at different levels of the urbanization index.

– whether designated as urban or rural – levels of overweight would be increasing rapidly in low-income populations, resulting in smaller disparities between low- and high-income groups. Hypotheses related to changing dietary patterns mirrored those for overweight. We expected that residents of more urbanized areas would consume large quantities of total dietary fat, animal foods and edible oils, and relatively low intakes of cereals and vegetables. We also expected that in urbanized settings, intakes of dietary fat, animal foods and edible oils would increase over time, displacing energy from cereals.

The urbanization index was used to classify areas as having high (top tertile) and low/moderate (bottom two tertiles) levels of urbanicity at each point in time. Similarly, individuals with per capita incomes within the top tertile were classified as having high incomes. Trends in overweight and dietary intakes in urban and rural communities at different levels of urbanicity were described using means and prevalences for each cross-section. Trends in low/moderate (hereafter "low") as against high-income groups within these communities were also examined. The analysis was repeated, excluding the province added in 1997 to ensure the comparability of trends. We also repeated a number of analyses with the additional exclusion of new households added in 1997, with no meaningful change in results, although numbers in some cells were sparse (not shown). All analysis was conducted using STATA version 7.0 (Stata Corporation 2002, College Station, Texas, United States).

RESULTS
Sample characteristics
The analysis sample included more than 3 000 men and 3 000 women in each round (Table 2). Over time, CHNS sample communities became significantly more urbanized, and there were large, statistically significant increases in deflated per capita household incomes (ttest p<0.05 for both income and urbanicity).

TABLE 2
Demographic, socio-economic and nutritional status characteristics of adults 20-45 years at baseline, China Health and Nutrition Survey (CHNS), 1991-1997[1]

	Men			Women		
	Urban	Rural	All	Urban	Rural	All
Sample size N (%)						
1991	1 063 (31)	2 340 (69)	3 403	1 140 (31)	2 483 (69)	3 623
1993	972 (30)	2 277 (70)	3 249	1 042 (30)	2 412 (70)	3 454
1997	977 (31)	2 146 (69)	3 123	983 (31)	2 153 (69)	3 136
Mean (sd) age*						
1991	31.5 (7.2)	31.4 (7.7)	31.4 (7.5)	30.6 (7.2)	30.7 (7.6)	30.7 (7.5)
1993	33.6 (7.3)	33.4 (7.7)	33.4 (7.6)	32.7 (7.2)	32.8 (7.6)	32.7 (7.5)
1997	37.6 (7.2)	37.7 (7.8)	37.7 (7.6)	37.4 (7.2)	37.7 (7.7)	37.6 (7.6)
Mean (sd) urbanicity score*						
1991	63.3 (9.3)	43.1 (11.5)	49.4 (14.3)	63.3 (9.3)	43.5 (11.5)	49.7 (14.2)
1993	65.4 (9.7)	44.9 (11.9)	51.0 (14.7)	65.3 (10.2)	45.1 (11.8)	51.2 (14.7)
1997	69.3 (10.1)	49.7 (12.8)	55.8 (15.1)	69.3 (10.3)	49.9 (13.0)	56.0 (15.2)
Mean (sd) deflated HH income/capita[2]*						
1991	1 439 (827)	1 034 (838)	1 161 (855)	1 426 (825)	1 061 (915)	1 176 (904)
1993	1 673 (1 327)	1 148 (1 168)	1 305 (1 241)	1 710 (1 447)	1 174 (1 197)	1 336 (1 301)
1997	2 527 (2 207)	1 840 (2 420)	2 054 (2 376)	2 521 (2 041)	1 874 (2 472)	2 076 (2 365)
Mean (sd) BMI*						
1991	21.8 (2.9)	21.3 (2.3)	21.5 (2.5)	21.9 (3.0)	21.7 (2.6)	21.8 (2.7)
1993	22.1 (2.7)	21.5 (2.3)	21.7 (2.4)	22.2 (3.1)	21.8 (2.7)	21.9 (2.8)
1997	23.1 (3.4)	22.1 (2.7)	22.4 (2.9)	23.1 (3.2)	22.4 (3.0)	22.6 (3.0)
Percentage overweight[3]*						
1991	12.4	6.4	8.3	15.7	10.8	12.4
1993	15.9	7.1	9.6	17.9	12.3	13.9
1997	27.4	13.1	17.5	24.4	18.4	20.2
Percentage underweight[4]*						
1991	8.9	7.0	7.6	9.6	8.4	8.8
1993	7.6	5.5	6.1	7.0	8.5	8.0
1997	3.9	4.5	4.4	4.4	5.8	5.4

[1] Baseline for this analysis = 1991. [2]Income deflated to 1988 yuan. [3]Overweight/obese defined as BMI≥25.0. [4]Underweight defined as BMI<18.5.
* chi-square (categorical) or ttest (continuous) p<0.05 for differences between consecutive rounds (1991-93 and 1993-97) in both men and women.

Although income and urbanicity were positively associated, correlations were moderate (r=0.16 in 1991, 0.33 in 1993 and 0.35 in 1997). Thus there was substantial heterogeneity in the distributions of high income and high urbanicity in the sample (Table 3a and 3b). For example, in both urban and rural areas, only about half of the residents in highly urbanized areas were high-income adults.

TABLE 3a
Distribution of the sample by urbanicity and income level[1]

	Urban men			Rural men		
	Low/mod	High	All	Low/mod	High	All
Distribution by urbanicity level – N (percentage low versus high urbanicity)						
1991	197 (19)	866 (81)	1 063	2 083 (89)	260 (11)	2 343
1993	195 (20)	777 (80)	972	1 983 (87)	294 (13)	2 277
1997	289 (30)	688 (70)	977	1 804 (84)	342 (16)	2 146
1997, excluding Heilongjiang	209 (24)	659 (76)	868	1 561 (82)	342 (16)	1 903
1997, excluding Heilongjiang and new HH	92 (15)	512 (70)	604	1 368 (82)	297 (86)	1 665
Distribution by income and urbanicity level – N (percentage high income)						
1991						
Low income N	129	397	526	1 605	133	1 738
High income N	68	469	537	476	126	602
% high income	*34.5*	*54.2*	*50.5*	*22.9*	*48.7*	*25.7*
1993						
Low income N	127	364	491	1 560	127	1 687
High income N	68	413	481	423	167	590
% high income	*34.9*	*53.2*	*49.5*	*21.3*	*56.8*	*25.9*
1997						
Low income N	140	384	524	1 379	182	1 561
High income N	148	302	450	424	160	584
% high income	*51.4*	*44.0*	*46.2*	*23.5*	*46.8*	*27.2*

TABLE 3b
Distribution of the sample by urbanicity and income level[1]

	Urban women			Rural women		
	Low/mod	High	All	Low/mod	High	All
Distribution by urbanicity level – N (percentage low versus high urbanicity)						
1991	222 (19)	918 (81)	1 140	2 191 (88)	293 (12)	2 484
1993	210 (20)	832 (80)	1 042	2 098 (87)	314 (13)	2 412
1997	292 (30)	691 (70)	983	1 792 (83)	361 (17)	2 153
1997, excluding Heilongjiang	213 (24)	658 (76)	871	1 547 (81)	361 (19)	1 908
1997, excluding Heilongjiang and new HH	93 (15)	508 (85)	601	1 327 (81)	314 (19)	1 641
Distribution by income and urbanicity level – N (percentage high income)						
1991						
Low income N	164	426	590	1 685	145	1 830
High income N	58	492	550	505	148	653
% high income	*26.1*	*53.6*	*48.3*	*23.1*	*50.5*	*26.3*
1993						
Low income N	137	389	526	1 630	135	1 765
High income N	73	443	516	468	179	647
% high income	*34.8*	*53.3*	*49.5*	*22.3*	*57.0*	*26.8*
1997						
Low income N	144	381	525	1 368	190	1 558
High income N	147	308	455	423	171	594
% high income	*50.5*	*44.7*	*46.4*	*23.6*	*47.4*	*27.6*

[1]Urbanicity level defined as high if in the top tertile of urbanicity index; income defined as high if per capita income in the top tertile.

Nutritional status changes
Prevalence of overweight increased
The prevalence of overweight doubled in men (8.3-17.5 percent) and increased by 63 percent in women (12.4-20.2 percent) in the six years between 1991 and 1997 (Table 2). Overweight was twice as common in urban than in rural areas in men, and 30-50 percent higher in urban than in rural women.

Overweight levels increased more rapidly in urbanized rural areas and less urbanized urban areas

Stratifying by urbanicity level (Table 4a and 4b) showed that, consistent with our hypotheses, overweight prevalence was higher – and increased more rapidly – in highly urbanized rural areas than in less urbanized areas. In urban areas, overweight prevalence increased 1.5 to 2.0 times more quickly in low- than high-urbanicity areas. The most striking increases in overweight were observed in men in less urbanized urban areas. By 1997, 31 percent of men living in these areas were overweight, and the prevalence had overtaken the level in more urbanized areas (24 percent). Similarly, overweight in urban women increased more rapidly in low- than in high-urbanicity areas.

TABLE 4a
Shifts in the prevalence of overweight/obesity in Chinese men, CHNS 1991-97[1]

	Urban men			Rural men		
	Low/mod	High	All	Low/mod	High	All
Overweight prevalence (%)						
1991	7.9	13.2	12.4	6.0	9.5	6.4
1993	23.3	14.1	15.9	6.3	12.0	7.1
1997	31.9	25.5	27.4	11.9	19.0	13.1
1997, excluding Heilongjiang	31.9	24.5	26.2	11.6	19.0	13.0
Prevalence Δ, 1991-1997	*24.0*	*12.3*	*15.0*	*5.9*	*9.5*	*6.7*
% Δ, 1991-1997	*+303.8*	*+93.2*	*+121.0*	*+98.3*	*+100.0*	*+104.7*
Overweight prevalence by income level (%)						
1991						
Low income	7.3	12.9	11.7	4.9	6.7	5.0
High income	8.9	13.5	13.0	9.9	12.0	10.4
High:low ratio	*1.2*	*1.0*	*1.1*	*2.0*	*1.8*	*2.1*
1993						
Low income	17.4	12.8	14.0	4.9	12.4	5.5
High income	34.9	15.2	17.8	11.3	11.8	11.4
High:low ratio	*2.0*	*1.2*	*1.3*	*2.3*	*1.0*	*2.1*
1997						
Low income	32.2	23.4	25.6	10.2	12.9	10.5
High income	31.7	27.8	29.1	17.5	25.6	19.8
High:low ratio	*1.0*	*1.2*	*1.1*	*1.7*	*2.0*	*1.9*

[1]Overweight/obese defined as BMI≥25.0. [2]For urban women in less urbanized areas, the 1997 prevalence of overweight in low- versus high-income groups is shown excluding Heilongjiang. Overweight prevalence was 23.3 versus 25.0 percent including Heilongjiang.

In urban areas, low-income overweight increased rapidly in both men and women

Further stratifying on income revealed that, in urban areas, disparities in overweight in high- versus low-income groups were generally small (Table 4a and 4b and Figure 2). Indeed, in the most urbanized areas, women with low incomes were as likely to be overweight as high-income women. Within low-, medium- and high-income tertiles, overweight prevalence among women in these highly urbanized communities was 15.9, 18.9 and 13.6 percent respectively in 1991, and 22.3, 25.7 and 23.0 percent respectively in 1997. Over time, both low- and high-income overweight increased considerably in urban areas, particularly in less urbanized settings. Among men, a large increase in high-income overweight between 1991 and 1993 was followed by a large increase in low-income overweight between 1993 and 1997. As a result, by 1997, overall increases among low-income urban dwellers were similar to those in high-income groups, and income disparities in prevalence were similar in 1991 and 1997.

TABLE 4b
Shifts in the prevalence of overweight/obesity in Chinese women, CHNS 1991-97[1]

	Urban women			Rural women		
	Low/mod	High	All	Low/mod	High	All
Overweight prevalence (%)						
1991	15.4	15.7	15.7	10.6	12.9	10.8
1993	17.0	18.2	17.9	11.9	14.7	12.3
1997	24.3	24.6	24.5	17.4	23.1	18.4
1997, excluding Heilongjiang	29.4	23.9	25.1	15.8	23.1	17.2
Prevalence Δ, 1991-1997	*14.0*	*8.9*	*8.8*	*6.8*	*10.2*	*7.6*
% Δ, 1991-1997	*+57.8*	*+56.7*	*+56.1*	*+64.2*	*+79.1*	*+70.4*
Overweight prevalence by income level (%)						
1991						
Low income	14.5	18.3	17.3	9.7	13.5	10.0
High income	17.9	13.6	14.0	13.5	12.4	13.3
High:low ratio	*1.2*	*0.7*	*0.8*	*1.4*	*0.9*	*1.3*
1993						
Low income	17.5	19.4	18.9	10.9	17.5	11.5
High income	16.0	17.0	16.9	15.3	12.7	14.5
High:low ratio	*0.9*	*0.9*	*0.9*	*1.4*	*0.7*	*1.3*
1997[2]						
Low income	23.4	25.7	25.1	15.7	18.6	16.1
High income	27.8	23.4	23.9	22.5	27.9	24.1
High:low ratio	*1.2*	*0.9*	*1.0*	*1.4*	*1.5*	*1.5*

[1]Overweight/obese defined as bmi≥25.0. [2]for urban women in less urbanized areas, the 1997 prevalence of overweight in low- versus high-income groups is shown excluding heilongjiang. Overweight prevalence was 23.3 versus 25.0 percent including heilongjiang.

FIGURE 2
Trends in overweight by urbanicity and income level

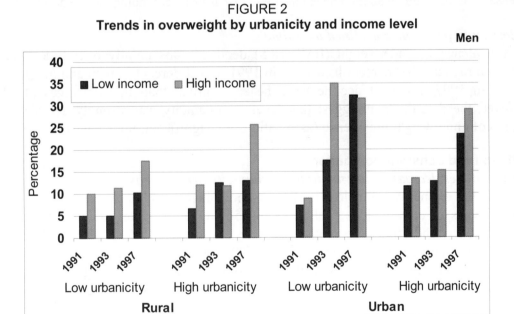

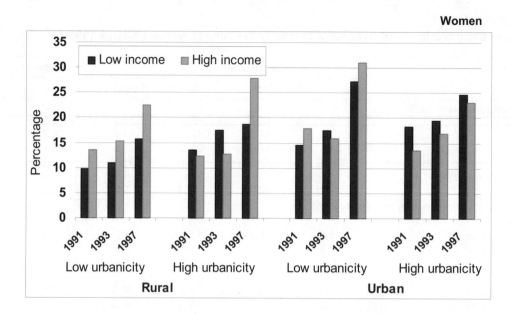

Recent increases in rural overweight were concentrated in high-income groups

In urbanized rural areas, low- and high-income groups had similar levels of overweight in 1991 and 1993. With rapid increases in overweight among high-income residents of these communities between 1993 and 1997, however, there were large disparities in 1997. In rural areas at low levels of urbanicity, overweight was about twice as prevalent in high- as in low-income rural men, and about 40 percent higher in high-income women. As there were similar increases in overweight at all income levels, these disparities were maintained over time.

Underweight prevalence declined over time

The prevalence of underweight (BMI<18.5) declined substantially over time, from 7.6 percent in men and 8.8 percent in women in 1991, to 4.4 percent in men and 5.4 percent in women in 1997. Rates of decline were faster in urban than in rural areas (Table 2). However, the data did not suggest that level of urbanicity was strongly associated with patterns of underweight prevalence (associations not significant; not shown).

Shifts in food consumption patterns

Energy intakes decreased, but not in low-urbanicity urban areas

Mean intakes of energy were close to recommended levels, and declined slightly over time in most types of communities (Table 5a and 5b). Overall, mean intakes declined from 101.8 percent of the Chinese recommended daily allowance (RDA) in 1991 to 95.2 percent in 1997, with means below the RDA in rural (92.0 percent) but not urban (102.7 percent) residents. Intakes also declined slightly in absolute terms. Mean energy intakes in each round were 2 943 (749), 2 820 (754) and 2 809 (1 099) in men, and 2 541 (636), 2 437 (748) and 2 422 (1 005) in women. However, in low-urbanicity urban areas – where the most dramatic increases in overweight prevalence took place – energy intakes increased or remained stable over time (from 101 to 106 percent of the RDA in men and 102 to 103 percent in women). This increase appeared to be even larger after restricting the data to individuals whose reported energy intakes were well within plausible levels for their estimated basal metabolic rate, using habitual ranges of activity considered normal in industrialized countries (from 100 to 109 percent). In absolute terms, mean (sd) intakes in these communities for 1991, 1993 and 1997, respectively, were 2 736 (704), 2 748 (751) and 2 806 (793) kcals among men, and 2 412 (668), 2 445 (679) and 2 361 (598) among women.

TABLE 5a
Shifts in mean intakes of energy, fat and selected food groups in urban and rural areas by level of urbanicity[1]

	Urban men			Rural men		
	Low/mod	High	All	Low/mod	High	All
Energy and dietary fat intakes						
Percentage of energy RDA						
1991	100.2	104.1	103.4	101.6	101.0	100.6
1993	96.6	100.9	100.0	95.9	96.2	96.0
1997	106.1	101.9	103.2	91.6	97.3	92.5
1997, excluding Heilongjiang	103.3	101.9	102.2	91.7	97.3	92.8
% Δ, 1991-97	+5.9	-2.1	-0.2	-9.8	-3.7	-8.1
Percentage of energy RDA, if intakes plausible						
1991, plausible	103.5	107.1	106.6	95.6	101.5	96.3
1993, plausible	96.9	105.5	103.9	92.5	100.1	93.6
1997, plausible	110.6	102.7	104.7	89.9	95.5	90.9
% Δ, 1991-97	+6.9	-4.1	-1.8	-6.0	-5.9	-5.6
Fat (as % kcals)						
1991	21.4	27.0	26.0	19.0	24.9	19.7
1993	25.7	29.6	28.7	19.9	28.6	21.0
1997	33.4	32.6	32.8	23.4	33.0	25.0
1997, excluding Heilongjiang	33.5	32.6	32.8	23.6	33.0	25.3
% Δ, 1991-97	+56.1	+20.7	+26.2	+23.2	+32.5	+26.9
% ate high fat[2]						
1991	15.1	36.5	32.7	11.3	26.3	13.1
1993	32.5	45.3	42.6	14.4	42.9	18.2
1997	58.8	59.3	59.2	22.5	55.3	27.9
1997, excluding Heilongjiang	59.7	59.5	59.5	23.1	55.3	28.9
% Δ, 1991-97	+289.4	+62.5	+81.0	+99.1	+110.3	+113.0
Food group intakes						
Percentage ate animal foods						
1991	80.9	94.4	92.0	68.0	92.2	70.8
1993	88.5	96.7	95.0	68.2	95.8	71.9
1997	94.3	97.8	96.7	74.4	94.7	77.7
1997, excluding Heilongjiang	93.4	97.7	96.6	75.2	94.7	78.8
% Δ, 1991-97	+16.6	+3.6	+5.1	+9.4	+2.7	+9.7
Animal foods (g)						
1991	105.3	174.5	162.1	84.7	157.0	93.1
1993	144.4	192.7	182.4	90.8	191.2	104.3
1997	190.9	203.4	199.5	100.6	213.7	118.6
1997, excluding Heilongjiang	199.2	202.6	201.7	106.6	213.7	126.1
% Δ, 1991-97	+81.3	+16.6	+23.1	+18.8	+36.1	+27.4
Edible oils (g)						
1991	34.4	44.2	42.7	35.9	40.8	36.5
1993	38.6	43.9	42.9	34.0	43.1	35.3
1997	55.7	43.7	47.7	43.4	46.4	43.9
1997, excluding Heilongjiang	57.5	43.0	46.8	41.2	46.4	42.2
% Δ, 1991-97	+61.9	-1.1	+11.7	+20.9	+13.7	+20.3
Vegetables (g)						
1991	339.8	313.4	318.1	381.0	343.8	376.6
1993	323.7	313.8	315.9	422.0	338.7	410.8
1997	335.3	307.9	316.4	376.0	367.0	374.6
1997, excludingHeilongjiang	337.4	308.4	315.5	367.6	367.0	367.5
% Δ, 1991-97	-1.3	-1.8	-0.5	-1.3	6.7	-0.5
Percentage energy, cereals						
1991	72.1	61.3	63.2	72.5	65.2	71.7
1993	67.6	58.2	60.2	71.4	58.4	69.6
1997	54.5	55.1	54.9	67.1	54.4	65.0
1997, excluding Heilongjiang	54.6	55.1	55.0	66.7	54.4	64.5
% Δ, 1991-97	-24.4	-10.1	-13.1	-7.4	-16.6	-9.3

TABLE 5b

Shifts in mean intakes of energy, fat and selected food groups in urban and rural areas by level of urbanicity[1]

	Urban women			Rural women		
	Low/mod	High	All	Low/mod	High	All
Energy and dietary fat intakes						
Percentage of energy RDA						
1991	102.4	103.1	102.9	101.9	101.6	101.8
1993	101.0	100.2	100.4	96.3	97.7	96.5
1997	103.1	102.0	102.3	90.1	98.9	91.6
1997, excluding Heilongjiang	100.7	102.0	101.7	90.7	98.9	92.3
% Δ, 1991-97	+0.7	-1.1	-0.6	-11.6	-2.7	-10.0
Percentage of energy RDA, if intakes plausible						
1991, plausible	98.2	104.5	103.5	94.8	97.8	95.2
1993, plausible	99.2	102.7	101.9	91.3	99.2	92.5
1997, plausible	107.6	99.9	101.8	86.4	95.7	88.0
% Δ, 1991-97	+9.6	-4.4	-1.6	-8.9	-2.1	-7.6
Fat (as % kcals)						
1991	21.8	27.3	26.3	19.2	25.5	20.0
1993	26.7	29.9	29.2	20.2	29.9	21.5
1997	33.0	33.9	33.7	24.0	34.0	25.8
1997, excluding Heilongjiang	33.4	33.9	33.8	24.1	34.0	26.0
% Δ, 1991-97	+51.4	+24.2	+28.1	+25.0	+33.3	+29.0
% ate high fat[2]						
1991	18.6	36.6	33.3	11.7	30.0	13.9
1993	31.0	46.6	43.4	14.6	45.0	18.6
1997	62.2	62.5	62.4	24.2	59.8	30.5
1997, excluding Heilongjiang	65.4	62.5	63.2	24.8	59.8	31.6
% Δ, 1991-97	+234.4	+70.8	+87.4	+106.8	+99.3	+119.4
Food group intakes						
Percentage ate animal foods						
1991	79.6	95.2	92.4	66.4	86.4	68.8
1993	89.9	96.4	95.1	65.9	93.8	69.6
1997	92.2	97.4	95.7	72.5	95.0	76.4
1997, excluding Heilongjiang	89.9	97.2	95.4	73.0	95.0	77.3
% Δ, 1991-97	+15.8	+2.3	+3.6	+9.2	+10.0	+11.0
Animal foods (g)						
1991	90.2	153.0	141.6	69.2	136.9	77.3
1993	116.5	158.4	149.7	72.7	165.0	85.0
1997	158.4	178.6	172.3	78.9	187.7	97.5
1997, excluding Heilongjiang	161.5	175.9	172.3	83.1	187.7	103.6
% Δ, 1991-97	+75.6	+16.7	+21.7	+14.0	+37.1	+26.1
Edible oils (g)						
1991	36.0	39.3	38.7	33.0	37.5	33.7
1993	34.5	38.6	37.9	31.6	39.6	32.8
1997	47.5	41.2	43.3	39.4	42.2	39.9
1997, excluding Heilongjiang	47.7	40.4	42.4	37.5	42.2	38.5
% Δ, 1991-97	+31.9	+4.8	+11.9	+19.4	+12.5	+18.4
Vegetables (g)						
1991	308.5	288.0	291.7	350.2	317.4	346.5
1993	311.4	290.0	294.4	395.8	319.6	385.7
1997	316.2	296.6	302.7	356.8	334.1	352.9
1997, excludingHeilongjiang	321.6	295.4	301.9	353.2	334.1	349.5
% Δ, 1991-97	2.5	3.0	3.8	1.9	5.3	1.8
Percentage energy, cereals						
1991	71.3	61.3	63.1	73.0	64.7	72.0
1993	66.7	58.6	60.3	71.7	57.9	69.8
1997	55.2	53.3	53.8	67.3	53.2	64.8
1997, excluding Heilongjiang	54.6	53.3	53.6	67.1	53.2	64.4
% Δ, 1991-97	-22.6	-13.1	-14.7	-7.8	-17.8	-10.0

[1]Low urbanicity = bottom two tertiles of index; high urbanicity = top tertile. [2]High fat defined as >30 percent of energy.

Total fat intakes increased dramatically in all environments, particularly in less urbanized urban areas

Overall, between 1991 and 1997, mean intakes of dietary fats increased from 21.8 to 27.7 percent of energy (see Table 5a and 5b). However, these means mask substantial heterogeneity across different types of communities. The largest increases were observed in less urbanized urban areas, where mean intakes increased by more than 50 percent, and in urbanized rural areas, where intakes increased by one-third. The proportion of adults consuming high-fat (>30 percent of energy) diets increased more than threefold in less urbanized urban areas, doubling in rural areas regardless of urbanicity level (Table 5a and 5b). Rates of increase were smaller in highly urbanized urban areas, where initial intakes were relatively high. As a result of these large increases, by 1997 more than 50 percent of residents in all urbanized areas consumed high-fat diets. As initial levels were very low, only half as many (about 25 percent) residents in low-urbanicity rural areas consumed similar diets.

Low-income adults increasingly consumed high-fat diets

High-fat diet consumption increased in both low- and high-income residents, although intakes remained higher in high-income groups (Figure 3). The proportion of high-income residents of urbanized rural areas consuming high-fat diets (70.6 percent of women and 64.4 percent of men) was similar to levels among high-income residents of urban areas (69.0 percent of women and 66.4 percent of men).

FIGURE 3
Trends in high-fat diet consumption by urbanicity and income level

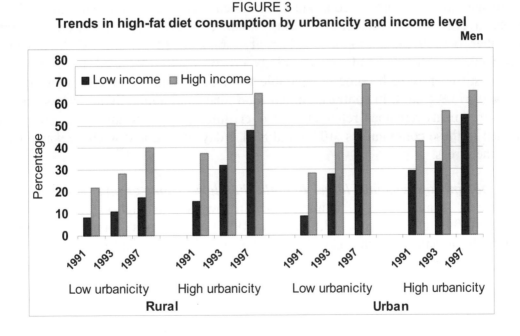

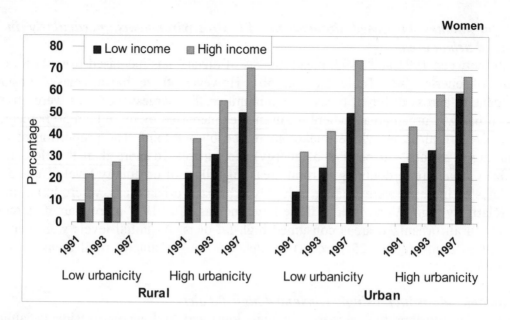

Animal food consumption remained low only in non-urbanized rural areas

From 1991 to 1997, mean intakes of animal foods (meats and poultry, fish and eggs) increased by about 25 percent, from 105.6 to 131.6 g/day. However, there was substantial variability in both amounts and rates of increase across different types of community settings (Table 5a and 5b). Both increases in consumption and ultimate levels of intake were substantial in less urbanized urban environments, as well as in urbanized rural areas. Increases over time were smaller in the most urbanized areas, where initial levels of intake were higher. By 1997, intakes in high-urbanicity rural areas (213.7 and 187.7 g/day in men and women, respectively) and low-urbanicity urban areas (199.2 and 161.5 g/day) had increased sufficiently to become comparable to those of high-urbanicity urban residents (202.6 and 175.9 g/day). In contrast, animal food intakes of adults living in less urbanized rural environments remained relatively flat over time. The mean amount of animal food consumed in these communities (103.3 and 83.1 g/day in men and women) was only half that in other areas.

Animal food intakes remained larger in high- than low-income groups

Disparities in mean intakes of animal foods in low- versus high-income groups were substantial (104.5 g/day versus 183.8 g/day in 1997) and, in most communities, persisted over time. In urbanized urban areas, disparities were relatively small in 1991 (26.9 g/day) but increased over time (50.8 g/day by 1997), as intakes increased largely in high-income subjects. Income disparities in the other communities were similar or somewhat larger in 1997: 66.5 g/day in less urbanized urban areas, 87.2 g/day in urbanized rural areas and 49.9 g/day in low-urbanicity rural areas.

FIGURE 4
Trends in animal food (g) consumption by urbanicity and income level

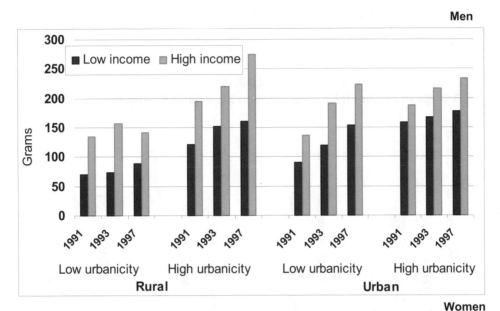

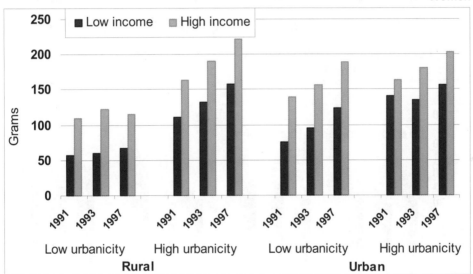

Edible oil consumption increased in rural areas and in less urbanized urban areas
Overall, consumption of plant oils also increased substantially over time, from 37.1 to 43.0g/day (Table 5a and 5b). As was observed with animal foods, intakes increased most dramatically between 1991 and 1997 in less urbanized urban areas (33.3 to 51.5 g/day), and there were large increases in urbanized rural areas (39.1 to 44.1 g/day). In contrast to animal foods, however, there were substantial increases in the most rural environments (34.4 to 41.3 g/day), and there were no increases in added oil consumption levels in the most urbanized areas (42.7 and 42.4 g/day).

In urban areas, low- and high-income groups had comparable trends in edible oil intakes
High-income adults generally consumed higher levels of added fats than low-income adults (Figure 5). However, in low-urbanicity urban areas both absolute intakes in 1997 and increases between 1991 and 1997 were similar, regardless of income. Intakes remained relatively flat over time in the most urbanized areas, regardless of income.

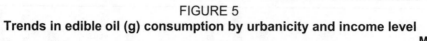

FIGURE 5
Trends in edible oil (g) consumption by urbanicity and income level

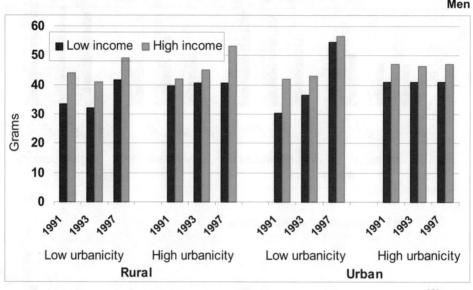

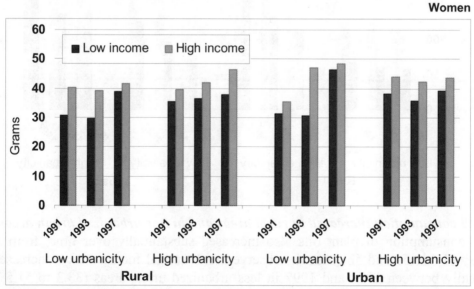

In rural areas, trends in oil intakes varied depending on urban context
In urbanized rural areas, both absolute levels and increases in edible oil intakes were concentrated in high-income adults (Figure 5). Income disparities in oil consumption increased over time in these communities. In low-urbanicity rural areas, however, high-income residents consumed much higher levels of added oils in 1991. However, as low-income groups increasingly consumed high quantities of edible oil, these income disparities fell over time.

Vegetable consumption was highest in the most rural settings

In contrast to animal foods and oils, mean intakes of vegetables were consistently higher in rural than in urban areas, as well as in low- rather than high-urbanicity areas (Table 5a and 5b). Vegetable consumption changed relatively little over time, although there were slight decreases in urban areas. Trends in rural areas were more irregular. Stratifying on income (Figure 6) showed that in the most urban areas, there was little difference in vegetable intakes by income group. However, there was substantial variation in the magnitude and direction of income disparities in other communities.

FIGURE 6
Trends in vegetable (g) consumption by urbanicity and income level

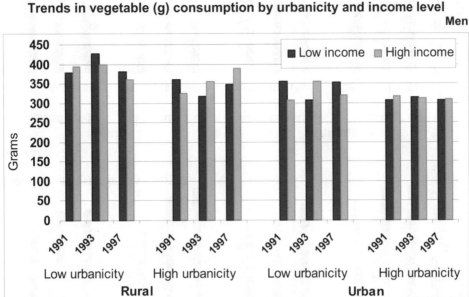

Cereal intakes fell in all communities

Intakes of cereals decreased substantially, from an average of 69.1 percent of energy in 1991 to 61.8 percent in 1997 (Table 5a and 5b and Figure 7). Reductions in the proportion of energy from cereals were smallest in residents of less urbanized rural areas (low-income 8 percent, high-income 9 percent). Intakes declined more substantially in all areas, but declines were particularly marked among residents of less urbanized urban areas.

FIGURE 7
Trends in cereal (% energy) consumption by urbanicity and income level
Men

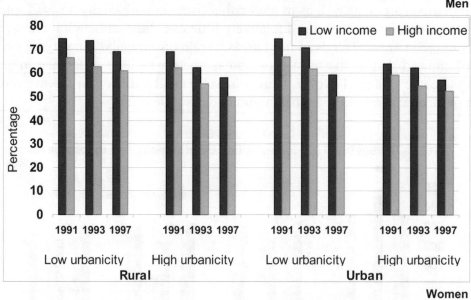

Women

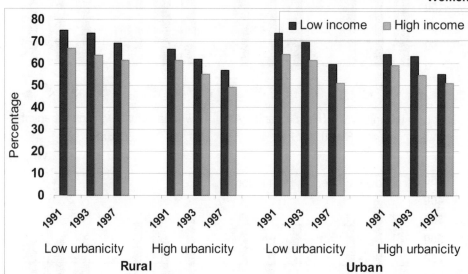

Food prices
Food prices fell more in urbanized than in truly rural areas
Relative prices for most food items were already lower in 1991 in urban than in rural areas (Table 6). Nonetheless, reductions over time in relative food prices were consistently substantially larger in urban than in rural areas. For example, reductions in the relative price of pork were nearly twice as large in urban (35.2 percent) as in rural areas (18.7 percent). Within both urban and rural areas, relative price reductions were also higher in more than in less urbanized communities (Figure 8).

TABLE 6
Shifts in food prices relative to prevailing wages, CHNS, 1991-1997[1]

	Urban			Rural			Urban/rural ratio
	Low/mod	High	All	Low/mod	High	All	
Fatty pork							
1991	0.74	0.71	0.71	0.76	0.59	0.75	0.95
1993	0.65	0.58	0.59	0.78	0.62	0.76	0.78
1997	0.48	0.46	0.46	0.65	0.42	0.61	0.75
% Δ, 1991-97	-35.1	-35.2	-35.2	-14.5	-28.8	-18.7	1.88
Fish							
1991	0.72	0.61	0.62	0.64	0.50	0.63	0.98
1993	0.62	0.57	0.58	0.66	0.53	0.64	0.91
1997	0.23	0.29	0.27	0.39	0.20	0.35	0.77
% Δ, 1991-97	-68.1	-52.5	-56.5	-39.1	-60.0	-44.4	1.27
Rapeseed oil							
1991	0.91	0.68	0.73	0.96	0.52	0.92	0.79
1993	0.61	0.42	0.46	0.67	0.48	0.65	0.71
1997	0.34	0.25	0.27	0.51	0.25	0.46	0.59
% Δ, 1991-97	-62.6	-63.2	-63.0	-46.9	-51.9	-50.0	1.26
Cabbage							
1991	0.050	0.052	0.051	0.053	0.033	0.051	1.00
1993	0.038	0.047	0.046	0.056	0.050	0.055	0.84
1997	0.038	0.050	0.047	0.066	0.032	0.061	0.77
% Δ, 1991-97	-24.0	-3.8	-7.8	24.5	-3.0	+19.6	3.51
Rice							
1991	0.140	0.129	0.131	0.144	0.121	0.142	0.92
1993	0.118	0.101	0.104	0.135	0.104	0.131	0.79
1997	0.076	0.095	0.090	0.152	0.058	0.135	0.67
% Δ, 1991-97	-45.7	-26.4	-31.3	5.6	-52.1	-4.9	6.39
Flour							
1991	0.122	0.131	0.130	0.148	0.121	0.146	0.89
1993	0.127	0.108	0.111	0.144	0.145	0.144	0.77
1997	0.068	0.081	0.077	0.153	0.068	0.137	0.56
% Δ, 1991-97	-44.3	-38.2	-40.8	3.4	-43.8	-6.2	6.58

[1]Data shown are CHNS community survey data; figures are free market prices for each item in each community, divided by prevailing daily wage for an ordinary male labourer reported for each community.

Reductions in prices were largest for oils and animal foods

Relative prices in urban areas declined dramatically for oils (63 percent) and animal foods (35-68 percent), with smaller reductions in the prices of rice (26-46 percent) and flour (38-44 percent). Price changes for cabbage (the main vegetable consumed) – already inexpensive – ranged from negligible (-7.8 percent) to moderate (-24 percent). Similar price changes were observed in urbanized rural areas, with large reductions in the relative prices of oils, animal foods and cereals, but small or negligible changes in cabbage prices. In comparison, in less urbanized rural areas, there were smaller relative price changes for animal foods as well as oils, while relative prices actually increased substantially for cabbage, with small increases in rice and flour prices.

FIGURE 8
Trends in pork prices relative to prevailing male wages by urbanicity level

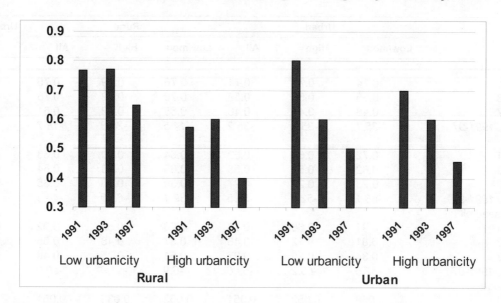

DISCUSSION

Urbanization is profoundly linked with the rapid shifts in the stage of the nutrition transition in China. In a very short time frame, between 1991 and 1997, there were extremely large increases in overweight in this sample of young Chinese adults. These increases were concentrated not in the most urbanized areas, but in less urbanized urban settings – smaller cities and suburban areas – where infrastructure and resources that characterize the urbanization process are being put into place. There were also very high increases in overweight in urbanized areas officially designated as rural, especially in areas where urbanicity levels were high. Particularly within urbanized settings, both absolute levels and increases in overweight among low-income adults were substantial. Indeed, in the most urbanized areas, low-income women generally had higher levels of overweight than those with higher incomes.

Increases in overweight were accompanied by striking changes in diet composition. During this six-year period, adult diets became much richer in dietary fats from both edible oils and animal foods. The majority of the increased fat consumption came from added oils, and the proportion of fat from added oils increased with time: 53.1 percent in 1991, 54.8 percent in 1993 and 60.7 percent in 1997. Edible oils and animal foods appear to have displaced cereals, consumption of which has declined drastically over the same period, particularly in urbanized areas. In contrast, consumption of vegetables remained fairly stable over time.

As with changes in overweight, there was important heterogeneity in these dietary shifts associated with levels of urbanicity. In general, the most striking changes took place in less urbanized urban areas and in urbanized rural areas – areas experiencing the most rapid increases in overweight. In less urbanized urban areas, there was a marked increase – 16.9 to 60.5 percent – in the proportion of adults consuming high-fat diets between 1991 and 1997. Similar trends took place in urbanized rural areas, with the prevalence of high-fat diets increasing from 28.3 to 57.7 percent. As a result, more than 50 percent of adults living in all urbanized areas had high-fat diets by 1997. However, the contribution of edible oils to these dietary fat increases was marked only in low-urbanicity urban communities; increases in edible oil intakes in urbanized rural areas were relatively small

(12.8 versus 54.7 percent). The proportion of fat from plants rose from 50.1 to 67.5 percent in less urbanized urban areas, while the proportion in urbanized rural areas was 49.2 to 49.5 percent in 1991 and 1997, respectively. These shifts in dietary composition may have contributed to the maintenance of high levels of energy intake in low-urbanicity urban environments. Mean energy intakes in these communities actually increased over time, in contrast to stable intakes or declines in other areas. Several studies suggest that increasing energy density, such as that resulting from greater added fat content, may promote larger food intakes (Rolls, 2000).

Edible oils also contributed to increases in fat consumption in truly rural areas. Although less than 25 percent of residents in these areas had high-fat diets, there were large increases in oil intakes in these communities (from 34.4 to 41.2/day), and the proportion of fat from plant oils rose sharply (56.5 to 66.9 percent). In contrast, oil consumption did not change meaningfully in the most urbanized areas (about 47 percent of total fats). Consequently, intakes in less urbanized areas eventually exceeded levels in highly urbanized urban settings; intakes in the most rural areas were not much lower than consumption levels in the most urbanized settings. By 1997, mean intakes of edible oils in all types of communities exceeded the maximums recommended by both Chinese (25 g/day) and United States dietary guidelines (about 44 g in a 2 500 kcal diet, given added fats constituted about 53 percent of total fats, assuming a total of 750 kcals/83 g of fat).

Traditionally, the Chinese diet contained small quantities of animal source foods, which helped to facilitate its low-fat content. As with dietary fats, there were particularly large increases in less urbanized urban areas and in urbanized rural areas. By 1997, animal food intakes remained low only in the most rural areas, where mean intakes were about half the size of those in other types of communities. Over time, animal foods and oils were substituted for cereals: shifts in cereal consumption within each type of community essentially mirrored changes in animal food and oil intakes, with the largest declines observed in low-urbanicity urban areas and highly urbanized rural areas. Following these increases, mean animal food consumption levels in all urbanized settings in 1997 were in the range recommended by Chinese dietary guidelines: 200 g in total (Chinese Nutrition Society, 2000). However, these recommendations emphasize lean meats, while the majority of meats consumed were high in fat. Mean animal food intakes were also comparable to the maximum amounts recommended in United States dietary guidelines (142-213 g based on two to three servings of 2-3 ounces/57-85 g each).

Economic and structural changes related to urbanization have probably played a key role in these dietary shifts. During this relatively short time period, there were very large decreases in food prices relative to wages. This was largely attributable to the faster increases in wages in urban areas. These changes made animal foods and edible oils increasingly accessible. In contrast to animal foods and oils, the relative price of cabbage actually increased over time in rural CHNS communities, remaining stable in urban areas. Furthermore, although there were substantial reductions in the price of cereals in urban areas, there was on average no change in relative prices of these foods in rural areas. As shown previously by Guo *et al.* (1999), consumers are highly responsive to changes in food prices; demand for animal foods such as pork and eggs, as well as for edible oils, is highly elastic. There has been a marked structural shift in the income-price-consumption relationships for key foods over time: a pronounced increase in the income elasticity of dietary fats, accompanied by income increases, has helped to promote higher intakes of fats (Guo *et al.*, 2000; Popkin and Du, 2003, in press). These changes in elasticity have been observed across the income spectrum, but have been most marked at the lower ends:

low-income group elasticities have changed the most, making them more likely to increase their intakes of vegetable oils and pork in response to price changes.

Dietary shifts were generally similar among subjects with relatively low incomes as in high-income groups. With regard to lower-income adults, individuals with high incomes consumed relatively high levels of animal foods and edible oils, and lower energy from cereals. However, particularly in urbanized areas, disparities in intakes across income groups were not always large, and tended to decrease over time. Thus in highly urbanized areas, more than 50 percent of low-income adults, and more than 65 percent of higher-income adults, consumed high-fat diets by 1997. In summary, dietary shifts characterized by increased intakes of animal foods and edible oils, reduced intakes of cereals and relatively little change in fruit and vegetables, have been observed in all urbanized areas, among both high- and low-income adults.

These dietary shifts have been accompanied by changes in activity, including declines in occupational activity and active commuting (Bell, Ge and Popkin, 2001; 2002). There have also been increases in sedentarism during leisure time, associated with growing television ownership, which reached 90 percent of this sample – 95 percent in highly urbanized areas – in 1997. Together, these changes have contributed to the growing overweight in Chinese adults and to the rising levels of chronic disease in China that have been documented elsewhere (e.g. Du *et al.*, 2002). Given the evidence that there is rising overweight in a variety of settings, and the extensive spread of adverse dietary changes, efforts to combat these obesogenic dietary trends need to target both low- and high-income groups, and to include urbanized rural areas as well as urban settings.

Policies and programmes to promote healthful dietary patterns

As part of its urbanization and development policies, China has emphasized rural development, using policies such as the promotion of township and village enterprises that have helped to reduce poverty and supported the development of infrastructure (FAO, 1999). Although not explicitly targeted at improving dietary quality, such policies undoubtedly play a role in the nature and amount of dietary change. By raising incomes and promoting infrastructure development, China's rural development policies may affect not only food security – a key objective – but also the structure of demand and food availability. Policies to counter increased demand for potentially obesogenic dietary patterns, characterized by larger intakes of added fats and animal foods, are needed to accompany rural and urban development efforts.

The National Plan of Nutrition Action developed in 1997 involved intersectoral cooperation between policy-makers in the health and agriculture ministries, as well as other institutes involved in nutrition and food hygiene (Zhai *et al.*, 2002). In addition to food self-sufficiency, the plan's objectives include increases in the production of alternative animal food (poultry and fish) and protein sources (soybeans), as well as in vegetables and fruit. Results thus far have been mixed. Meat production has expanded substantially over time, almost keeping up with demand: meat imports were 1.7 percent of the total supply in 1990 and 3.6 percent in 2001 (FAO, 2003). Although poultry consumption remains much lower than other meats (67.7 g/day in 1997), both production and intakes have increased, from 7.3 to 12.9 g/day between 1991 and 1997. Similarly, fish intakes increased from 22.6 to 27.8 g/day. However, expansion of soybean production has been slower (Geissler, 1999). Both availability (13.7 kcals/capita/day in 2001; FAO 2003) and reported intakes (39.0 g/day in 1991 and 44.6 g/day in 1997 in the CHNS) of pulses remain low.

Subsidies, price adjustments and other policies have been used to promote vegetable production and consumption in urban areas, as well as in regions where consumption is low (Zhai *et al.*, 2002). The impact of these policies is thought to be positive, although data are limited. Indeed, while vegetable consumption declined substantially during the 1980s, changes in intakes have been smaller and more inconsistent in the 1990s (Du *et al.*, 2002). In contrast with intake data, food availability data suggest that there have been substantial increases in vegetable production in China, from 67 to 141 kcals/capita/day from 1990 to 2000 (FAO, 2003). However, the correlation with intakes may be low, as has been found in other countries (Pomerleau, Lock and McKee, 2003). As we have shown, consumption of vegetables is now substantially lower in urbanized areas than in very rural settings, suggesting that, with urbanization, vegetable consumption may be vulnerable to further declines. Additional efforts to maintain and, if possible, increase vegetable intakes may be needed.

China has also implemented a number of other policies and programmes with the aim of promoting lifestyle shifts – including dietary changes – to help slow the increases in obesity and chronic disease. One demonstration project funded by the World Bank and the World Health Organization (WHO) in the city of Tianjin (one of China's largest cities) has focused on improving health in an urban centre. After six years, lower rates of hypertension and stroke mortality in the demonstration areas compared to the city as a whole suggest that the project achieved some success in reducing risk factors for these conditions (Zhai *et al.*, 2002). The extent to which changes in diet and activity patterns played a role is uncertain (Tian *et al.*, 1995a; b). Another important initiative has been in developing education efforts to encourage healthful dietary patterns, including the development of dietary guidelines and the "Chinese pagoda" (Chinese Nutrition Society, 2000). Dissemination efforts have not been widespread and, despite a positive impact on knowledge, there has been little evidence of change in dietary behaviour (Zhao *et al.*, 2001). In addition to efforts to influence dietary patterns, a 1995 policy asked schools to emphasize physical education as well as classroom learning, to promote higher levels of activity and help to reduce early obesity (Zhai *et al.*, 2002). Again, there are few data on the impact of these policies, which are believed to be limited so far.

A wide range of other policy and programme options may be considered to combat further the unhealthy dietary trends associated with urbanization. Studies of food group elasticities in China, as well as intervention studies in the United States, suggest that price changes that favour more rather than less healthy foods may be highly effective (French, 2003; Guo *et al.*, 1999). Because of the cross-price elasticities (which influence how foods are substituted for others when prices change), as well as persistent undernutrition in some areas, price policies must be carefully considered to ensure the absence of adverse effects (Guo *et al.*, 1999; Haddad, 2003). Agriculture and trade policies to influence food supply, such as policies to promote greater availability of soybeans, fruit and vegetables, should be pursued further. It is also important to identify effective nutrition education strategies. Food labels may be one effective approach (Neuhouser, Kristal and Patterson, 1999). In addition, researchers in Brazil have suggested that widespread mass media exposure publicizing the epidemic of obesity, as well as obesity prevention measures, may have helped to shift diet and activity patterns in higher socio-economic status groups (Monteiro *et al.*, 2000; 2002). Given the widespread access to mass media, similar efforts may be beneficial in China. Aggressive food marketing and changes in the food supply are thought to be central forces underlying dietary shifts observed in countries undergoing globalization, urbanization and the nutrition transition (Chopra, Galbraith and Darnton-Hill, 2002; Lang, 1999). Policies to affect the food supply, as well as efforts to market more healthful dietary practices, may be the most direct routes to reduce or reverse these shifts.

Bibliography

Bell, A.C., Ge, K. & Popkin, B.M. 2001. Weight gain and its predictors in Chinese adults. *Int. J. Obes. Relat. Metab. Disord.*, 25(7): 1079-86.

Bell, A.C., Ge, K. & Popkin, B.M. 2002. The road to obesity or the path to prevention: motorized transportation and obesity in China. *Obes. Res.*, 10(4): 277-83.

Bolling, C. & Somwaru, A. 2001. US food companies access foreign markets though direct investment. *Food Rev.*, 24(3): 23-28.

Cee, J. & Theiler, S. 1999. US French fries heat up China's fast food industry. *USDA FAS (Foreign Agricultural Service) online* (www.fas.usda.gov/info/agexporter/1999/usfrench.html).

Chen, S. & Wang, Y. 2001. *China's growth and poverty reduction: Recent trends between 1990 and 1999.* Washington, DC, World Bank (econ.worldbank.org/files/2369_wps2651.pdf). Accessed August 24, 2003.

Chinese Nutrition Society. 2000. Dietary guidelines and the food guide pagoda. *J. Am. Diet. Assoc.*, 100(8): 886-7.

Chopra, M., Galbraith, S. & Darnton-Hill, I. 2002. A global response to a global problem: the epidemic of overnutrition. *Bull. World Health Org.*, 80: 952-958.

Doak, C.M., Adair, L.S., Monteiro, C. & Popkin, B.M. 2000. Overweight and underweight coexist within households in Brazil, China and Russia. *J. Nutr.*, 130(12): 2965-71.

Drewnowski, A. & Popkin, B.M. 1997. The nutrition transition: new trends in the global diet. *Nutr. Rev.*, 55(2): 31-43.

Du, S., Lu, B., Zhai, F. & Popkin, B.M. 2002. A new stage of the nutrition transition in China. *Public Health Nutr.*, 5: 169-174.

FAO Regional Office for Asia and the Pacific. 1999. Annex 3. Agricultural policy and food security in China. In *Poverty alleviation and food security in Asia: lessons and challenges.* December 1998. FAO RAP Publication 1999/1 (www.fao.org/DOCREP/004/AB981E/ab981e00.htm#Contents).

Food and Agriculture Organization of the United Nations (FAO). 2003. *Food balance sheets* (apps.fao.org).

French, S.A. 2003. Pricing effects on food choices. *J. Nutr.*, 133(3): 841S-843S.

Geissler, C. 1999. China: the soyabean-pork dilemma. *Proc. Nutr. Soc.*, 58(2): 345-53.

Gittelsohn, J., Haberle, H., Vastine, A.E., Dyckman, W. & Palafox, N.A. 2003. Macro- and microlevel processes affect food choice and nutritional status in the Republic of the Marshall Islands. *J. Nutr.*, 133(1): 310S-313S.

Guo, X., Mroz, T., Popkin, B.M. & Zhai, F. 2000. Structural changes in the impact of income on food consumption in China, 1989-93. *Econ. Dev. Cultural Change,* 48: 737-760.

Guo, X., Popkin, B.M., Mroz, T.A. & Zhai, F. 1999. Food price policy can favorably alter macronutrient intake in China. *J. Nutr.*, 129(5): 994-1001.

Haddad, L. 2003. Redirecting the nutrition transition: what can food policy do? In *Food policy options: preventing and controlling nutrition-related non-communicable diseases.* Report of a World Health Organization and World Bank Consultation. Washington, DC, World Bank.

Hu, G. & Tian, H. 2001. A comparison of dietary and non-dietary factors of hypertension and normal blood pressure in a Chinese population. *J. Hum. Hypertens.*, 15(7): 487-93.

Lang T. 1999. Diet, health and globalization: five key questions. *Proc. Nutr. Soc.*, 58(2): 335-43.

Marr, J. & Hatfield, A. 1997. Fast-food restaurants: just what eastern China's consumers ordered. *US Department of Agriculture FAS (Foreign Agricultural Service) online* (www.fas.usda.gov/info/agexporter/1997/fastfood.html).

Martorell, R., Khan, L.K., Hughes, M.L. & Grummer-Strawn, L.M. 1998. Obesity in Latin American women and children. *J. Nutr.*, 128(9): 1464-73.

Mendez, M.A., Stookey, J.D., Adair, L.S. & Popkin, B.M. 2003. *Measuring urbanization and its potential impact on health: the China case.* Carolina Population Center, University of North Carolina at Chapel Hill. (unpublished manuscript)

Monteiro, C.A., Conde, W.L., Lu, B. & Popkin, B.M. 2003. *Is obesity fuelling inequities in health in the developing world?* São Paulo University Department of Nutrition and Carolina Population Center, University of North Carolina at Chapel Hill. (unpublished manuscript)

Monteiro, C.A. , D'A Benicio, M.H., Conde, W.L. & Popkin, B.M. 2000. Shifting obesity trends in Brazil. *Eur. J. Clin. Nutr.*, 54(4): 342-6.

Monteiro, C.A. ,Wolney, L.C. & Popkin, B.M. 2002. Is obesity replacing or adding to undernutrition? Evidence from different social classes in Brazil. *Public Health Nutr.*, 5(1A): 105-12.

Neuhouser, M.L., Kristal, A.R. & Patterson, R.E. 1999. Use of food nutrition labels is associated with lower fat intake. *J. Am. Diet. Assoc.*, 99(1): 45-53.

Pomerleau, J., Lock, K. & McKee, M. 2003. Discrepancies between ecological and individual data on fruit and vegetable consumption in fifteen countries. *Br. J. Nutr.*, 89(6): 827-34.

Popkin, B.M. 2003. The nutrition transition in the developing world. *Dev. Policy. Rev.* (in press)

Popkin, B.M. & Du, S. 2003. Dynamics of the nutrition transition and their implications for the animal foods sector: a worried perspective. *J. Nutr.* (in press)

Popkin, B.M., Lu, B. & Zhai, F. 2003. Understanding the nutrition transition: measuring rapid dietary changes in transitional countries. *Public Health Nutr.* (in press)

Reardon, T., Timmer, C.P. & Berdegue, J.A. 2003. The rise of supermarkets in Latin America and Asia: implications for international markets for fruits and vegetables. *In* A. Regmi & M. Gehlhar, eds. *Global markets for high value food products.* Agricultural Information Bulletin, US Department of Agriculture Economic Research Service. Washington, DC, USDA.

Rolls, B.J. 2000. The role of energy density in the overconsumption of fat. *J. Nutr.*, 130(2S Suppl): 268S-271S.

Rosenthal, E. 2002. Beijing Journal; Buicks, Starbucks and fried chicken. Still China? *The New York Times*, 25 February.

Tian, H.G., Guo, Z.Y., Hu, G., Yu, S.J., Sun, W., Pietinen, P. & Nissinen, A. 1995b. Changes in sodium intake and blood pressure in a community-based intervention project in China. *J. Hum. Hypertens.*, 9(12): 959-68.

Tian, H.G., Nan, Y., Liang, X.Q., Yang, X.L., Shao, R.C., Pietinen, P. & Nissinen, A. 1995a. Relationship between serum lipids and dietary and non-dietary factors in a Chinese population. *Eur. J. Clin. Nutr.,* 49(12): 871-82.

United Nations Population Division. 2002. *World urbanization prospects: the 2001 revision* (www.un.org/esa/population/publications/wup2001/WUP2001Annextab.pdf). Accessed 19 July 2003.

Wang, Y., Monteiro, C. & Popkin, B.M. 2002. Trends of obesity and underweight in older children and adolescents in the United States, Brazil, China and Russia. *Am. J. Clin. Nutr.*, 75(6): 971-7.

World Bank. 2001. *World Development Indicators 2001*. Washington, DC. 396 pp.

Zhai, F., Fu, D., Du, S., Ge, K., Chen, C. & Popkin, B.M. 2002. What is China doing in policy-making to push back the negative aspects of the nutrition transition? *Public Health Nutr.*, 5(1A): 269-273.

Zhao, L., Zhai, F., Li, D. & Li, Y. 2001. A survey on the effects of the dietary guideline nutrition education project (English abstract). *Wei Sheng Yan Jiu*, 30(3): 176-9.

Annex

Overview of the China Health and Nutrition Survey urbanization index

Component	Variables used to generate the component score
Population size	Population
Population density	Population, area
Housing-related infrastructure	Sewer lines, water lines, electric lines and natural gas available in community
Transportation infrastructure	Road type of high quality (dirt, gravel, paved); distance to bus stop and distance to train station short (maximum if ≤1km)
Health facilities	Highest quality of service available in community or neighbouring area (university hospital, private hospital, city hospital, neighbourhood clinic, work unit clinic, village clinic)
Education facilities	Variety of educational facilities available in community or neighbouring area (preschool, primary school, middle school, upper school, vocational school)
Market availability	Free market stores selling variety of goods located within community, weighted based on number of days per week that stores are open
Communication infrastructure	Television station, radio station, cinema, newspaper, telephone network, postal service, fax service available in community
Economic indices	Average male wages above median; large percentage working outside agriculture; large percentage employed in community
Sanitation	Water plant available; community environment sanitary (excreta absent)

Globalization, urbanization and nutrition transition in a developing island country: a case study in Fiji

Jimaima Tunidau Schultz[1]*

INTRODUCTION

Definitions of globalization vary considerably, with the term often meaning whatever its user wants it to mean. Contrary to some claims, there is no widely accepted conceptual or operational definition, although it is possible to identify at least four, often overlapping approaches (Reich, 1998).[2] Given this diversity, it is hardly surprising that its outcomes are hotly disputed, even among those who adopt a similar approach.

From a Pacific island (developing world) perspective, globalization equates with development, and development implies change in at least three areas: economics and trade (from subsistence-and-barter to monetized economy); technological (from traditional/manual-mechanical to modern/electronic); and sociocultural (from traditional knowledge, beliefs and values to new knowledge, beliefs and values). Although development and change might benefit a community, or at least some of its members, this is not an automatic or uniform outcome. As this paper outlines, development, change and globalization have been far from even or beneficial for those in Fiji or in the wider Pacific. Globalization carries with it many human and social implications often ignored by those whose thinking appears to be dominated by economic models, trade flows and visions of a new economic order.

---

[1] Lifestyle Health Adviser
Secretariat of the Pacific Community (SPC)
Noumea
New Caledonia
E-mail: jimaimas@spc.int

* The author wishes to acknowledge the collaboration of R.F Schultz and P. Vatucawaqa in the preparation of this paper.

[2] Approaches to globalization include the following (Reich, 1998), with some blurring of boundaries.

  i)   As a contemporary historical period that began around the end of the Cold War when political/ideological alliances in place since the end of the Second World War began to change.

  ii) As an economic phenomenon that includes deregulated markets; privatization of assets; a retreat of the state from its social responsibilities; cross-national distribution of products; diffusion of technology; and integrated capital markets.

  iii) As an essentially sociopolitical phenomenon, with globalization typified by a blending of values around the principles of capitalism and democracy with an American emphasis, i.e. American hegemony. "Globalization is the latest label for capitalism, colonialism and imperialism expansions combined" (Finau, Wainiqolo and Cuboni, 2002:13).

  iv) As a technologically driven social revolution involving a shift from industrial capitalism to a post-industrial concept of economic relations leading to the emergence of a "whole new economy". This group sees the world as a single, specialized but interdependent market and refers to globally integrated production; the privatization of state assets; and technological linkages across national borders

In this paper, Fiji will be presented as a case study. However, by way of introduction a few background observations will be made to place the Pacific region in context before referring more specifically to Fiji.

The 22 island nations of the Pacific cover an area about the size of Europe, Asia and North America. The total regional population is small, with approximately 7.6 million people divided into three main cultural groups: the largest is Melanesian (around 6.4 million), then Polynesian with approximately 0.62 million and the smallest, Micronesia, has a population of approximately half a million. In terms of countries, Papua New Guinea has the largest population, with 4.6 million persons. Tokelau has the smallest, with 1 500 inhabitants. Fiji's population of 0.82 million in 2003 falls in between (Pacific Regional Statistics, 2003).

Before the Second World War, each island nation was essentially self-sufficient and culturally self-contained, living in an ecologically balanced relationship with land and ocean. Anthropological evidence indicates that the Melanesian and Polynesian people in particular had good nutritional status, were physically impressive and lived in healthy, robust, communally oriented societies (Coyne, 2000). While this may sound like romanticizing the past, it is a true reflection of historical reports.

Since the 1950s, international actors have introduced the concept of development into the region. Effective subsistence-and-barter economies have been gradually, sometimes abruptly, replaced by monetized economies dependent on cash crops, world markets and gyrating commodity prices. With this have come new wants rather than needs, new lifestyles, the notion of unemployment and the invention of poverty. At least three iniquities are experienced: (i) the concept of "development dependency"; (ii) inequitable distributions of wealth; and (iii) various forms of deficiency and deprivation. The people and governments of the region have had to battle with a particular view of the world that others wish to create.

"There is a sense in which rapid economic progress is impossible without painful adjustments. Ancient philosophies have to be scrapped; old social institutions have to disintegrate; bonds of cast, creed and race have to burst; and large numbers of persons who cannot keep up with progress have to have their expectations of a comfortable life frustrated. Very few communities are willing to pay the full price of economic progress."

Measures for the Economic Development of Underdeveloped Countries. New York, Department of Economic and Social Affairs, United Nations, 1951. *In* Escobar, 1995: 3.

What has been ignored by some is that traditional societies had developed ways of defining and treating human, rather than corporate needs. These were, and to some extent still are, based on visions of community and sufficiency. Furthermore, they were effective. Unemployment, poverty and other forms of deprivation and lifestyle diseases were not an issue. These are the gifts of development.

Communities do not live or function in a social vacuum. Our cultures contain important value differences that reflect substantial differences in priorities and preferences. Yet much discourse on economic development, trade and technological change ignores this basic reality.

TRENDS AND CHANGES
Demographic profiles
Fiji's population (approximately 820 000 in 2003), consists of two very different ethnic groups: indigenous Fijians (51 percent of the total) and Indians (44 percent) who were transported to Fiji

by a colonial government between the 1880s and 1926 to work in the sugar industry. A third category, a mixture of Rotumans, represents the remaining 5 percent (Fiji Bureau of Statistics [FBS], 2003).

Three demographic pyramids are shown. Figure 1 shows the total population, Figure 2 indigenous Fijians and Figure 3 Indians. Figures 2 and 3 indicate important differences between the two ethnic communities. The Indian profile shows: (i) a drop in fertility over the past decade; and (ii) minimum to no-growth in people of 25-44 years old consistent with considerable emigration. These characteristics are also consistent with the social and political uncertainties faced by the Indian community following the military coups of 1987 (see Broad economic patterns on p. 211).

FIGURE 1
Population pyramid for total population, 1996

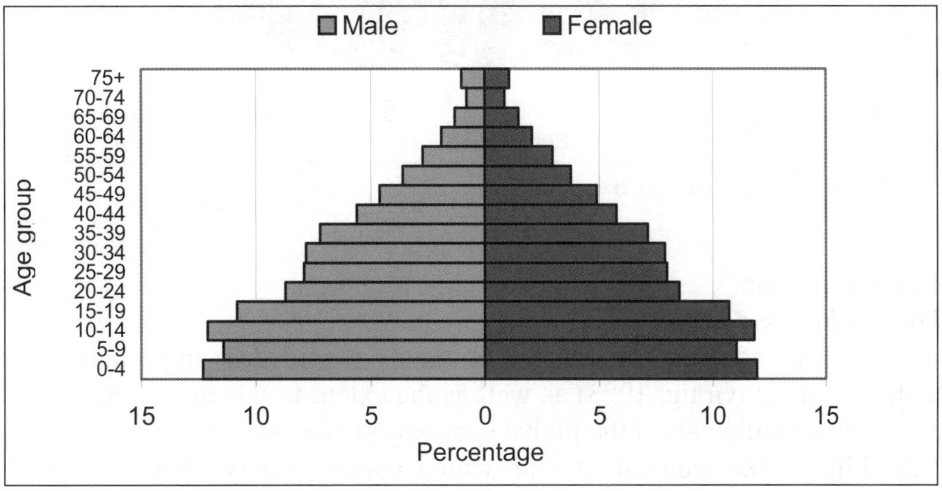

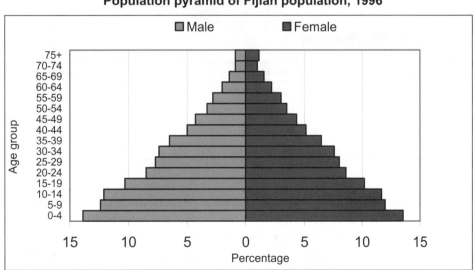

Source: 1996 Population and Housing Census.

FIGURE 2
Population pyramid of Fijian population, 1996

Source: 1996 Population and Housing Census.

FIGURE 3
Population pyramid of Indian population, 1996

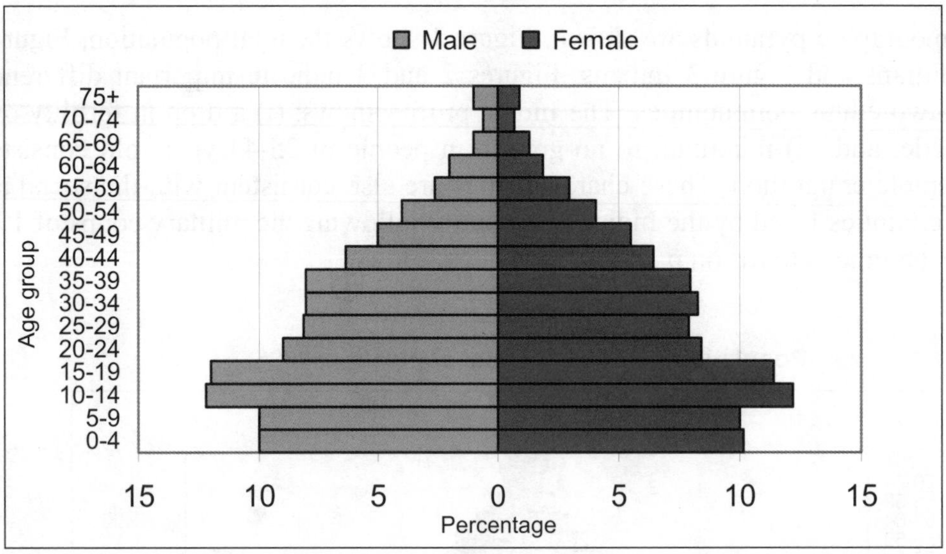

Source: 1996 Population and Housing Census.

Trends in urbanization
Population mobility and urbanization
Population mobility and urbanization are commonly regarded as important indicators of economic development (Graig, 1993) as well as the extent to which a country has become monetized and potentially part of the global economy (Chandra, 1990).

By 1996, Fiji's urban population represented approximately 46 percent of the total population (Table 1). This suggests a relatively urbanized community when compared to similar developing countries. United Nations statistics indicated that similar countries possessed an average urbanization level of around 34 percent into the mid-1990s.

TABLE 1
Urbanization rates for Fiji, 1966-1986

Year	Urban population	% of total population	Urbanization rate
1966	159 259	33.4	2.8
1976	218 495	37.2	3.9
1986	277 025	38.7	1.5
1996	359 495	46.4	(not provided)

Source: FBS, 1989; FBS ,1998.

Fiji's urban population is unevenly distributed across its three main islands (Viti Levu, Vanua Levu and Taveuni) and 300 smaller islands. By the mid-1990s, the main island of Viti Levu accounted for a little over 90 percent of Fiji's total urban population which, in turn, accounted for around 45 percent of that island's total population. Of Viti Levu's urban population, almost all (93 percent) lived in five urban areas: the greater Suva area (158 000), Nausori (14 000), Lautoka (39 000), Nadi (15 200) and Ba (10 300) (FBS, 1998). This uneven distribution converts to population densities of between 67 and 90 persons/km^2 for the Central Division (containing the greater Suva area), to only seven per km^2 in the smaller scattered islands of the Eastern Division (FBS, 1998).

Reasons for a disproportionate and growing urban population in the greater Suva area are attributed to three main factors: (i) search for paid employment and a cash income – the "push" of rural poverty combined with the "pull" of urban employment; (ii) education for children and young adults; and (iii) curiosity mixed with the lure of town/city excitement. However, since the early 1980s, at least three factors have combined to stall economic development and create a decline in urban employment. These factors are: (i) difficult trading conditions and falling commodity prices as a consequence of globalization; (ii) drought followed by cyclones; and (iii) inappropriate advice from the International Monetary Fund (IMF) pushing a globalization agenda (Lal, 1992; Robertson and Tamanisau, 1988).

Two problems of urbanization

Urbanization and urban drift associated with economic development have created at least two different sets of problems.

One relates to the provision of housing, infrastructure and other services to accommodate a rapidly growing urban population. These costly developments, constrained by budgetary considerations, place government and other agencies under unrealistic pressure to perform and deliver.

The other lies in the need to provide employment for new and old urban dwellers, many of whom possess few marketable skills. First-generation indigenous Fijian urban dwellers in particular usually leave behind a village-level subsistence-and-barter existence: their challenge is to learn new survival skills in a competitive, cash-based economy where the lifestyle is different, few paid jobs are available and urban poverty and survival become a new reality.

Commonly regarded as indicators of development (e.g. Millennium Development Goal indicators), infrastructure, services and amenities are considered next.

A possible third problem is the creation of a sustainable food supply for the urbanized communities.

Indices of development and change

Amenities and services: indicators of development

Standard indices indicate that Fiji has a relatively high level of human development with a Human Development Index (HDI) rating of 0.754 (UNDP, 2003).

Adult literacy in English is 93 percent for Fijians, and around 85 percent for Indians, while approximately 98 percent of children between six and 14 years of age attend school (Department of Information, 1998).

Fiji recently undertook a Household Income and Expenditure Survey (HIES), the results of which were published in 2002. Relevant data from this survey are indicated together with Bureau of Statistics census data (for the whole of Fiji), to permit comparison (Table 2).

TABLE 2
Comparison of HIES 2002 and the 1996 census

Amenity	Urban		All Fiji	
	HIES	% of total	Census 1996	% of total
House (with concrete outer wall) – more permanent	40 903	48.9	33 614	49.7
Safe water	80 412	96.1	62 845	92.9
Electricity	75 647	90.5	58 957	87.1
Television	64 212	76.8	46 698	69.0
Telephone	48 969	58.6	31 500	46.5
Use of car	21 815	26.0	17 349	25.6

Source: FBS, 2003.

Perhaps not surprisingly, Table 2 indicates that urban households generally possess a higher percentage of basic amenities with the largest urban/rural differences in urban access to television and a telephone. Approximately 60 percent of Fiji's population have direct access to commercially generated electricity and of this, around 40 percent is generated from local resources (e.g. hydropower), and 60 percent using imported fuel (Department of Information, 1998).

Transport
Air. Fiji has a large international airport (Nadi), a secondary international airport close to Suva, a successful profit-making international airline (Air Pacific), and smaller privately owned domestic air carriers servicing numerous smaller airstrips in regional centres and outer islands. Nadi International Airport is the biggest and most developed international airport in the Pacific Region. It is regarded as the Pacific gateway to the rest of the world.

Sea. As a maritime country, shipping and other maritime services are well established, with an inter-island shipping fleet, roll-on roll-off ferries, private fishing fleets, wharves, container terminals and a quarantine and customs service in major coastal centres. Although services exist, inter-island shipping is still problematic and often infrequent.

Roads. The three large islands have a good to adequate system of major roads and bridges linked by a network of sealed and unsealed secondary roads. Overall, approximately 20 percent are tar-sealed while on Viti Levu, the figure is almost 80 percent (Department of Information, 1998). These are serviced by a system of privately owned bus lines and taxis that provide a relatively inexpensive form of transport.

Vehicle registrations. In 2001, 2 207 new private vehicles were registered; in 2002 this increased to 3 580, an increase of just over 60 percent. The number of registered new buses was 25 in 2001 and 40 in 2002 (a 60 percent increase). Newly registered taxis, rental and hired cars were 213 in 2001 and 323 in 2003 (a 52 percent increase) (FBS, 2003). Motorcycles are relatively rare. Total vehicle numbers for the country could not be ascertained making a per capita calculation unavailable.

The combination of an effective public transport system (buses and taxis), and increasing numbers of privately owned vehicles, suggest an overall decrease in walking activity. This provides a very crude societal indicator of decreasing physical activity among the adult population.

Technology diffusion

Fiji is serviced by an effective international (Worldwide Direct Dialling) and national telecommunications system including mobile phones (owned by approximately one in eight persons) and a small number of Internet cafés (The Review, 2003).

No statistics for computers were available, although most businesses and many private homes in urban areas possess their own computers.

Television transmission covers most of the main islands using English, with limited coverage in Fijian and Hindi. Two satellite receiver dishes permit international retransmission of programmes; a pay television service (Sky Fiji) is also available.

Broad economic patterns

The main feature of Fiji's economic structure is a dependency on primary industry, which is easily upset by weather conditions and fluctuations in international prices.

Economic development in Fiji since 1970 might be described in terms of four to five identifiable cycles: (i) growth between 1970 and 1979/80; (ii) slowdown and recession between 1980/81 and 1991/92; (iii) growth between 1992 and 1998/99; (iv) slowdown and regression from 1999 to 2002; and (v) recovery and limited growth in 2003.

It is notable that both periods of major economic stagnation and recession (ii and iv above), were followed by an increase in severe political instability (military coups in 1987 and an attempted coup in 2000). Once set in motion, these politically destabilizing events further damaged an already weakened economy, causing additional widespread economic hardship.

The economic and political antecedents to the 1987 coups have been well documented, with causes commonly attributed to four main factors: (i) an economic recession attributed to falling commodity prices linked to globalization; (ii) government implementation of "structural adjustments" and a wage freeze advocated by international organizations such as the World Bank and International Monetary Fund according to a globalization agenda; (iii) social disruption and cultural degradation as a consequence of economic development and modernization; and (iv) local political opportunism (Schultz, 2003). There are currently signs of a tentative economic recovery; however, the political situation remains fragile.

Between 1997 and 2001, Fiji had an annual trade deficit from F$500 to F$600 million with food imports representing either the third or fourth largest import (after manufactured goods and machinery and transport equipment), approximately equal to imported mineral fuel. In 2002, the annual gross domestic product (GDP) per head of the population was F$4 222 (approximately US$2 250) (FTIB, 2003).

ROLE OF DEVELOPMENT AND URBANIZATION ON FOOD SUPPLY

In Fiji, notions of development have been strongly influenced by advice tendered by the World Bank and International Monetary Fund, based on principles of economic globalization (Finau, Wainiqolo and Cuboni, 2002). In this setting, economic development has changed not only the Fijian economy, but the distribution and nature of the population from a rural subsistence-and-barter community to an urban wage-dependent monetized one. Fiji now has an agricultural economy based on one main cash crop – sugar, currently under threat – and a few abandoned, unsuccessful cash crops (bananas, cocoa and coffee), ginger and kava (*yaqona*) with a doubtful future, and highly vulnerable non-food manufactures (garments, textiles, footware and some woodchips). There is limited food processing that includes wheat and rice milling, and processing of milk, meat and ginger.

Increasing urbanization has generated the need for a reliable food supply for the urban population. To some extent, nearby rural areas have benefited by moving into vegetable, milk and meat production. However, once self-sufficient in food, Fiji has become increasingly reliant on imported processed foods. Distribution has been a growth industry with many small corner stores plus a rapid increase in larger shops and supermarkets. Fiji now has six identifiable foodstore chains and approximately 70 supermarkets (Chaudhari, 2003).

Knowledge of the food supply chain/system contributes to a better understanding of a nation's food security system. An analysis of the urban food supply system in Fiji identified the food marketing channels (Baxter, 1980). Figure 4 illustrates the flow of commodities from the point of production to the final consumer. It will be noted from the figure that both local and imported foods make up Fiji's food supply system. However, an important growing industry in Fiji, the food manufacturing sector, has not been included. Raw ingredients are imported and processed in the country. They include cereals and meat. The processed products are on the supermarket shelves and in small stores throughout the country.

The distribution pattern illustrated in Figure 4, plus cost, determines the choice available to families. In general terms, the more complex the distribution chain, the greater the cost to consumers, even though the food might be locally produced (Schultz, 1997).

FIGURE 4
Produce marketing channels

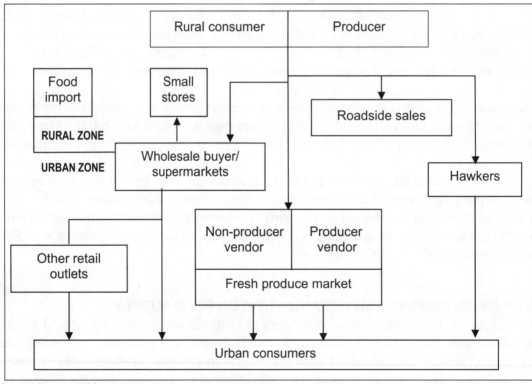

Source: Baxter, 1980.

Baxter (1980) identified a number of factors contributing to a reliance on a cash-based food supply chain in Fiji. These include the following.

• Families cut off from traditional lands and unable to grow their own food. They become totally reliant on cash (or limited credit) to buy food.

- As urban centres spread, more land is required for housing and industrial purposes with less available for planting food. Home food gardens become fewer.
- Despite a reasonable transport system, traditional family/clan food support is no longer available.

As a consequence, the cheaper imported foods become a major source of food supply with nutritional quality usually compromised by cost. An example is fish – fresh fish is more expensive than tinned fish, so tinned fish is consumed. Tinned corned beef may also be perceived to be cheaper than most fresh meat, so tinned meat is eaten (Schultz, 1997).

Dietary change
Predevelopment
Prior to development, in order to survive, communities were self-sufficient and food secure via subsistence and barter. In times of plenty, food was shared and excess food was preserved using traditional methods. The communal and mutual care philosophy of Fijian society meant that no one went hungry.

The traditional diet consisted of food from both land and sea, usually consumed twice a day: morning and evening. Meals were simple, balanced and nutritious, consisting of starchy root crops as the main energy source; fish, crabs and shellfish as protein; and local green leafy vegetables as an accompaniment. Coconut used in cooking was the main source of fat. Meat was eaten only occasionally (pork, chicken and turtle), usually at special feasts. Fruit and grilled starchy roots were eaten while gardening. Leftover starchy foods from a previous meal were eaten when out fishing. The main drink was green coconut juice.

Post-development
Development brought many dietary changes, including eating patterns and types of food. The number of times food was consumed during a day increased, and the nature of the food changed from unprocessed to refined and processed. Indians brought their own eating patterns based on cereals and lentils. An impact of development on diet is that more variety became available.

During the early period of urbanization, food supply to urban areas was generally insufficient and of limited variety. Food importation began to service the ever more numerous colonial expatriate population in the country. This marked the beginning of an increasing dependency on overseas food sources. Fiji changed from being self-sufficient to relying more and more on imported food such as rice, tinned meat and fish, wheat flour, mutton, beef, pork, sweet biscuits and sugary drinks. For the Fijian urban population, cost, availability and convenience are increasingly becoming important determinants of eating patterns (ACIAR, 2002). From an economic perspective, food imports also impacted on the national balance of payments and foreign exchange reserves.

Eating patterns have changed more among indigenous Fijians than Indians (ACIAR, 2002). On a day-to-day basis, urban Fijians have shifted from the more traditional but expensive taro (*dalo*), to cheaper cassava and bread, followed (in order of importance) by rice and wheat flour biscuits. Intake of breadfruit and plantains remains about the same. Intake of animal protein (red meat, both fresh and tinned) has increased substantially compared to fish. Food choice for Fijians is determined mainly by value for money followed by ease of preparation. For Indians, value for money and personal preference were the two major determinants of choice (ACIAR, 2002).

Role of imported and traditional foods

Both local and imported foods play important roles in the diet of the Fijian population as previously illustrated in Figure 4. For example, urban dwellers typically purchase fresh food from fresh produce markets, roadside sales, hawkers or supermarkets; a low-income subgroup still attempts to maintain home-grown food, generally starchy local food (cassava), grown on vacant land wherever it can be found (Saito, 1995). Cultural food patterns remain strong especially at festival and feast times (Schultz, 1997).

Imported food

Figure 5 shows the comparative percentages of major food groups imported in 1985 and 1992 to 1996. As can be seen, all pulses were imported, followed by vegetable oil and fat, cereals (80 percent or more imported), and vegetables, meat, milk and animal fat (from 60 to 80 percent imported).

FIGURE 5
Percentage of food imported by food group

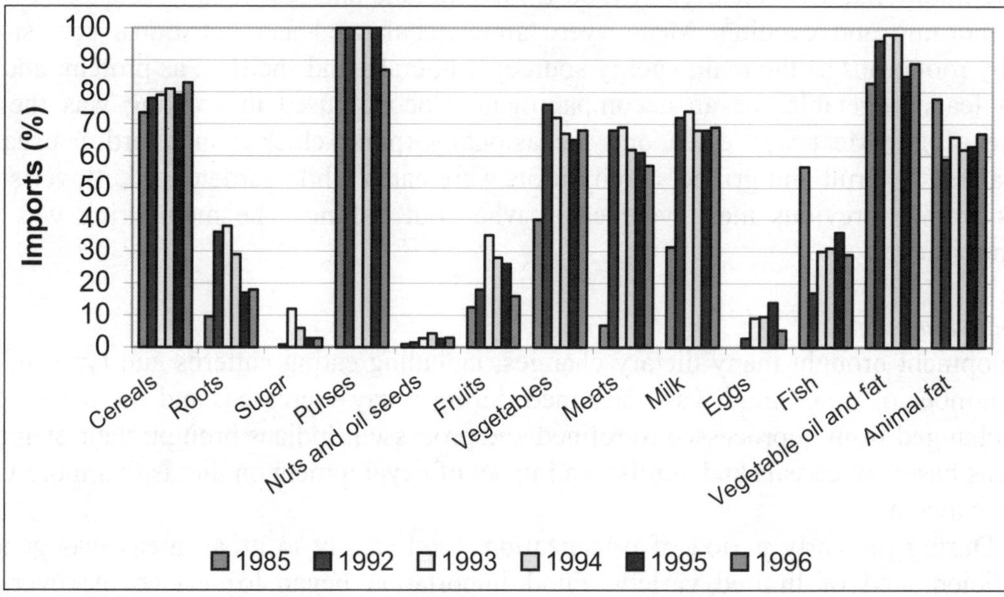

Source: National Food and Nutrition Centre, 2003a.

A different breakdown shows the percentages of energy supply on a per capita basis derived from imports as well as from locally grown food (Figure 6). These data indicate a consistent pattern of just over half the total dietary energy being supplied by imported food between 1992 and 1996.

FIGURE 6
Percentages of energy supply (per capita/day) derived from imports and from locally available foods, 1985-1996

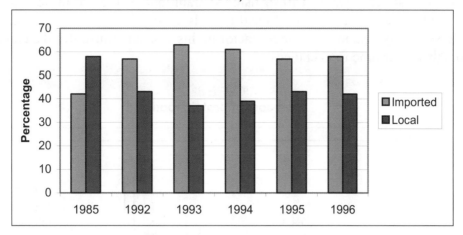

Source: National Food and Nutrition Centre, 2003a.

Figure 7 shows the availability of kcals from four major energy food groups – rice, flour, cassava and taro – in 1985 and 1992-1995. The figure clearly shows that cereal has become a major energy food. It has replaced the traditional starchy root taro (*dalo*). Cassava appears to be more important than taro. Although taro is a "status" and more nutritious food, its relatively high cost has made it less accessible to the economically poor families in urban areas.

FIGURE 7
Sources of kcals from cereals and root crops, 1985-1995

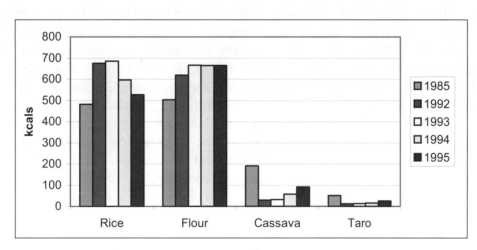

Source: National Food and Nutrition Centre, 2003a.

Although not included in Figure 7, the case of noodles is interesting. In the 1982 national survey, they did not appear as a food item but ten years later (1992), they appeared in the top 12 of the common energy foods eaten in both urban and rural areas, especially among Fijians (Saito, 1995). Generally speaking, commercially processed food has become an indispensable part of Fiji's diet and, overall, there has been a marked increase in the consumption of animal food products, animal fat and vegetable oil: a change more evident in urban areas (Saito, 1995; ACIAR, 2002). A reported increase in cereal intake (e.g. rice) as an energy source has been attributed to its lower cost.

In general terms, cost affects food choice among urban populations. Figure 8 indicates a gradual increase in the unit cost of protein foods over the years (1986-2001). Tinned fish and lamb chops are cheaper than fresh fish, the traditional source of protein in the Fijian diet. Although a popular food item, tinned meat is clearly the most expensive. However, taste preference may be a much stronger factor in this case and illustrates the complexity of the factors that determine food choices.

FIGURE 8
Unit cost of protein food

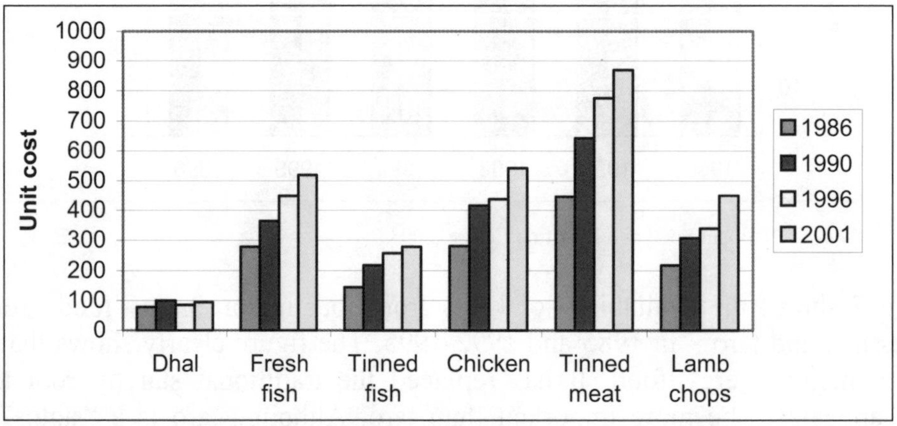

Source: National Food and Nutrition Centre, 2003a.

Emerging new food outlets and food hygiene concerns

Supermarkets are the most striking feature of the urban food supply system. The growth in this industry has been remarkable over the last 15 years. As stated previously, Fiji now has six relatively large supermarket stores with approximately 70 chains operating in urban centres. Supermarkets carry both local and imported processed foods with limited amounts of local fresh foods. The major urban areas have also seen a proliferation of small fast food services, restaurants, street vendors, street barbecues and home-based caterers. Large global fast food providers such as McDonald's, Kentucky Fried Chicken and various pizza chains have appeared during the past decade. Although legislation relating to food and hygiene standards as well as food labelling is in place to protect the consumer, government monitoring and enforcement are inconsistent. The food hygiene standards of the larger commercial chains appear to be better than in local food outlets, but the nutritional status of their products has been the subject of considerable debate. Evidence linking overconsumption of these and similar fast foods to obesity in Fiji remains problematic

Food security

Fiji's increasing reliance on substantial quantities of imported food leaves the country open to outside political and economic pressures. Figures 5 and 6 illustrate Fiji's vulnerability, especially in circumstances where food is increasingly being used as a political weapon by larger developed countries to coerce susceptible countries such as Fiji. During the coups of 1987 and the failed coup in 2000, Fiji's trade partners applied food sanctions in an attempt to punish the insurgents. Unfortunately, such sanctions represent a blunt instrument, with innocent women and children the first to suffer when this strategy is adopted.

Given that Fiji often suffers from cyclones that can devastate local food production, imported food (processed or fresh) is unavoidable if enough food is to be available for the population. The question that needs to be addressed is the level of reliance on imported food to complement the local supply.

National data show that Fiji has more kcals available per capita/day compared to FAO's stated nutrient requirement (National Food and Nutrition Centre, 2003b). Unfortunately, these figures hide the real picture – that of uneven distribution of food within all sectors of the population. Based on the definition of food security, Fiji is not food secure, in the author's view.

IMPACT OF GLOBALIZATION ON LIFESTYLE[3] IN URBAN AREAS

A number of societal characteristics have been attributed to globalization and economic development in Fiji and the Pacific Region. These include changed values involving an encouragement of nuclear rather than extended family households, individualism rather than communalism, the accumulation of wealth rather than sharing, and employment by others instead of self-sufficiency (Finau, Wainiqolo and Cuboni, 2002). These characteristics are contrary to indigenous cultural values and are perceived to assist in undermining them.

The global marketing of products and lifestyles via television in small island countries such as Fiji has become common. Subtle as well as aggressive advertising by transnational tobacco and alcohol companies, in particular, both in print and electronically, appears to be aimed at younger receptive age groups. Generally, such advertising portrays lifestyles that are economically unachievable in local circumstances, generating expectations and a sense of envy and frustration that are socially disruptive for individuals and groups. Between 1997 and 2001 the value of imported alcoholic beverages and tobacco increased by 19 percent (Fiji Bureau of Statistics, 2002a).

While it is difficult to gain a clear picture of alcohol and tobacco consumption over time because of few systematically collected data, available information indicates a prevalence rate for smoking of 46 percent in 1992. It also appears that smoking increased by about 24 percent between 1980 and 1994 (Khaleghian, 2003). An increase in import figures for alcohol and tobacco as indicated above, suggests a growing market.

Data from the Global Youth Tobacco Survey conducted in Fijian schools (1 629 students aged 13 to 15 years) showed that one in five students had smoked their first cigarette before their tenth birthday. One in ten was a current smoker at the time of the survey. More than half the current smokers have fathers who smoke (UNICEF and WHO, 1999). The same survey also found that 40 percent of students had started drinking before the age of ten. About 62 percent of students reported binge drinking. The survey also found that some students were using marijuana, with 7 percent admitting to current use.

Kava (*Piper methysticum*) was consumed by five years of age, and 24 percent of students were drinking it regularly. Of concern is the practice of "wash-down" where, after a kava session, the drink changes to alcohol. Youth drink home brews if they cannot afford to buy alcohol. Anecdotal information indicates that in some instances, young people turn to glue- or petrol-sniffing and marijuana to keep them "high". In order to pay for their habits, youth resort to robbery and other crimes as a way of obtaining money. Increasing unemployment is likely to exacerbate both substance abuse and crime in urban areas.

An issue of concern in Fiji is that overseas litigation against the large transnational tobacco and alcohol companies is causing these companies to cast around for easier

---

[3]   Lifestyle refers to wide-ranging behaviours including work patterns, dietary patterns, physical activity, smoking and alcohol consumption. Lifestyle changes are often more pronounced in urban situations where modernization is the norm.

markets. In this respect, and despite smaller populations, the Pacific Region appears to be attracting renewed attention.

A survey of physical activity levels in urban Fiji reported that 58 percent of the population was engaged in sedentary work (clerical activities in the public service, industry and business) (Fiji Bureau of Statistics, 2002b). Also, more people in urban areas (61.4 percent) reported being engaged in "light physical work" compared to those in rural areas (38.8 percent) (Saito, 1995). These results may be directly linked to the differences in lifestyles between urban and rural areas. Urban centres have easy access to a cheaper transport system, television and so on that discourage physical activity.

New forms of entertainment such as nightclubs and bars where licences are often justified on the grounds that they are fulfilling the needs of international tourists, also attract young local people whose liking for these venues tends to lead to family conflict and disputes.

Generally speaking, the influence of globalization is not limited to product promotion *per se*. It also focuses on lifestyle change as a more comprehensive and effective marketing strategy. In this respect, its influence is more subtle and insidious, providing a marketing climate that shows little concern about the negative social implications of cultural degradation (de Vries, 1996), an important issue in this part of the world (Baker, Hanna and Baker, 1986; Finau, Wainiqolo and Cuboni, 2002; Schultz, 2003).

The changing role of women

Increasing numbers of urban women have taken on additional wage-earning responsibilities outside the home to help make ends meet. At the same time they have maintained their traditional role as mother, nurturer and housekeeper. This additional workload has had little to do with self-fulfilment and more to do with economic necessity to ensure family survival in an urban setting.

Women constitute 35.5 percent of the economically active population, and 64 percent of them are engaged in the money economy. Women also make up the largest percentage of those engaged in subsistence activity without a cash income (67.3 percent) (FBS, 2002b). Unemployment rates are highest in urban and peri-urban areas and concern mainly indigenous Fijians.

Women account for a significant percentage of workers in manufacturing (38.1 percent), services (37.6 percent), finance (36.3 percent) and the wholesale and retail trade (36.1 percent) (FBS, 2003). Women in the workforce with young infants often breastfeed for a shorter duration (Saito, 1995) and breastmilk is substituted with infant formula, placing an additional economic burden on the family or the mother.

In urban areas where there is limited support from the extended family, wage-earning women are left with little choice but to hire a child minder or house girl for child care. This has far-reaching consequences because house girls are generally young with little understanding of the relationship between proper child care (food and socialization) and child development. Not only does child care absorb precious income, but it generally provides inadequate care for the child (Schultz, 1997).

MALNUTRITION

Despite Fiji's comparatively high level of development, malnutrition and micronutrient deficiencies are still prevalent in some sectors of the community, with young children and women the most vulnerable.

Birth of underweight infants (below 2 500 g) affects 21 percent of Indian infants and 4 percent of Fijian babies (Saito, 1995). Although most Fijian children are born with above average weight, their growth slows after three to five months. Hospital records indicate that this relates especially to Protein Energy Malnutrition (PEM), with Fijian babies under three years of age forming the largest group (Saito, 1995). The most common reasons are poverty and inappropriate weaning foods.

Underweight remains a problem for Indian children aged five to nine years (32 percent compared to 4 percent of Fijians of the same age group). Although there has been some improvement in the rate of underweight children since the 1993 National Nutrition Survey, the problem remains high among Indian children (Saito, 1995).

Although breastfeeding initiation is high (92 percent), after three months it declines to below 50 percent for Fijian mothers and approximately 10 percent among Indian women (Saito, 1995). Use of infant formula is strongly encouraged by the multinational manufacturers who provide free samples to hospitals and health clinics. Use of infant formula is associated with two main problems in Fiji: poor hygiene and excessive dilution of the formula to save money (Schultz, 1997). Both practices can result in diarrhoeal disease which contributes to malnutrition. This creates a vicious cycle between malnutrition and diarrhoea and is more of a problem in urban areas because of the shorter duration of breastfeeding.

The prevalence of anaemia in both children and women is high. Forty percent of children under five years and 32 percent of adult Fijian and Indian women are anaemic. Anaemia is typically linked to two outcomes: in Indian women it contributes to low birth weight and results in low energy levels and low productivity in the workplace (Saito, 1995). Anaemia is more prevalent in low-income groups and is attributed to low consumption of iron-rich foods (inadequate iron-rich vegetable sources among Indian women in particular) (Schultz, 1997). Other contributing factors are worm infestation and defaulting antenatal and postnatal care generally linked to poverty.

The National Nutrition Survey carried out in 1993 found that 56 percent of Fiji's adult population (18 years and over) were malnourished (under- and overnutrition) (Saito, 1995). Using body mass index (BMI) as an indicator, 44 percent were within the healthy weight range, 32.7 percent were identified as overweight or obese and 23.3 percent as underweight. More men than women were within the healthy weight range (51.5 and 38.4 percent, respectively). By contrast, more women than men were classified as either overweight or obese (41 and 24 percent, respectively) and more Fijians (37.8 percent) than Indians (26 percent) were in these categories. The survey also found a higher proportion of overweight and obesity in urban areas (34 percent) than in rural areas (23 percent), and the proportion of overweight and obese was significantly higher among those adults who were engaged in light or sedentary activity than those who had high levels of physical activity. Underweight was found mostly among Indian men (30 percent) and women (26 percent) compared with Fijians (19 percent men and 15 percent women).

TRENDS IN HEALTH STATUS IN THE URBAN ENVIRONMENT

It is argued that globalization has created a double health burden for developing small island countries such as Fiji. On the one hand, many communicable diseases commonly associated with poverty are still prevalent, including diarrhoea, respiratory infections and mosquito-borne and parasitic diseases. At the same time, newer non-communicable diseases (NCDs) and lifestyle-related diseases closely linked to economic development and modernization are on the increase because of changing lifestyle patterns, more availability of foods rich in fat, sugar and salt and more consumption of tobacco and alcohol. In urban areas, in particular, increased prevalence rates for circulatory disorders (coronary artery diseases, strokes and diabetes) have been attributed to changing lifestyle patterns. Cervical and breast cancers are also more common.

The percentage of deaths in Fiji through heart disease increased from 18 percent in 1960 to 38 percent in 1987 to 1988. Cardiovascular disease has been the leading cause of death in the country for the last decade (between 45 to 50 percent of all deaths) (Khaleghian, 2003; Coyne, 2000). The high prevalence of cardiovascular disease risk factors such as smoking, obesity, diabetes and hypertension in urban areas is of concern.

In 1980, a clinical survey reported that the rates of diabetes among Fijians living in urban areas had increased tenfold to 6.6 percent (Coyne, 2000). The 1993 National Nutrition Survey found rates of self-reported diabetes were less than 1 percent of those under 44 years of age, but rose to 10 percent in those above 45 years (Saito, 1995). Indians had markedly higher rates of diabetes with 6.9 percent compared to 3.3 percent of Fijians. The mean BMI of those with diabetes (27 kg/m^2) was significantly higher than those without diabetes (24 kg/m^2). It is suggested that this self-reported survey might have underestimated the true prevalence rates, given that diabetes ranked as the third leading primary cause of hospital admission in 1994 (Coyne, 2000). In 1996 diabetes-related amputation was around ten per week.

Cancer ranks third as a cause of death in Fiji (Coyne, 2000). The three most common cancers in women are cervix, breast and ovary while in men the three most common are prostate, lung and liver. Cancer incidence tends to be higher in wealthier Pacific island countries (Khaleghian, 2003) and Fiji is one of the most developed. Risk factors for most cancers include smoking, alcohol and high-fat diets. Consumption of vegetables and fruit has been linked to cancer prevention. Consumption of these foods has been on the decline, particularly in urban areas.

Obesity is a risk factor for many other NCDs. It is a health problem in its own right as well as a risk factor for cardiovascular disease, diabetes and hypertension. Both longitudinal and cross-sectional studies of anthropometric changes clearly show that modernization and western-influenced lifestyles sustain patterns of significant weight gain in Pacific peoples (Baker, Hanna and Baker, 1986; Friedlaender, 1987). Available evidence indicates that the problem of obesity will not simply go away but will continue to increase in the Pacific as a consequence of changes in lifestyle and diet.

While Fiji represents a particular example, the general principles outlining the linkages between globalization and NCD epidemics have been described by Beaglehole and Yach (2003), who identified a nutritional transition towards diets with a high proportion of saturated fat and sugars which they attributed to global trade and marketing developments. This transition involves the replacement of a traditional diet rich in fruit and vegetables by a diet rich in calories provided by animal fats and low in complex carbohydrates. This diet, in combination with tobacco use and little physical activity, leads to population-wide atherosclerosis and the widespread distribution of NCDs.

One problem ignored or overlooked by supporters of globalization is the limited economic and human resource capacity in small island countries to implement strategies believed to be appropriate. By their nature, NCDs are chronic, long-term diseases and each patient is likely to require health services over many years. At the same time, national economies are suffering as a result of the increasing number of premature deaths of individuals in their prime productive years. According to Khaleghian (2003), the total estimated disease burden for low- to middle-income countries such as Fiji shows that NCDs as a whole account for 42.5 percent of all disability-adjusted life years (DALYs) lost in 1998 as compared to 40.4 percent for communicable diseases and 16 percent for injuries. The largest contribution to lost DALYs was the burden caused by cardiovascular diseases and cancer, responsible for 37.3 percent of all NCD-related DALYs lost in 1998 (Khaleghian, 2003).

The total cost of NCDs in 1998 for Fiji was estimated to be 1.5 percent of its GDP. Direct cost estimates for NCDs as a percentage of the total health budget for 1998 were just over 11 percent (Khaleghian, 2003). This means that for Fiji with its small economy, the economic cost of NCDs is enormous. Its health system is increasingly burdened by the high and long-term cost of diagnosis and treatment. Sending patients overseas for special treatment is an additional burden on the economy.

PROGRAMMES

From the perspective of a small Pacific island country, problems associated with globalization are perceived to lie beyond their power to influence. There is a perception of helplessness and impotence. This means that few programmes, if any, designed to address problems identified with globalization are funded.

One example from Fiji is that of the National Plan of Action for Nutrition. This plan was endorsed by parliament in 1998. However, more than five years later, no resources have been allocated to implement the plan. Clearly, it is not regarded as a national priority. Yet this was not the impression in 1998. Alternatively, it may be regarded as simply too difficult: a pointless exercise given the international forces perceived to be conspiring to undermine any such plan.

Expenditure on health in Fiji indicated that 72 percent of the budget was to be spent on curative measures, 2.6 percent allocated to prevention strategies and 24.6 percent spent on administration (Khaleghian, 2003). The percentage of health expenditure on preventive measures is indicative of the kind of budget allocated to nutrition promotion

Since 1980, the Ministry of Health has implemented a number of projects to prevent non-communicable and other nutritional deficiency diseases. A few examples are the following.

(i)　　A food garden project to address maternal and child health in the early 1980s.

(ii)　　Anti-tobacco legislation passed by parliament.

(iii)　　In 1999, parliament passed a bill banning the sale (and importation) of fatty meat called mutton flaps in Fiji.

(iv)　　In 1999 an Obesity Environmental Audit project was piloted in a peri-urban area of Suva.

(v)　　The Ministry of Health is currently working on legislation to fortify flour with iron to address the problem of anaemia.

(vi)　　Parliament passed in 2003 a Food Safety Bill which focuses on trade.

Two comments are relevant. First, unfortunately, with the exception of the food garden project, these undertakings have not been evaluated. Their effectiveness is often presumed but unsubstantiated. The food garden project appeared successful while funding from the United Nations Children's Fund (UNICEF) was available. However, since UNICEF's priority has changed, funding has dried up, and the project has died. Apart from an initial evaluation, no impact evaluation has been carried out.

Second, anecdotal evidence indicates that although a ban on the import and sale of mutton flaps is in place, fatty mutton pieces are still sold in supermarkets. Importers are now importing carcasses and then cutting and selling the fatty pieces under other names.

CONCLUSIONS

Generally speaking, the available evidence indicates considerable social, cultural, lifestyle, health and nutrition status change in Fiji over the past two decades. Whether this is attributed to development, urbanization, modernization or globalization, or perhaps all four, is an issue of definition and considerable debate relating to assumptions about the nature of causality.

Many sociocultural indicators of change are qualitative in nature and difficult to quantify. However, this does not mean that they are less important than more readily measured clinically defined markers of health and nutrition. Unfortunately, only the readily measured indicators tend to be used and this provides a simplistic impression that fails to reflect the complex nature of the problem.

Taken overall, evidence of negative social, nutritional and health outcomes linked to globalization and its companion concepts is consistent over a wide range of indicators.

The effectiveness of health and nutrition interventions in Fiji remains to be clearly demonstrated. Factors contributing to this situation include the inappropriateness of many imported interventions; lack of local ownership of these interventions; inadequate/insufficient resources; competing priorities; and absence of evaluation.

RECOMMENDATIONS

The following are based on some of the critical problems and challenges raised in this paper.

- Although multisectoral partnerships are regarded as highly desirable, in reality there are many institutional organizations and personal impediments to be overcome if these are to be implemented. Therefore it is recommended that the Food and Agriculture Organization of the United Nations (FAO) assist small island countries to develop relevant knowledge, skills and attitudes required to facilitate effective cooperative partnerships.

- Whereas since the late 1980s, many small island countries have developed national plans and policies for nutrition designed to address food security, to date very few of these plans have been developed beyond draft form. Therefore it is recommended that FAO provide practical assistance to small island countries in the form of funding and expertise to facilitate the review, adoption and implementation of these plans and policies.

- In recent years FAO has focused on Codex Alimentarius, which is primarily concerned with international trade, but very little has been done about food safety and handling at the community and household level. It is therefore recommended that FAO implement a two-prong approach to food safety issues and initiates community education programmes designed to improve food handling, preparation, processing and storage in small island countries.

Bibliography

Australian Centre for International Agricultural Research (ACIAR). 2002. *Determinants of food choice in Fiji: their role in demand for nutritionally dense food and nutrition security.* ACIAR Project Final Report. Canberra.

Baker, P.T., Hanna, J.M. & Baker, T.S., eds. 1986. *The changing Samoans: behaviour and health in transition.* New York, Oxford University Press.

Baxter, M. 1980. *Foods in Fiji.* Monograph No. 22. Suva, University of the South Pacific, Development Studies Centre.

Beaglehole, R. & Yach, D. 2003. Globalization and the prevention and control of non-communicable diseases: the negated chronic diseases of adults. *Lancet,* 362: 903-08.

Chandra, R. 1990. Patterns and processes of urbanization in Fiji. *In* R. Chandra & J. Bryant, eds. *Population of Fiji.* Noumea, South Pacific Commission.

Chaudhari, A. 2003. Mix and merge. *The Review,* 1-2 (1 September).

Coyne, T. 2000. *Lifestyle diseases in Pacific communities.* Noumea, Secretariat of the Pacific Community.

Department of Information. 1998. *Fiji today.* Suva, Ministry of National Planning and Information.

De Vries, M. W. 1996. Trauma in cultural perspective. *In* B.A. van der Kolk, A.C. McFarlane & L. Weisaeth, eds. *Traumatic stress.* New York, Guilford Press.

Escobar, A. 1995. *Encountering development: the making and unmaking of the Third World.* Princeton, New Jersey, United States, Princeton University Press.

FAO, RAPA. 1992. *Selected indicators of food and agriculture development in the Asia-Pacific Region, 1981-1991.* Bangkok.

Fiji Bureau of Statistics (FBS). 1989. *Census of Population and Housing Report of 1986.* Suva, Fiji Government Printer.

Fiji Bureau of Statistics (FBS). 1998. *Census of Population and Housing Report of 1996.* Suva, Fiji Government Printer.

Fiji Bureau of Statistics (FBS). 2002a. *Current economic statistics.* July issue. Suva.

Fiji Bureau of Statistics (FBS). 2002b. *Household Income and Expenditure Survey (HIES) 2002-2003.* Statistical News No. 66. Suva.

Fiji Bureau of Statistics (FBS). 2003. *Fiji in profile* (www.statsfiji.gov.fj/f_general.html.

Finau, S., Wainiqolo, I.L. & Cuboni, G.G. 2002. *Health transition and globalization in the Pacific: vestiges of colonialism?* Suva, School of Public Health and Primary Care, Fiji School of Medicine.

Friedlaender, J.S. 1987. *The Solomon Island Project: a long-term study of health, human biology and culture change.* Oxford, United Kingdom, Clarendon Press.

FTIB (Fiji Trade and Industry Board). 2003. (www.ftib.org.fj/contents/fiji_economy/aboutfj/economy.htm).

Graig, E. 1993. Stress as a consequence of the urban physical environment. *In* L. Goldberger & S. Breznitz, eds. *Handbook of stress.* Second ed. New York, Free Press.

Khaleghian, P. 2003. *Non-communicable diseases in Pacific countries: disease burden, economic cost and policy options.* Noumea, Secretariat of the Pacific Community and the World Bank.

Lal, B.V. 1992. *Broken waves: a history of the Fiji islands in the 20th century.* Honolulu, University of Hawaii Press.

Ministry of Agriculture, Fisheries, Forests & Agricultural Landlord and Tenants Act (ALTA). (MAFFA). 2001. (unpublished data)

National Food and Nutrition Centre. 2003a. *Fiji Food Balance Sheet Report 2000.* Suva.

National Food and Nutrition Centre. 2003b. *Fiji Food Balance Sheet Report 2001.* (in print)

Pacific Regional Statistics. 2003. ABC Radio International (www.abc.net.au/ra/pacific/places/stat_table.htm).

Reich, S. 1998. *What is globalization? Four possible answers.* Working Paper No. 261. University of Notre Dame, Canada, Kellogg Institute for International Studies.

Robertson, R. T. & Tamanisau, A. 1988. *Fiji: shattered coups.* Leichardt, Australia, Pluto Press.

Saito, S. 1995. *1993 National Nutrition Survey Main Report.* Suva, National Food and Nutrition Committee.

Schultz, J.T. 1997. *Food, society and development.* Suva, University of the South Pacific.

Schultz, R.F. 2003. *Social change, mental health and military coups.* (Ph.D. thesis, assessment pending)

Secretariat of the Pacific Community (SPC). 1999. *Fiji islands population profile.* Noumea.

The Review (anonymous author). 2003. *Extending the reach.* Feature Article 1. September.

United Nations Development Programme (UNDP). 2003. *Human Development Report.* Millennium Development Goals: a compact among nations to end human poverty. New York, Oxford University Press (www.undp.org/hdr2003).

UNICEF & WHO. 1999. *Substance use among adolescents in Fiji*. Suva, Fiji National Health Promotion Centre, United Nations Children's Fund and the World Health Organization.

Impact of globalization on the food consumption of urban India

Swarna Sadasivam Vepa[1]

INTRODUCTION

At first sight the link between globalization and food intake appears to be rather remote. However, its influence can be substantially high, although it works mostly through employment, incomes, prices and the market influence on food preferences. Globalization means bringing the domestic economy closer to the international economy in many ways. It is a consequence of liberalization and decontrol. The rationale behind liberalization and globalization was to bring competition and efficiency into the economy. They are part of structural reforms. Change in the existing structure is expected to contribute to efficiency in the long term and lead to absorption of labour, increase in incomes and overall prosperity.

One of the expected impacts on dietary patterns relates to higher incomes. The consumption pattern shifts away from cereals and towards more expensive protective foods. The second expected impact is the shift towards more processed foods. Third is the market influence of popular fast foods promoted through advertising by transnational corporations. Changes in the dietary pattern in turn influence the nutritional status of the population. Some effects such as fewer cereals and more protective foods in the diet can improve nutritional status, while a shift towards high-fat, high-sugar snack foods may lead to obesity and chronic diseases. Another adverse impact may be displacement of the poor by structural reforms. This group experiences lower affordability and a reduced calorie intake leading to growth disorders, such as stunting. A more severe impact may be on higher infant mortality rates and lower life expectancies.

The impacts of globalization differ from country to country, and between and within communities, depending upon the losers and winners in the process of change. It is difficult to trace these impacts in a sequential manner and to apportion total impacts between globalization and other forces at work in the economy. Reasons for the sedentary lifestyles of middle-class and upper-class urban workers, and deterioration of the low-income diets of rural migrants can be found elsewhere in the pattern of economic growth, not necessarily related to globalization.

This paper attempts to examine urban dietary patterns in India, in the backdrop of globalization and its influence on employment, incomes and market forces. The paper consists of three parts. The first part looks at the extent of globalization and urbanization and their impact on employment, incomes, imports and consumerism. The second part considers the dietary patterns of the urban population and attempts to link them to globalization. Certain aspects of the consumption patterns of the non-poor and the poor

[1] Dr Swarna Sadasivam Vepa
Programme Director and Ford Foundation Chair for Women and Sustainable Food Security
M.S. Swaminathan Research Foundation, Chennai, India
E-mail: svepa@mssrf.res.in

have been considered at the all-India level and across the regions in the urban areas of the country, within the limitations of the data. The increasing intake of processed foods by those not so poor and the low calorie intake of the poor in various states have been analysed. The third part briefly touches upon the implications of these consumption patterns on the nutritional status of the population.

BACKDROP OF INDIAN GLOBALIZATION AND URBANIZATION

July 1991 marked the beginning of globalization in India. It was a critical turning-point in the economic history of the country. Record low foreign exchange reserves triggered a financial crisis since they were barely enough to meet the import needs of two or three weeks. Under these circumstances, India decided to open up its economy. It devalued its currency; decontrolled the foreign exchange; unshackled its industry; privatized part of the public sector; removed subsidies on many items; removed import duty on several items; lowered the barriers; and invited foreign competition. In the decade that followed, liberalization and globalization proceeded unchallenged, albeit slowly and there was no looking back.

As a result, more than a decade later, India now has foreign exchange reserves worth more than US$100 billion. The Federal Bank, known as the Reserve Bank of India, has been struggling to keep the value of the rupee reasonably low against other currencies. The economy was able to maintain for most of the decade a gross domestic product (GDP) growth of 6 percent per annum. This is one side of the story, which sounds like a success story and an advertisement for globalization.

However, the other side of the story is a far cry from success. The growth of GDP in the past decade owes more to that of the service sector than the manufacturing one, which decreased from 29 percent in 1990 to 26 percent in 2001, while that of the service sector increased from 39 to about 49 percent.

Yet there were more losers than winners in the process. The gain in income came from reduced employment and more capital-intensive and labour-substituting investment. The increased productivity per worker was because of a reduction in the number of persons employed in the restructuring that took place across industry. Regular employment shrank and there was an increase in casual work. The rate of growth of employment decreased to 1.9 percent in 1993-2000, compared to the previous period of 1983-1993/1994 at 2 percent. Unemployment increased from 5.9 percent in 1993-1994 to 7.32 percent in 1999-2000. As per the economic census, the growth of workers in the establishments[2] came down to 1.7 percent in 1990-1998 from 2.84 percent in 1980-1990 (GOI, Ministry of Statistics and Programme Implementation, 2001).

The elasticity of employment with respect to income has decreased in all sectors. In the manufacturing sector, it decreased from 0.38 percent in 1983 to 1993 to 0.33 percent in 1993-1994 to 1999-2000. Regarding electricity, gas and water supplies, employment shrank with an increase in these infrastructure facilities. It changed from a positive elasticity of 0.63 percent between 1983 and 1993 to a negative elasticity of -0.52 percent between 1993 and 1994 and 1999-2000.[3]

---

[2]   Establishments refer to the units of economic activity undertaken with the help of at least one hired worker on a fairly regular basis (Planning Commission, 1998).

[3]   This means a 1 percent increase in the sector income has led to an increase of 0.30 percent in manufacturing employment. A negative elasticity means that a 1 percent increase in income in the electricity, gas and water supply sector led to a decline in employment by more than 0.5 percent.

In community social and personal services, employment elasticity changed from a positive 0.68 to -0.25 percent over the same period. The primary sector employment either shrank or had an elasticity close to zero (GOI, Planning Commission, 2002). For the economy as a whole the employment elasticity came down from 0.52 to 0.16 percent over the same period (GOI, Planning Commission, 2002). In other words, the economy lost its capacity to absorb more labour. As a consequence, unemployment has increased, particularly in the lower-income groups. Unemployment in these lowest-expenditure classes was close to 10 percent, while it was less among the higher-income groups (Table 1).

TABLE 1
Unemployment rate by expenditure class

Serial no.	Expenditure class	Unemployment rate (current dailystatus/percentage)
1	0-300	9.61
2	300-350	9.67
3	350-425	8.20
4	425-500	9.20
5	500-575	9.20
6	575-665	8.63
7	665-775	8.18
8	775-915	7.18
9	915-1 120	6.65
10	1 120-1 500	5.68
11	1 500-1 925	4.67
12	>1 925	4.10

Source: GOI, Planning Commission, 2001.

Another interesting feature of the Indian economy is that the decade of globalization and the fairly high growth of industry compared to agriculture have led to a lower than expected level of urbanization.[4] The growth of the urban population is lower than in the previous decade. It decelerated from 3.1 percent in 1981 to 1991 to 2.75 percent in 1991-2001. The urban/rural growth differential was lower in 1991 to 2001 at 1.08 percent, compared to 1.70 percent between 1971 and 1991. The share of urban population increased only moderately from 25.71 percent in 1991 to 27.78 percent in 2001 (GOI, Planning Commission, 2002). Compared to the rest of Asia where about 37 percent of the population live in urban areas, India had fewer than 30 percent living in these areas by the turn of the century. There were 35 urban agglomerations with a population of more than one million in 2001 and about 37 percent of the urban population live there. There are two mega cities, Mumbai and Delhi, with a population of more than ten million. The population of the metropolitan cities grew at 2.56 percent in 1991 to 2001 as against the urban rate of growth of 2.75 percent. However, there are pockets of phenomenal growth such as the union territory of Delhi. The major reason is that the growth in GDP during this decade was a result of reduced employment and increased labour productivity, together with an increase

---

[4]   Urbanization is a process whereby more and more people come to live in towns and cities rather than stay in villages. Typically in a developing country the degree of urbanization is low but the rate of growth of the urban population is high and concentrated in a few big cities.

in incremental capital out-ratios, rather than caused by a shift of the population into high-paid jobs or an expansion of employment. Thus it is also obvious that the benefits favoured a few highly paid employees and profit-making industrialists rather than an expansion of employment opportunities in urban areas. This is probably the reason for the quick downturn of GDP growth in the past two years, which had a narrow base of a few high-growth industries rather than a broad base spread over more industries and people.

Globalization, processed food imports and domestic expansion

Imports of food such as cereals and cereal products, cashew nuts and edible oils have increased since globalization began. The imports of many food items were liberalized by putting them on "open general licensing", which does not require permission from the government. Import duties were reduced to negligible or zero levels on many food items. As a result, the food-related imports of cereals and products surged from 308 000 tonnes in 1990 to 1 620 000 tonnes in 1999-2000 (GOI, Planning Commission, 2002). Edible oil imports increased from 526 000 tonnes in 1990 to 4 190 000 tonnes in 2002 (GOI, Planning Commission, 2002). Food-related imports represent about 4.5 percent of the total imports of about US$51 billion, constituting approximately US$3 billion (GOI, Planning Commission, 2002). Essential food items such as edible oils and pulses make up the bulk of the imports, while the processed food sector is much smaller. The impact on consumption does not vary dramatically, because of these imports, since they are less elastic to income changes. Compared to the food market turnover of about US$70 billion, US$3 billion worth of imports are not significant so far. However, in specific sectors imports may influence urban consumption. Imports of processed foods, particularly milk products and fruit and vegetables have increased substantially. The impact of imported processed foods appears to be small for the country as a whole.

The entry of many transnational corporations into the country and expansion of the already existing food processing ones is impressive. Food products, beverages and tobacco together have a weight of about 11.5 percent in the index of industrial production. The food products industry recorded a growth of 4.20 percent in 1999-2000 and 10.12 percent in 2000-2001 (GOI, Ministry of Food Processing Industries, 2003). Thereafter there was a negative growth of -1.68 in the following year. The problem was the economic downturn in all sectors in 2000-02 (GOI, Ministry of Food Processing Industries, 2003).

The turnover of the total food market is approximately Rs250 000 crores (US$69.4 billion) out of which value-added food products comprise Rs80 000 crores (US$22.2 billion). Since liberalization, several billion dollars worth of foreign capital have invaded the various segments of the food and agroprocessing industry. The food processing industry is poised to attract phenomenal investment of around Rs92 000 crores during the Tenth Five-Year Plan period (2002-2007). However much depends upon the increase in the purchasing power of the people (GOI, Ministry of Food Processing Industries, 2003).

To sum up, we may conclude that liberalization and globalization undoubtedly benefited India in achieving higher efficiency and competitiveness but did not lead to higher absorption of labour. Urbanization proceeded slowly and unemployment has spread. The impact on consumption of lower-income groups is expected to be negative. The expected impact on the higher-income groups is a shift to more expensive foods, imported processed foods and the spread of popular brands of fast foods, both Indian and foreign.

PATTERNS OF URBAN CONSUMPTION

As incomes go up, the food basket becomes more diversified. Cereal consumption decreases and the consumption of other foods increases. Even though people spend a smaller share of their income on food, they spend more in absolute terms. The urban food basket is the most diversified. Urban people consume fewer cereals and more of other items. Protective foods such as pulses, fruit and vegetables, milk, eggs and meat (including mutton) are easily available in the urban environment. If prosperity arising from economic growth and the influence of globalization were positive, then we would expect a more balanced diet away from cereals and towards protective high-protein foods, vegetables and fruit at the average level.

In addition to the change in the consumption pattern over time at the all-India level, we have also examined the consumption basket at the state level. Differences between prosperous states such as Delhi, Punjab and Haryana on the one hand and underprivileged states such as Orissa and Bihar on the other capture the impact of globalization on the consumption pattern.

Trends in average consumption

Data on the physical quantities of consumption of various items have been collected and published by the National Sample Survey Organization (GOI, National Sample Survey Organization, 2001a). For urban India as a whole from 1987 to 1988 and from 1999 to 2000 consumption has changed. Consumption of rice and wheat has decreased marginally. Milk and egg consumption records an increase. Substantial increases over the various time periods are seen in the consumption of tea, biscuits, salted snacks, prepared sweets, edible oils, sugar and country sugar (jaggary). There is a decline in the intake of fruit and vegetables. Thus it seems that diets have shifted towards more sugars and fats, less fruit and fewer vegetables. There is no evidence of a substantial shift of average diets towards nutritive and protective foods. The phenomenal growth in biscuit consumption and tea is more a result of prosperity and changing preferences. Therefore the impact of globalization on these two items appears to be at best indirect (Table 2).

TABLE 2
Change in the pattern of consumption of selected food items of the urban population (kg/month/per capita)

Food items	1987-88	1993-94	1999-2000
Rice	5.26	5.13	5.10
Wheat/flour	4.37	4.44	4.45
Pulses	0.87	0.77	0.85
Liquid milk (litres)	4.26	4.89	5.10
Eggs (number)	1.43	1.48	2.06
Milk fat	0.04	0.05	0.07
Edible oils	0.41	0.46	0.74
Flesh foods	0.39	0.40	0.46
Vegetables	3.94	3.09	3.00
Leafy vegetables	0.40	0.15	0.17
Mangoes	n.a.	0.12	0.16
Bananas (number)	5.10	4.48	5.00
Lemons (number)	n.a.	1.23	1.39
Sugar/jaggary	0.97	0.97	1.32
Tea leaf (g)	60.43	63.93	70.44
Biscuits	0.07	n.a.	2.06
Salted refreshments	0.04	n.a.	1.36
Prepared sweets	0.11	n.a.	0.40

Source: GOI, National Sample Survey Organization, 2001a.

Consumption across the expenditure classes

The pattern of consumption across the expenditure classes among the urban population reveals the same tendency. Per capita consumption of foods rich in protein such as pulses, milk products, eggs, fish and meat is far from adequate in all income classes. Consumption of pulses is barely above the Indian Council of Medical Research (ICMR) norm only in the highest three income classes, constituting about 20 percent of the population. None of the expenditure groups consume adequate quantities of eggs, fish and meat. Forty percent of the population consume milk below the norm of 150 ml.

Consumption of foods such as fruit that provide vitamins and micronutrients is fairly low, even in the diets of the higher-income classes. Fruit consumption is barely above the ICMR norm in any expenditure class, with the exception of the highest class, constituting 5 percent of the population. Consequently, 95 percent of the people have diets that are lacking in fruit. Vegetables are consumed in almost all expenditure classes (100-300 g/per capita/day). This would appear to be adequate. Part of the quantity consumed is in the form of tubers, which are rich in carbohydrates, leaving the diets inadequate in green and yellow vegetables (Table 3).

TABLE 3
Per capita consumption of selected food items for all India, urban (g/day)

Serial no.	MPCE[1] class (Rs)	Cereals and cereal substitutes	Pulses and pulse products	Milk, liquid (litres)	Milk products	Edible oils	Eggs, fish and meat	Vegetables	Fruit (fresh)	Sugar and *gur*	Beverages and processed foods
1	0-300	299.67	16.67	42.33	0.00	10.33	8.13	113.27	5.15	16.00	35.33
2	300-350	338.33	20.00	56.00	0.33	12.33	11.29	141.42	8.17	19.33	60.67
3	350-425	341.67	22.33	73.67	0.33	14.67	14.42	150.92	9.13	25.67	70.53
4	425-500	358.33	27.33	95.33	1.67	20.67	17.75	164.43	9.61	27.33	117.20
5	500-575	353.67	30.00	114.00	3.33	22.00	19.54	180.60	13.19	29.67	93.81
6	575-665	360.00	32.00	144.33	4.00	25.00	21.92	186.07	15.57	34.67	124.68
7	665-775	356.33	37.67	171.67	5.33	28.33	23.63	193.29	19.21	35.33	181.85
8	775-915	355.33	35.67	192.67	5.67	26.33	25.50	214.21	23.39	36.67	186.25
9	915-1 120	350.00	38.00	226.33	12.00	28.00	28.54	218.51	28.76	38.67	213.28
10	1 120-1 500	350.67	44.67	263.67	11.00	29.67	32.96	238.30	36.38	41.00	265.17
11	1 500-1 925	331.33	45.33	334.67	14.67	32.33	35.25	268.44	56.76	43.67	351.25
12	1 925 and more	324.00	49.00	401.33	17.67	35.00	52.92	299.32	79.70	49.33	427.41
	All classes	347.33	33.33	170.00	6.33	24.00	23.92	196.72	22.48	33.33	166.66

[1] MPCE: monthly per capita expenditure
Source: GOI, National Sample Survey Organization, 2001a.

Processed and ready to eat foods – consumption and production
It is interesting to note from Table 3 that in urban areas consumption of processed foods and ready to eat foods has gone up together with income. The tendency is clear across all expenditure classes except in the lowest three classes, consisting of about 20 percent of the population. Consumption of beverages, biscuits, processed foods, salted snacks, prepared sweets and other purchased foods constitutes 100-427 g/per capita/day, from the lowest to the highest expenditure class. Average consumption is about 167 g/per capita/day. This is probably an indication of the increasing consumption of snack foods and high-calorie foods such as sweets, which are purchased away from the home. Energy-wise they may contribute to as many as 1 000 kcals in the daily diet, or 30 to 40 percent of the required calories in the high-income classes.[5]

A look at the consumer food industry of India further reveals the possible impact of globalization on urban diets. The consumer food industry in the country is not big, but has grown in certain aspects in the post-liberalization period. The industry mainly consists of cereal- and sugar-based products such as bread, biscuits, cakes, pastries, pasta, cornflakes and ready to eat/cook products. Bread and biscuits constitute the largest segment of the consumer food industry. About 40 percent of bread is produced in the organized sector while 74 percent of biscuits are produced in the same sector (GOI, Ministry of Food Processing Industries, 2003). Other products have a smaller share in the organized sector.

---

[5] Approximately100 g of processed cereals and sugar-based foods can provide up to 200 kcals or more.

Various transnationals have entered the domestic market, increasing investment and competition in the post-liberalization period.

Some cocoa products, soft drinks, alcoholic beverages, and mineral and packaged water are also important in the consumer food industry. Soft drinks constitute a significant contribution as the third largest industry after packed tea and biscuits. This has attracted the largest foreign direct investment in the country of over US$1 billion in recent years. Production was about 6.6 billion bottles in 2001-2002 (GOI, Ministry of Food Processing Industries, 2003).

The consumption of fizzy drinks, pizzas and potato crisps, etc. has increased in the diets of the urban population, as witnessed by the sales increase in these items. Undoubtedly, globalization has facilitated the entry of branded products and outlets into the market, such as Coca-Cola, Pepsi-Cola, Pizza Hut, Domino's Pizza and Mcdonald's, primarily for the more affluent consumers. Other local products of a cheaper variety, both by branded and unbranded producers, flood the markets. Globalization is the main cause of the expanding market for ready to eat foods. Although the branded product market is not very big, it is growing. For example, Amul is an established company producing milk powder and butter in India. However, it has started competing with global brands for cheese and pizza in recent years (Bhushan and Damodaran, 2001).[6]

A number of unbranded producers flood the markets with cheaper products such as potato crisps and pizzas to woo consumers and suit the pockets of the lower-income groups. Domino sells about 100 000 pizzas a day, Pizza Hut 40 000 and Amul about 50 000 frozen pizzas a day (Pizzamarketplace.com, 2003). The prices range any where between Rs20 for an Amul frozen pizza to Rs450 for a special premium large pizza from Domino (Pizzamarketplace.com 2003). The unbranded market tends to be larger.

Since liberalization in 1991, total investment in the processed food sector has been in the range of US$156 billion (of this, foreign direct investment has been about US$2 billion). Thus urban consumption patterns are influenced by globalization across all expenditure groups except the lowest. Direct consumption of popular global brands on the one hand and the consumption of cheaper substitutes on the other have increased the overall consumption of processed foods (GOI, Ministry of Food Processing Industries, 2003).

It is noteworthy that the processing of meat, poultry, fish, eggs, milk, vegetables and fruit has not shown any significant increase. About 15 percent of the milk and 2 percent of fruit and vegetables are processed. Egg and poultry meat production increased from about 0.58 million tonnes in 1995 to 0.97 million tonnes in 2001 (GOI, Ministry of Food Processing Industries, 2003).

The food processing industry as well as urban consumption patterns are highly skewed towards cereal- and sugar-based products and not towards meat, fish, poultry, milk and vegetables.

Average consumption across the states

A study of dietary patterns across the states strengthens the observation above. We have calculated an index of consumption by taking the ratio of requirement to actual consumption. An index value of one indicates that the requirement is the same as consumption. An index value higher than one indicates consumption above the requirement and an index value of less than one indicates consumption below the requirement. The ICMR calculated the requirement of various food items at the average

---

[6]   Also see the Times News network, 2003.

level in a balanced diet for a reference person. These norms are reliable at the average level for the population as a whole (Table 4).

TABLE 4
Per capita consumption index of food items with ICMR norm

Serial no.	State	Cereals	Sugar	Pulses	Total vegetables	Fruit	Edible oils	Milk	Eggs	Meats	Fish and prawns
	ICMR norm (g)	420	30	40	125	50	22	150	45	25	25
1	Andhra Pradesh	0.87	0.74	0.73	0.78	0.64	0.91	0.88	0.24	0.39	0.11
2	Assam	0.97	0.71	0.63	0.60	0.53	0.83	0.43	0.25	0.31	1.05
3	Bihar	1.01	0.74	0.78	0.74	0.53	0.79	0.68	0.12	0.27	0.21
4	Gujarat	0.67	1.29	0.86	0.88	0.68	1.59	1.32	0.08	0.16	0.04
5	Haryana	0.74	1.66	0.88	0.75	0.80	0.95	1.81	0.09	0.09	0.00
6	Himachal Pradesh	0.82	1.29	1.17	0.82	0.82	1.11	2.02	0.23	0.24	0.01
7	Jammu and Kashmir	1.02	0.80	0.78	0.98	0.86	1.17	1.60	0.20	0.75	0.01
8	Karnataka	0.81	1.08	0.87	0.76	0.75	0.89	1.01	0.23	0.44	0.16
9	Kerala	0.73	0.98	0.58	0.44	0.68	0.70	0.70	0.30	0.44	2.51
10	Madhya Pradesh	0.88	1.13	0.83	0.86	0.55	0.97	0.87	0.10	0.16	0.07
11	Maharashtra	0.74	1.28	0.85	0.85	0.77	1.27	0.96	0.18	0.39	0.20
12	Orissa	1.15	0.73	0.62	0.91	0.52	0.65	0.39	0.16	0.25	0.47
13	Punjab	0.73	1.80	0.98	0.97	0.78	1.02	1.95	0.14	0.11	0.00
14	Rajasthan	0.92	1.29	0.80	0.79	0.50	0.94	1.54	0.05	0.15	0.00
15	Tamil Nadu	0.77	0.83	0.85	0.84	0.78	0.88	0.95	0.34	0.47	0.24
16	Uttar Pradesh	0.86	1.18	0.82	0.70	0.76	0.91	1.05	0.11	0.32	0.04
17	West Bengal	0.89	0.76	0.50	0.77	0.62	1.03	0.53	0.43	0.33	1.15
18	Delhi	0.68	1.19	0.98	0.88	1.29	1.12	1.75	0.18	0.35	0.16
19	Chandigarh	0.69	1.50	1.16	0.97	1.22	1.15	2.11	0.23	0.17	0.00
20	Pondicherry	0.76	0.74	0.83	0.89	0.62	0.97	0.93	0.41	0.35	0.57
	All India	0.83	1.11	0.83	0.81	0.71	1.09	1.02	0.19	0.32	0.29

Source: GOI, National Sample Survey Organization, 2001a.

The consumption of sugar was above the ICMR norm in 11 out of 20 states. Sugar consumption in all the other states varied between 74 and 98 percent of the requirement. The lowest level of sugar consumption per capita, at about 74 percent, was in Assam. Edible oil consumption was above the prescribed norm in eight out of 20 states. Most of the calorie decrease caused by less than the recommended level of cereal consumption in the average urban diet in many states was compensated by higher levels of consumption of other energy foods, particularly sugar, edible oils and probably milk fats. Average calorie consumption was higher in wealthier states, such as Punjab and Haryana, with fewer cereals and more fats and sugar. The average urban consumption of poorer states such as Orissa and Bihar contained more cereals in the diet.

Food intake of the urban lower-income classes

It has been found that for urban India as a whole and also for many states across the urban expenditure classes, cereal consumption has been declining since the 1970s. This trend is clear from the National Sample Surveys (NSS). The average urban Indian's per capita monthly consumption of cereals decreased from 11.36 kg in 1970 to 1971 to 10.63 kg in 1993 and 1994, and further to 10.42 kg in 1999 to 2000. In 1993 to 1994, cereal consumption by the lowest 10 percent was 9.51 kg per capita per month. It marginally increased to 9.55 kg in 1999 to 2000. However, despite this increase, the calorie intake of the lowest 10 percent decreased over the same period, from 1 893 kcals per consumer unit to 1 889 kcals. Many others who have analysed the NSS data have also noticed the decreasing trend even for the lower expenditure classes (Radha Krishnan, 2002).

Decreases in average cereal consumption are not of concern, as the average calorie intake of the urban population in all the states was found to be fairly high and above 2 100 kcals, both in 1993 to 1994 and in 1999 to 2000. Before the calorie data are analysed, some explanations are in order. The consumption data for 1999-2000 have been alleged to be overestimated. However, what is striking is that despite this bias towards overestimation, the actual calorie intake of the lowest deciles in many states was quite low and below acceptable levels.

In all the states the lowest 10 percent consumed less cereal than the average for the state itself. This is an alarming trend, since it means no growth in calorie intake. The average calorie intake for the lowest 10 percent in the urban areas for the country as a whole has remained stagnant. At least for the poor, cereal consumption and calorie intake go together, since cereals provide the major part of the calories consumed (Table 5). The per capita monthly cereal consumption of the poorest 10 percent was lowest in Kerala at 6.93 kg. It was also low in Gujarat, Haryana, Tamil Nadu, Pondicherry, Karnataka and Uttar Pradesh at about 8 kg per capita per month.

TABLE 5
Cereal consumption and calorie intake (urban areas)

Serial no.	State	Cereal consumption of the lowest 10 percent	Cereal consumption for all classes	Calorie intake by the lowest 10 percent	Calorie Intake by all classes	Cereal consumption of the lowest 10 percent	Cereal consumption for all classes	Calorie intake by the lowest 10 percent	Calorie intake by all classes
			(1999-2000)				(1993-1994)		
		(kg/month)	(kg/month)	(kcal/cu/day)*	(kcal/cu/day)	(kg/month)	(kg/month)	(kcal/cu/day)	(kcal/cu/day)
1	Andhra Pradesh	9.67	10.94	1 842	2 508	9.64	11.30	1 768	2 455
2	Assam	10.68	12.26	1 876	2 630	10.65	12.05	1 950	2 543
3	Bihar	9.87	12.70	1 813	2 645	10.48	12.82	1 860	2 667
4	Gujarat	7.62	8.49	1 829	2 518	7.89	8.96	1 744	2 491
5	Haryana	7.66	9.36	1 692	2 665	9.19	10.46	1 886	2 616
6	Himachal Pradesh	10.47	10.33	2 222	3 218	12.47	11.01	2 366	2 914
7	Jammu and Kashmir	11.51	12.84	2 357	5 955	11.48	11.48	2 397	2 950
8	Karnataka	8.57	10.21	1 776	2 494	8.39	10.87	1 662	2 485
9	Kerala	6.93	9.25	1 581	2 498	7.18	9.46	1 549	2 445
10	Madhya Pradesh	9.51	11.09	1 867	2 904	10.17	11.32	1 917	2 556
11	Maharashtra	9.74	9.35	1 867	2 484	9.43	9.37	1 835	2 432
12	Orissa	13.03	14.51	2 100	2 802	11.39	13.36	1 962	2 754
13	Punjab	8.06	9.21	1 979	2 667	7.96	9.01	1 903	2 569
14	Rajasthan	10.19	11.56	2 071	2 869	10.35	11.52	1 983	2 704
15	Tamil Nadu	8.04	9.65	1 676	2 509	7.28	10.05	1 442	2 366
16	Uttar Pradesh	8.83	10.79	1 765	2 610	9.91	11.08	1 890	2 615
17	West Bengal	10.03	11.17	1 900	2 597	10.56	11.64	1 914	2 587
18	Delhi	7.96	8.61	1 943	2 623	7.35	8.99	1 758	2 895
19	Chandigarh	7.03	8.74	1 803	2 741	8.34	9.00	1 946	2 839
20	Pondicherry	8.20	9.62	1 665	2 441	7.94	10.27	1 545	2 440
	All India	9.55	10.42	1 890	2 637	9.51	10.63	1 893	2 542

*kcal/cu/day = kilocalories/consumer unit/day.
Source: GOI, National Sample Survey Organization, 2001b,c; 1995; 1997.

The calorie consumption of the poorest deciles across the states was high only in Himachal Pradesh, Jammu and Kashmir, Orissa and Rajasthan. Even if 1 900 kcals are considered a reasonable level of consumption per consumer unit per day for moderate urban workers, only the poorest in the Punjab, Delhi and West Bengal qualified as having an adequate food intake. In many states, low levels of calorie intake accompanied lower levels of cereal consumption. Particularly low levels of cereal consumption and calorie intake by urban lower-income groups were seen in Andhra Pradesh, Karnataka, Tamil Nadu, Pondicherry, Kerala, Maharashtra, Gujarat, Madhya Pradesh, Uttar Pradesh, Chandigarh, Assam and Bihar.

The shortfall of calories consumed over the adopted norm indicates the depth of hunger. It can therefore be said that the urban poor in the states mentioned above experience various depths of hunger. Kerala, with the lowest level of 1 580 kcals and Tamil Nadu, with 1 675 kcals per consumer unit per day, show grave hunger. We considered 1 890 kcals per consumer unit per day as the acceptable level of calorie intake for urban people and estimated the percentage of population consuming less than this level. Consumer unit is more appropriate than person as a unit, since it is adjusted for sex and age composition.

The cutoff point of 1 890 kcals chosen was higher than the FAO figure of 1 810 chosen in calculations for the number of hungry. This was adjusted for the sex and age composition of India (FAO, 2000). It constitutes 70 percent of the international norm of 2 700 kcals.

In urban India as a whole, 13.4 percent of the population consume less than 1 890 kcals.[7] The percentage varies between 1.40 percent in Jammu and Kashmir to 19.10 percent in Tamil Nadu. In Delhi about 10.5 percent of the population consume less than this norm. A possible explanation for the falling calorie intake of the lowest deciles is the widespread unemployment and the adverse impacts of globalization.

Some economists do not take the problem of low levels of consumption by the lower deciles seriously; average consumption is given more importance. They observe that the slowdown in cereal demand is a result of changes in the tastes and preferences of the people. Wherever infrastructure developments and prosperity related to globalization and imports themselves make more of the other food items available, cereal consumption decreases. It is argued that this is not a sign of deterioration in human welfare (Rao, 2000). The demonstration effect and the availability of a variety of foods, some of which may be more nutritious than cereals, could be some of the reasons for an increase in the cost of calories consumed by the urban poor.

Another important point is that those consuming diets deficient in calories are not able to utilize the other nutrients effectively since, in the absence of sufficient calories, protein and other nutrients are not well utilized. Furthermore, many micronutrients are better absorbed by the body only if a balanced diet sufficient in calories is eaten. Varieties of foods that enhance the absorption of nutrients are ideal. For example, the absorption of iron improves if there are traces of vitamin C in food. Hence, the bottom line for better nutritional status is the minimum calorie intake per consumer unit. Sufficient calories should be consumed, and it is advantageous if they come from a variety of foods.

We may conclude that globalization has not helped the urban poor to improve their consumption via increased incomes as expected. The data show that while the rich may have benefited from globalization and prosperity, the poor have lost out. Job and income losses have caused the poor to eat less. We cannot attribute the decrease in calorie intake by the urban poor entirely to globalization.

Imported essential food items have undoubtedly improved food availability. Imports of pulses and edible oils, for example, seem to have particularly benefited the urban rich rather than the urban poor.

NUTRITIONAL STATUS OF THE URBAN POPULATION
Nutritional disorders in children

Nutritional problems can occur across all expenditure classes for both rich and poor when diets are unbalanced. The risk for those with protein calorie malnourishment is higher than for others. Protein-energy malnutrition can impair the immune system, leaving malnourished children less able to battle common diseases such as measles and diarrhoea. Unbalanced diets lead to many deficiencies and result in growth disorders. In India only 49 percent of the people consume iodized salt and 167 million people are at risk of iodine deficiency disorders (GOI Micronutrient Initiative and UNICEF, 1997). About 52 percent of women were found to have anaemia out of the 88 percent women covered by national family health surveys (International Institute of Population Sciences, 2000).

---

[7]   The estimates of number of hungry by FAO are based on the calorie supply and its distribution across the expenditure classes, based on certain assumptions. Our estimates are directly based on the sample survey and hence there is a discrepancy in the percentage of hungry.

Undernutrition that occurs during childhood, adolescence and pregnancy has an additive negative impact on the birth weight of infants. These infants are more likely to be underweight or stunted in early life. Undernutrition in early childhood has serious consequences. Underweight children tend to have more severe illnesses, including diarrhoea and pneumonia.

Underweight children under five years of age can be classified as severely underweight and moderately underweight. Children whose weight for age Z score is below three standard deviations of the National Centre for Health Statistics (NCHS)/World Health Organization (WHO) international reference curve are classified as severely underweight. Those having a weight for age Z score below two standard deviations of the reference curve are classified as moderately underweight. Stunted children (low height-for-age) are similarly classified as severely stunted and moderately stunted.

In urban India, 15.4 percent of children are severely stunted and 35.6 percent moderately stunted; about 11.6 percent of children are severely underweight and 38.4 percent are moderately underweight. In the case of the percentage of severely stunted children under three years of age, Bihar was in the worst position with 24 percent, followed by Uttar Pradesh with 22 percent, Rajasthan with 21 percent and Assam with 20 percent. Kerala occupied the best position in this regard with only 7 percent of severely stunted children under three years of age. Andhra Pradesh and West Bengal were in the next best position with 9.3 and 9.5 percent respectively (Table 6).

Madhya Pradesh had the largest percentage of severely underweight children under three years of age with 19 percent. Orissa and Uttar Pradesh followed with a figure close to 16 percent. Kerala, Punjab, Assam and Andhra Pradesh were at the other end of the scale with 2.9 to 7 percent of severely underweight children under three years of age.

TABLE 6
Underweight, stunting and wasting (urban India), 1998-1999

Serial no.	State	Underweight (-3 SD)	Stunting (-3 SD)	Wasting (-3 SD)	Underweight (-2 SD)	Stunting (-2 SD)	Wasting (-2 SD)
1	Andhra Pradesh	6.8	9.3	0.4	28.6	29.7	7.6
2	Assam	6.5	20.2	1.6	27.3	37.1	10.4
3	Bihar	12.1	24.2	3.8	47.4	42.2	17.1
4	Gujarat	9.4	18.8	2.1	38.1	38.5	11.3
5	Haryana	7.6	18.1	1.0	31.3	40.3	5.5
6	Himachal Pradesh	–	–	–	–	–	–
7	Jammu and Kashmir	–	–	–	–	–	–
8	Karnataka	–	–	–	–	–	–
9	Kerala	2.9	7.1	0.7	22.4	18.5	10.9
10	Madhya Pradesh	19.5	19.6	4.0	44.3	39.8	17.3
11	Maharashtra	10.9	11.1	1.6	44.1	33.3	15.7
12	Orissa	16.7	14.3	3.6	45.3	37.0	23.6
13	Punjab	6.1	11.4	0.5	18.6	29.4	7.4
14	Rajasthan	15.1	21.4	1.3	46.0	44.0	8.6
15	Tamil Nadu	9.6	11.8	4.5	33.5	27.1	20.6
16	Uttar Pradesh	16.3	21.8	2.4	42.6	46.7	9.5
17	West Bengal	9.3	9.5	0.8	31.5	25.5	11.1
18	Delhi	10.1	18.0	4.1	34.7	36.8	12.5
19	Chandigarh	–	–	–	–	–	–
20	Pondicherry	–	–	–	–	–	–
	All India	11.6	15.4	2.2	38.4	35.6	13.1

Source: International Institute of Population Sciences, 2000 (Table 7.10).

Problem of obesity of the non-poor

Obesity is a condition where there is excessive accumulation of fat in the body. It can occur among all classes, not necessarily only in the affluent ones. The main reasons for obesity are sedentary lifestyles and a large intake of calories. A body mass index (BMI) of more than 30 is the main indicator of obesity. Obesity data are scarce for urban India. Information on adult BMI is available for rural areas from the National Nutrition Monitoring Bureau, but not for urban areas. A few case studies are occasionally conducted in the urban sector. It is not possible to generalize for the country as a whole.

The Nutrition Foundation of India (1999) conducted a reliable survey in Delhi. Its study reveals that obesity prevails mostly among the middle class. One percent of men and 4 percent of women in the slums are found to be obese. Among the middle classes, 32.2 percent of men and 50 percent of women are obese (Nutrition Foundation of India, 1999). [8]

---

[8]   See also Kamla Krishnaswamy, 1999.

Obesity was higher in the age group of 40 and above. Obesity of the middle classes is prevalent in all the developed countries. The proportion for European countries appears to be higher than India at 50 percent, but India is catching up fast without the same level of affluence.

The prevalence of abdominal adiposity was higher than overweight and obesity. Forty-nine percent of males and about 35 percent of females had abdominal adiposity (Nutrition Foundation of India, 1999).

While we cannot attribute all the blame for obesity on globalization, it is a definite consequence of a shift in dietary patterns, with more sugars, fats and carbohydrates. Processed and ready to eat foods available on the market may have contributed to the increase in obesity.

CONCLUSION

We may conclude that the impact of globalization on low-income groups has been one of undernourishment because of the failure to create more jobs and provide higher incomes. Its impact on the middle- and higher-classes is increased consumption of high-calorie foods and increased incidence of obesity. A dietary pattern devoid of balanced diets across all classes is responsible for the incidence of micronutrient deficiencies and related problems such as iodine deficiency disorders, anaemia and growth disorders in children. The situation requires a three-pronged strategy of nutrition education, food fortification and enhanced safety nets for the poor.

Bibliography

Bhushan, R. & Damodaran, H. 2001. Will Amul's pizzas trigger a price war? *Hindu Business Line,* 3 August 2001 (www.thehindubusinessline.com/).

Food and Agriculture Organization of the United Nations. 2000. *The State of Food Insecurity in the World*. Rome.

Government of India (GOI), Micronutrient Initiative & UNICEF. 1997. Strategy for elimination of micronutrient malnutrition in India. Proceedings of the workshop held in Jaipur from 1 to 2 November 1995.

GOI, Ministry of Food Processing Industries. 2003. *Annual report 2002-03*. New Delhi.

GOI, Ministry of Statistics and Programme Implementation. 2001. *Economic Census 1998. All-India Report*. New Delhi. May.

GOI, National Sample Survey Organization. Ministry of Statistics and Programme Implementation. 1995. *Employment and unemployment situation in India,* 1993-94. NSS 50th Round Report No. 402. New Delhi.

GOI, National Sample Survey Organization. Ministry of Statistics and Programme Implementation. 1997. *Sarvekshana,* Vol. XXI, No. 2, October-December. New Delhi.

GOI, National Sample Survey Organization. Ministry of Statistics and Programme Implementation. 2001a. *Consumption of some important commodities in India, 1999-2000*. NSS 55th Round Report No. 461. New Delhi.

GOI, National Sample Survey Organization. Ministry of Statistics and Programme Implementation. 2001b. *Level and pattern of consumer expenditure in India, 1999-2000*. NSS 55th Round Report No. 457. New Delhi.

GOI, National Sample Survey Organization. Ministry of Statistics and Programme Implementation. 2001c. *Nutritional intake in India, 1999-2000*. NSS 55th Round Report No. 471. New Delhi.

GOI, Planning Commission. 2001. *Report of the task force on employment opportunities*. New Delhi. (mimeo)

GOI, Planning Commission. 2002. *Tenth Five-Year Plan 2002-2007*. New Delhi (www.planningcommission.nic.in/plans/planrel/fiveyr/welcome.html).

International Institute of Population Sciences. 2000. *National Family Health Survey 2, 1998-99*. Mumbai, India.

Kamla Krishnaswamy. 1999. *Obesity in urban middle classes*. New Delhi, Nutrition Foundation of India.

Nutrition Foundation of India. 1999. *Investigation of current prevalence, nature and etiology of obesity in urban communities*. New Delhi (www.nutritionfoundationofindia.org/research4.asp).

Pizzamarketplace.com. 2003. Pizza continues slicing into India restaurant market. News story, 14 July (www.pizzamarketplace.com/news_story_16186.htm).

Radha Krishnan, R. 2002. Food and nutrition security. *In K.* Parikh & R. Radha Krishnan, eds. *India Development Report 2002*. India, Oxford University Press.

Rao, Ch. Hanumanth. 2000. Declining demand for food grains in rural India: implications. *Economic and Political Weekly,* 35(4).

Times News network. 2003. Vyas: power behind the Amul brand. *The Economic Times, 7* May (www.economictimes.com/).

Globalization, food consumption, health and nutrition in urban areas: a case study from the Philippines

Maria Regina A. Pedro, Corazon VC. Barba and Luz V. Candelaria[1]

INTRODUCTION

The last 30 years witnessed rapid urbanization in the Philippines, from 32 percent in 1970 to 54 percent in 1995. At present, 59 percent of the population lives in urban areas, with a recorded growth of 5.14 percent. This total is expected to increase to 68 percent in 2015 (Florentino, Pedro and Molano, 1996; Population Commission, 2002). Much of the growth of the urban population in the last ten years can be traced to efforts in opening up the Philippine economy.

Some of the most important trends with regard to globalization include: i) the rapid rise in trade, with increasing export orientation; ii) growth of the services sector, e.g. information and communication, finance and insurance, tourism and transportation; and iii) the increasing borderlessness of production and consumption (Ofreneo, 1997). The opening up of the country's economy through various liberalization efforts and the growth of the services sector have significantly affected the agriculture sector, and contributed to the acceleration of urbanization and its consequences.

Although the motive force of globalization has been primarily economic, it has penetrated other realms that may also have had significant impacts on the Filipino people's food consumption patterns and nutritional status. Cultural influences from the developed nations, including affluent lifestyles and overconsumption, are being transmitted daily by means of television, advertising, tourism and education. Consequently, lifestyle-related diseases have been closely associated with globalization.

This paper seeks to identify the impacts of globalization and urbanization on food consumption, health and nutrition in order to identify strategies and interventions to protect the health and nutrition of the population.

[1] Maria Regina A. Pedro
Corazon VC. Barba
Luz V. Candelaria
Food and Nutrition Research Institute
Department of Science and Technology
Philippines
E-mail: mrap@fnri.dost.gov.ph

TABLE 1
Urbanization trends in the Philippines

Indicators	1960	1970	1975	1980	1990	1995	2001
Urban percentage	29.8	31.8	33.3	37.2	48.6	54.1	59.1
Urban growth (%)	2.7	4.0	3.0	4.9	5.0	5.0	5.14
Rural growth (%)	2.5	2.6	2.6	1.5	0.3	0.3	-

Source: Population Commission, 2002.

Demographic profile and urbanization trends

The Philippines had an estimated population of 82 million in 2003. This rose from 76.5 million in 2000 and 68.8 million in 1995, at a growth rate of 2.36 percent per year since 1995 (National Statistics Office, 2000). The population growth is 3.3 percent in Metro Manila and 1.0-1.7 percent in the other regions. In Metro Manila, the population stood at 200 000 at the turn of the twentieth century, and ballooned to 9.9 million in 1999. This metropolitan region now constitutes 13 percent of the country's population. Population projections of the National Statistics Office, based on the 1995 census, show that the Philippine population will grow to 106 million in 2020. Metro Manila is predicted to reach 19 million in the year 2016.

The rapid population growth in the country is explained by the transition from high to low mortality, and continued high fertility. The Philippines' infant mortality rate has improved from 45 to 30 per 1 000 live births, while life expectancy at birth has increased from 67 to 71 years for females and 64 to 65 years for males, from 1990 to 2000. Actual fertility is one and a half births more than replacement fertility, and one birth more than the desired fertility (Duque, 2003).

In the metropolitan areas, the congestion – from 10 717 to 50 042 persons per km^2 in areas of central Manila, and an average of 15 617 persons per km^2 for the region, as against 566 persons per km^2 in rural areas (Asian Development Bank, 2000) – is also a significant result of massive rural to urban migration. Since the 1980s, approximately 300 families have been migrating each month to Manila from the provinces, contributing to the expansion of squatter colonies. In Metro Manila, there are approximately 591 of these colonies (Lamberte, 2000). There also has been an emergence of new "metropolises", in addition to Metro Manila, in other regions of the country, including Metro Cebu, Bacolod and Iloilo in the Visayas and Metro Davao, Cagayan de Oro and General Santos City in Mindanao. Overall, it has been estimated that 35 percent of the urban population are squatters and slum-dwellers.

Table 2 presents the in- and out-migration picture in Metro Manila and the other regions of the country for the period 1985 to 1990, revealing a net emigration from ten out of the 15 regions probably to Metro Manila and the industrial zones in the Southern Tagalog region and the growth centres in Cagayan de Oro (Northern Mindanao region) and Davao (Southern Mindanao region). For most of these regions, females outnumbered males as out-migrants, many of them being deployed as overseas Filipino workers (OFWs), while there were more male migrants to the industrial/growth centres in the Southern Tagalog and Northern and Southern Mindanao regions. According to the Philippine Overseas Employment Agency, a significant number of OFWs have been deployed to various countries, mostly in the Middle East (45 percent), Asia (42.5 percent) and Europe (7 percent). For 2002, the number of OFWs on record was 891 908, an increase of 2.8 percent from the total deployment in 2001 (Reyes, 2003).

TABLE 2
Net migration rate by region and gender, 1985-1990, per thousand population

Region	Male	Female
Metro Manila	10 161	29 291
Cordillera Adm. region	- 2 118	- 1 877
Northern Luzon	- 7 088	-10 272
Cagayan Valley	- 6 360	-12 892
Central Luzon	2 397	2 548
Southern Tagalog	22 085	20 174
Bicol	-24 699	-31 248
Western Visayas	-10 473	-15 960
Central Visayas	- 9 619	-11 749
Eastern Visayas	-17 930	-25 936
Western Mindanao	- 2 483	- 5 184
Northern Mindanao	8 074	3 579
Southern Mindanao	5 186	1 867
Central Mindanao	- 6 149	- 8 294
Adm. Region of Muslim Mindanao	- 5 332	- 4 904

Source: 1995-based national and regional population projections (cf. Reyes, 2003).

The Philippines' population structure reveals a high dependency ratio (Figure 1), and is expected to make the demographic transition between 2015 and 2025, when the elderly population becomes more significant (Asian Development Bank, 2000; Duque, 2003).

As the country moves towards a demographic transition, and the labour force increases, there has, however, been no significant increase in employment. The unemployment rate has been high, and increased from 8.9 percent in 1993 to 10.1 percent in 2000. In April 2003, the unemployment rate was placed at 12.6 percent, or 4.3 million Filipinos, based on a recent labour survey by the National Statistics Office.

Meanwhile, agriculture remained the major area of employment, even though the number and the proportion of those employed in the sector decreased between 1993 and 2000 (Table 3). Employment in the manufacturing sector, on the other hand, has increased, while job creation in the services sector has been significant. With regard to gender, more women are slowly being drawn into the labour force, particularly in the services sector.

FIGURE 1
**Population pyramid of the Philippines, 2000
(per '000 population)**

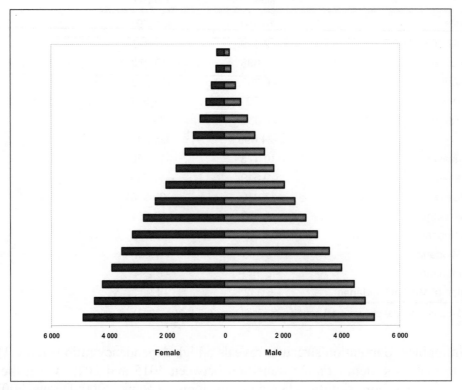

Source: Templo, 2003.

TABLE 3
Labour and employment statistics, 1993-2000

	1993	1995	2000
Labour force	26 822 000	28 040 000	30 908 000
Employed	24 443 000	25 698 000	27 775 000
Agriculture	11 194 000	11 323 000	10 401 000
Manufacturing	2 455 000	2 571 000	2 792 000
Unemployed	2 379 000	2 342 000	3 133 000
Unemployment rate (%)	8.9	8.4	10.1

Source: Asian Development Bank, 2002.

Nearly a third (28.4 percent) of families in the Philippines were poor in 2000 – defined as having an income below the level required to sustain a minimum food and non-food bundle. Poverty improvement has been confined to urban areas, where the incidence dipped significantly from 30.1 percent in 1988 to 19.9 percent in 2000 (Templo, 2003). Nearly 75 percent of the poor lived in the rural areas in 2000, and approximately half (41.4 percent) of rural families lived below the poverty line (Templo, 2003).

Other indicators of globalization

The effects of globalization have also been in terms of trends in information communication and technology and transportation, enhancing cross-cultural influences with regard to consumption patterns and lifestyles as well as transmission of diseases. With regard to crime, Metro Manila contributes significantly to the total reported crime cases against property as well as non-index cases.

Crime in the Philippines has been extensively linked to the increasing problem of drug use. In 1999, 83 drug syndicates (including transnationally organized ones), with a membership of approximately 560 000 drug pushers operated in the country. Related transnational crimes are the trafficking and smuggling of persons, terrorism and smuggling of firearms, and piracy of intellectual property rights, among others.

TABLE 4
Other indicators of globalization

	1995	2001	2002
Information communication and technology[1]			
Internet users ('000)	-	2000[2]	-
Main telephone lines (per 1 000 households)	21	40	-
Mobile phone subscribers ('000)	1 344[3]	12 159	-
Total estimated PCs ('000)	-	1 700	-
(per 100 households)	1.2	2.2	-
TV/CATV networks	1 053[3]	1 432	-
Transportation[4]			
Registered motor vehicles	-	3 865 862	4 182 673
Crime [5]			
Crime against persons[6]			
Philippines	28 670	23 634	25 706
Metro Manila	3 933	2 589	3 168
Crime against property[7]			
Philippines	13 341	14 407	18 054
Metro Manila	5 331	6 147	5 315

[1] *Source*: National Telecommunications Commission.
[2] 2000.
[3] 1997.
[4] *Source*: Land Transportation Office, Department of Transportation and Communication.
[5] *Source*: Philippine National Police; includes reported cases.
[6] Includes murder, homicide, physical injury, and rape.
[7] Includes robbery and theft.

ROLE OF GLOBALIZATION AND URBANIZATION ON DIETARY CHANGE
Evolution of the urban food supply

Globalization has had significant effects on the food supply. The most important of these is the increase in the importation of agricultural commodities.

Three food commodities where imports have contributed significantly are dairy products, cereals, and fats and oils. Imports contributed >50 percent of the total supply of milk and milk products from 1993 to 1999. Next to dairy products, 20-30 percent of the total supply of cereals and cereal products between 1993 and 1999 came from importation (Table 5).

Rice is the country's staple – importation peaked in 1998, at 31 percent of the total rice supply (versus practically 0 percent in 1993, and 11 percent in 1996 and 1999), to make up for low production during the year. Domestic production of corn, starchy roots and tubers, sugars and vegetables was also lowest in 1998.

Wheat flour imports, with the growing importance of bread and bakery products in the Filipino diet, have contributed >50 percent of the domestic supply since 1996. For nearly all food commodities, except milk and milk products and eggs, the contribution of imports to the total supply, by commodity, grew sharply after 1993. These included fats and oils, starchy roots and tubers, fruit and vegetables, meat and meat products, fish and other marine products. For milk and milk products and eggs, the contribution of imports was relatively steady from 1993 to 1999.

TABLE 5
Food importation and contribution percentage to total domestic food supply by commodity, the Philippines, 1993-1999

Commodity	Imports (in tonnes)				% of total domestic supply			
	1993	1996	1998	1999	1993	1996	1998	1999
Cereals and cereal products	3 652 098	3 244 959	4 181 426	3 153 148	25.0	18.8	28.2	18.3
Rice	111	862 384	2 170 835	836 378	0.0	10.8	31.3	10.8
Wheat flour	19 354	1 921 523	1 392 467	1 958 666	1.3	55.8	55.6	55.6
Starchy roots and tubers	1 659	20 292	19 508	25 675	0.1	0.6	0.7	0.9
Sugar and syrups	28 136	259 554	466 250	172 018	0.1	1.0	2.3	0.7
Pulses and nuts	91 806	194 413	202 071	343 243	0.8	1.7	1.7	3.1
Vegetables	7 012	22 243	40 835	57 022	0.3	0.8	4.4	6.0
Fruit	72 250	133 372	126 700	176 305	1.1	1.7	2.0	2.9
Fats and oils	21 487	45 244	46 902	89 740	6.9	13.4	14.1	24.0
Miscellaneous	30 809	49 088	55 034	42 434	0.9	1.2	1.1	1.0
Meat and products	1 467	9 556	183 611	130 302	0.1	0.4	6.4	4.5
Fish and other marine products	665	5 616	117 629	177 621	0.0	0.2	3.1	4.6
Milk and products	139 090	179 666	173 659	206 213	53.7	55.6	56.6	57.3
Eggs	3 796	3 139	3 142	2 857	1.5	1.2	1.1	1.0

Source: Philippine Institute of Development Studies, 2003.

While domestic production in general did not grow at the same rate as the population, the country managed to maintain its total domestic food supply at 1 000-1 200 g per capita/day from 1993 to 1999. This translated to about 2 000 kcals of energy available per capita/day in 1993, and 2 200-2 400 kcals per capita/day from 1996 to 1999, distribution patterns, food losses and wastage notwithstanding (Table 6). Per capita/day protein supply was 58.8 g in 1993 and 66-69 g per capita/day from 1996 to 1999 (Table 6). The Philippine recommended dietary allowances (RDAs) for energy and protein for the reference male of 20-39 years old are 2 570 kcals and 60 g protein, respectively; while the per capita RDA for energy was estimated at 1 968 kcals in 1995 and 1 979 kcals for 2001, based on the National Statistics Office population structure.

TABLE 6
Per capita food, energy and protein supply, by commodity, the Philippines, 1993-1999

Commodity	1993			1996			1998			1999		
	Per cap/d (g)	Energy (kcal)	Protein (g)	Per cap/d (g)	Energy (kcal)	Protein (g)	Per cap/d (g)	Energy (kcal)	Protein (g)	Per cap/d (g)	Energy (kcal)	Protein (g)
Cereals and cereal products	279.1	945	20.2	367.5	1 227	26.0	311.1	1 055	22.6	332.6	1 147	24.5
Starchy roots and tubers	66.6	103	0.8	65.5	102	0.9	53.2	84	0.7	52.4	84	0.6
Sugars and syrups	46.2	161	0.0	47.7	166	0.0	45.0	162	0.0	45.5	161	0.0
Pulses and nuts	34.1	47	1.6	33.5	48	1.7	33.0	49	1.8	31.1	50	2.0
Vegetables	97.1	46	2.4	100.1	48	2.5	29.8	15	0.8	29.9	15	0.8
Fruit	220.1	138	1.4	253.1	162	1.7	185.4	131	1.3	170.5	123	1.2
Fats and oils	12.4	94	0.0	12.5	95	0.1	11.7	95	0.1	12.5	106	0.1
Miscellaneous	129.7	249	8.0	142.4	244	10.3	171.7	318	12.2	213.6	362	13.4
Meat and products	71.5	138	10.3	80.3	154	11.5	89.9	170	12.9	89.4	171	12.8
Fish and other marine products	96.3	77	11.6	93.6	77	11.4	92.8	75	11.1	93.6	78	11.4
Milk and products	6.2	19	1.3	7.2	21	1.5	6.6	19	1.3	7.7	22	1.5
Eggs	9.2	13	1.0	9.2	13	1.0	9.5	14	1.0	9.4	14	1.0
TOTAL	1 067	2 032	58.8	1 212	2 356	68.6	1 040	2 186	65.8	1 088	2 330	69.3

Source: Philippine Institute of Development Studies, 2003.

Table 7 compares the country's per capita food supply and the mean one-day food consumption in 1993 in Metro Manila, and rural households in selected regions and the Philippines in general. It shows some indication of the distribution of the country's food supply to the urban and rural regions. There have been no food consumption studies in the Philippines since 1993, so it is not possible to show recent trends. The next Food Consumption Survey, among children up to five years old and pregnant and lactating women, is being carried out as one of the components of the 2003 or Sixth National Nutrition Survey by the Food and Nutrition Research Institute, Department of Science and Technology. Table 8 presents the translation of the per capita food consumption of 1993 to energy and nutrients.

With regard to cereals, rice consumption in 1993 was lowest among the urban households of Metro Manila, compared to rural households of the Philippines and in Northern Luzon, Eastern Visayas and the Administrative Region of Muslim Mindanao (ARMM). However, the consumption of other cereals, which included bread and bakery products, was highest in Metro Manila. Like bread and bakery products, the consumption of sugars, fats and oils, fish, meat and poultry, eggs, and milk and milk products was also higher in Metro Manila compared to rural areas. The consumption of green leafy and yellow vegetables in Metro Manila was lower compared to the rural households in the regions presented, except in Eastern Visayas and rural households of the Philippines.

In terms of mean per capita one-day energy and nutrient intake and percentage age adequacy, there are differences between urban (Metro Manila) and rural households. Percentage energy adequacy was lower among households of Metro Manila than rural households, except in Bicol (80.6 percent) and Western Visayas (74.0 percent). Mean vitamin A intake was adequate in Metro Manila but inadequate among rural households in all regions of the country including Northern Luzon, Eastern Visayas and ARMM. There were no wide differences in the intake of protein, calcium and thiamine between Metro Manila and Northern Luzon.

TABLE 7
Per capita food supply and mean one-day food consumption of Metro Manila and rural households by selected regions, the Philippines, 1993

Food commodity	Per capita food supply (g)	Mean one-day food consumption (g)				
		Metro Manila	Philippines	Northern Luzon	Eastern Visayas	ARMM
Cereals and cereal products	279	293	364	386	394	417
Rice	*212*	*252*	*300*	*368*	*362*	*405*
Other cereals	*12*	*40*	*15*	*15*	*22*	*9*
Starchy roots and tubers	67	12	21	11	18	75
Sugars and syrups	46	23	17	18	16	12
Dried beans and nuts	34	10	8	13	3	2
GLY vegetables	97[1]	18	34	52	15	48
Other fruit and vegetables	220[2]	113	126	152	102	79
Vitamin C-rich fruits		34	26	68	15	8
Beverages and condiments	130	29	16	9	25	8
Fats % oils	12	14	11	10	11	10
Fish, meat and poultry	168	181	133	136	177	111
Eggs	9	16	9	11	6	5
Milk and products	6	86	24	29	17	12
TOTAL	1 068	824				

[1] Includes all vegetables.
[2] Includes all fruit only.
Source: PIDS, 2003; FNRI-DOST, 2001; Molano *et al.*, 2003 (unpublished paper).

TABLE 8
Mean per capita one-day energy and nutrient intake and percentage adequacy of households in Metro Manila and rural households in the Philippines and selected regions, 1993

	Metro Manila	Philippines	Northern Luzon	Eastern Visayas	ARMM
Energy					
Intake (kcals)	1 651	1 696	1 808	1 837	1 828
% adequacy	85.7	88.6	95.1	93.3	93.1
Protein					
Intake (g)	52.2	49.1	51.8	55.0	47.3
% adequacy	110.6	104.9	109.0	113.0	96.4
Iron					
Intake (mg)	10.2	9.9	10.8	12.8	9.5
% adequacy	63.0	64.3	72.0	87.2	59.3
Calcium					
Intake (g)	0.41	0.39	0.42	0.36	0.30
% adequacy	70.7	66.1	72.5	62.3	52.1
Vitamin A					
Intake (RE)	582.7	327.9	344.1	249.8	229.5
% adequacy	131.6	73.8	76.3	54.7	50.6
Thiamine					
Intake (mg)	0.74	0.65	0.78	0.65	0.58
% adequacy	75.5	66.3	80.3	65.0	58.1
Niacin					
Intake (mg)	16.8	15.8	17.5	19.8	17.3
% adequacy	91.3	86.3	96.1	104.8	92.6
Riboflavin					
Intake (mg)	0.70	0.51	0.58	0.50	0.40
% adequacy	70.7	52.0	59.1	49.2	40.5
Ascorbic acid					
Intake (mg)	41.9	48.7	76.2	28.7	38.3
% adequacy	65.7	76.6	120.7	44.5	57.1

Source: FNRI-DOST, 2001; Molano *et al.*, 2003 (unpublished paper).

The proportion of households with <100 percent per capita energy adequacy was about the same in urban and rural areas (69.6 and 69.2 percent, respectively), while there were fewer urban (42.8 percent) than rural (46.1 percent) households with <100 percent per capita protein adequacy.

Dietary changes from 1978 to 1993

Table 9 presents the trends in the food consumption of Filipino households from 1978, when the First National Nutrition Survey was conducted, to 1993, the Fourth National Nutrition Survey. In examining the data, one should take note of the increasing urbanization of the country, from 32 percent in 1970 to 40 percent in 1980, 50 percent in 1990 and 52 percent at present.

From 1978 to 1993, the daily per capita consumption of cereals, cereal products and vegetables decreased while the consumption of meat, meat products and eggs increased in Philippine households, which include both rural and urban areas (Figures 2a and 2b). There was also a decreasing trend, from 1982 to 1993, in the consumption of starchy roots and tubers, beverages, condiments, and fish and shellfish, as well as in terms of the total food consumed.

In Metro Manila, there was a trend towards lower intake of sugars, and fats and oils, which are energy-dense food groups. There was also a trend towards lower intake of vegetables, as well as fruit (for the period 1982 to 1993). The trend in the consumption of cereals and cereal products from 1978 to 1993 showed small increasing intakes, which may be attributed to bread and bakery products more than to rice and rice products. As in the general Philippine situation, the trend in Metro Manila was towards increased intake of animal foods and lower intake of plant foods from 1978 to 1993. The trend was also towards increased total food intake from 1978 to 1982 and decreasing total food consumption from 1982 to 1993.

In terms of daily per capita energy and nutrient intakes, there was a trend towards lower energy intake for the Philippines, in general, from 1982 to 1993, as well as for Metro Manila, in particular, from 1978 to 1993 (Table 10). There was also a sustained decreasing per capita intake of calcium and ascorbic acid among households, in general, and in Metro Manila.

TABLE 9
Trends in per capita food consumption (g), 1978-1993, the Philippines and Metro Manila[1]

Food groups	Philippines				Metro Manila			
	1978	1982	1987	1993	1978	1982	1987	1993
Cereals and cereal products	367	356	345	340	286	287	292	293
Starchy roots and tubers	37	42	22	17	15	18		12
Sugars and syrups	19	22	24	19	50	30	21	23
Dried beans, nuts and seeds	8	10	10	10	10	14	14	10
Vegetables	145	130	111	106	138	120	101	87
Fruit	104	102	107	77	132	162	102	78
Beverages	8	16	12	9	20	37	21	29
Condiments	12	15	14	11				
Oils and fats	13	14	14	12	27	23	17	14
Meat and meat products	23	32	37	48	66	86	83	86
Eggs	8	9	10	12	16	14	14	16
Fish and shellfish	102	113	111	99	106	93	105	95
Milk and milk products	42	44	43	44	74	83	70	86
TOTAL	889	905	860	803	940	967	868	824

[1] 1978 to 1993 data were taken from the Philippines' National Nutrition Surveys (NNS), conducted every five years, by the Food and Nutrition Research Institute, Department of Science and Technology. The 1998 NNS did not have a food consumption survey component.
Source: FNRI-DOST, 2001; Molano *et al.*, 2003 (unpublished paper).

FIGURE 2a
**Cereal and vegetable consumption and urbanization trends,
the Philippines, 1978-1993**

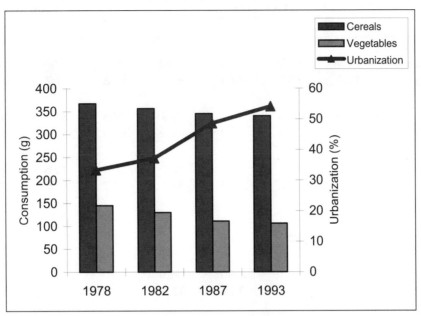

Source: FNRI-DOST, 2002; National Statistics Office, 2000.

FIGURE 2b
**Meat consumption and urbanization trends,
the Philippines, 1978-1993**

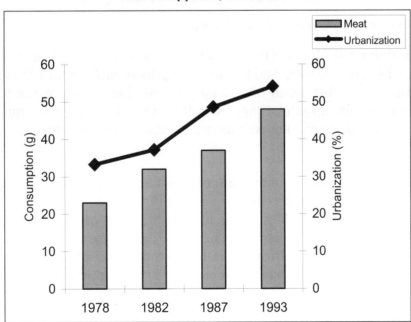

Source: FNRI-DOST, 2002; National Statistics Office, 2000.

TABLE 10
Trends of per capita nutrient intake and adequacy, the Philippines and Metro Manila[1]

	Philippines				Metro Manila			
	1978	1982	1987	1993	1978	1982	1987	1993
Energy								
Intake (kcals)	1 804	1 808	1 753	1 683	1 908	1 797	1 751	1 651
% adequacy	88.6	89.0	87.1	87.8	92.8	87.7	86.4	85.7
Protein								
Intake (g)	53.0	50.6	49.7	49.9	49.6	51.9	50.5	52.2
% adequacy	102.9	99.6	98.2	106.2	94.5	100.8	98.2	110.6
Iron								
Intake (mg)	11.0	10.8	10.7	10.1	10.4	10.6	10.5	10.2
% adequacy	91.7	91.5	91.5	64.7	83.2	85.5	86.8	63.0
Calcium								
Intake (g)	0.44	0.45	0.42	0.39	0.47	0.44	0.43	0.41
% adequacy		80.4	75.0	67.0	85.2	78.6	74.1	70.7
Vitamin A								
Intake (RE)			389.7	391.9			447.2	582.7
% adequacy			75.9	88.1			85.6	131.6
Ascorbic acid								
Intake (mg)	66.8	61.6	53.6	46.7	58.3	55.3	47.6	41.9
% adequacy		91.1	80.0	73.2	85.1	81.3	70.7	65.7

[1] 1978 to 1993 data were taken from the Philippines' National Nutrition Surveys (NNS), conducted every five years, by the Food and Nutrition Research Institute, Department of Science and Technology. The 1998 NNS did not have a food consumption survey component.
Source: FNRI-DOST, 2001; Molano *et al.*, 2003 (unpublished paper).

Florentino, Pedro and Molano (1996) attributed the positive trends in 1978 to 1982 to the improved economic situation, and the decreasing food intake from 1982 to 1987 to the economic crisis and fluctuation in food supply during that period. While the Philippine economy started to pick up after 1986, from 1988 to 1990, a period fraught with coup attempts and natural disasters, the country again experienced negative and slow growth through 1993 (Templo, 2003).

Importance of street foods and emergence of fast food chains

Street foods have played an important role in the Filipino diet, especially in urban areas. From the 1970s to the present, the street food trade has evolved into a large and complex food sector that provides both an important means of income for vendors and an affordable source of food for the people. Urban street food vending has provided employment and income for many, and gives economic support to small farmers as an outlet for rural produce. In some cities, such as Iloilo in the central Philippines, up to 25 percent of the labour force is involved in street food vending (De Guzman *et al.*, 1987). Most street food enterprises consist of a single person or are household-based, with family members helping to make or sell the product (De Guzman *et al.*, 1987). Some vendors also employ one or two paid assistants. Street food vendors/owner-vendors in Metro Manila are mostly migrants from the provinces.

Simple and traditional foods sold by street food vendors include fried and boiled snacks, packed snacks, soups, local cakes, grilled food (mostly meat), sandwiches, eggs, fruit and bakery products, as well as hot and cold beverages. A study by FNRI-DOST revealed that a street food meal can provide a reference adult male (20-39 years old) with 21 percent of the RDA for energy, and 28 percent of the RDA for protein. A street food snack provides 13 percent and 12 percent of the RDA for energy and protein, respectively.

IMPACT OF GLOBALIZATION ON LIFESTYLES IN URBAN AREAS
Physical activity patterns

Florentino, Villavieja and Laña (2002) studied the dietary and physical activity patterns of schoolchildren in Metro Manila, and noted the following.

- In private (fee-paying) schools in Metro Manila, 31 percent of schoolchildren consume less than 100 percent RDA for energy vis-à-vis 55 percent of schoolchildren from public schools not meeting the requirements.
- In private schools, 17.3 percent consume >150 percent RDA for energy vis-à-vis 7.4 percent in public schools.
- With regard to physical activity, other than sleeping and the hours spent in the classroom, urban schoolchildren in public and private schools spend more than one hour watching television, about one hour doing homework, and half an hour for indoor games. Children in private schools spend more time for homework and indoor games than children in public schools. Indoor games usually include computer and electronic games, board or card games, among others.
- Travel time to school takes from 15 minutes to half an hour. The children commute to school by means of a public or private vehicle, although about half of the public schoolchildren walk. Household chores and outdoor games both take up 30 to 40 minutes each; the public schoolchildren spend more time than children in the private schools in these activities.

While the picture presented above refers to schoolchildren in urban areas, a large proportion of children aged from five to 17 are out of school or partly working to earn money for their tuition as well as help put food on the table. From the October 2001 Survey on Children by the National Statistics Office (NSO, 2003), the national total of working children was estimated at 4 018 million (62.2 percent) of the total number of children aged from five to 17. Of the total working children, 246 000 (6.1 percent) were aged five to nine, 1.9 million (48 percent) were from ten to 14, and 1.8 million (46 percent) belonged to the 15-17 age group. There were more male working children (63 percent) than females, and seven out of ten working children lived in rural areas (about 1.2 million were in urban areas). Fifty-nine percent (59.4) of all working children in the country, and 52.4 percent of the urban working children claim they are exposed to various physical, chemical and biological hazards in their working environment.

There are approximately 1.5 million street children in the Philippines. In Metro Manila alone, there are 50 000 to 75 000. These numbers include children who work on the streets but maintain contact with their families (i.e. at the end of each day they return home) (70 percent); children who see the streets as their home and seek income from them (25 percent); and children who are completely disconnected from their biological families and are abandoned and neglected (5 percent) (Banaag, 1997). Street children live in households below the poverty line and belong to the estimated 2.5 million squatter families in Metro Manila (UNICEF, 1988).

In a survey carried out in Manila, the street children were aged eight to 15, and had been working in the streets for an average of 5.3 years (range = less than one to 15 years). The children earned between US$1.47 and >$4.50 a day and used this money to help augment family income or earn income for their own survival. The street activities they engaged in included street vending, scavenging scrap materials, begging, cleaning cars, and acting as a "barker" for public utility vehicles (Bacos *et al.*, 2002, unpublished paper). Negative and deviant behaviour, such as gambling, use of prohibitive drugs, and adolescent sexual activity were also noted in the same survey and in other studies (Lamberte, 2000).

Smoking
In 1994, the Philippines produced 85 360 million cigarettes or 1.6 percent of the world's total production. The annual average per capita consumption of an adult (aged 15 and above) increased from 2 010 manufactured cigarettes in 1970 to 1972, to 2 110 manufactured cigarettes in 1980. Consumption fell to 1 770 manufactured cigarettes in 1992.

Two sources of data show that smoking prevalence was 33 percent in 1998 (Duante *et al.*, 2001) and 23.5 percent in 2000 (Tiglau, Baltazar and Baquiloid, 2001).

PREVALENCE OF MALNUTRITION IN URBAN AREAS
Nutritional status of children
Tables 11 and 12 show the trends in the nutritional status of preschool and school-age children in the Philippines, and in Metro Manila alone, from 1989/90 through 2001.

TABLE 11
Trends in the nutritional status of preschool and school-age children, the Philippines

	Prevalence (percentage)					
	1989/90	1992	1993	1996	1998	2001
Up to five years old						
Underweight	34.5	34.0	29.9	30.8	32.0	30.6
Stunting	39.9	36.8	34.3	34.5	34.0	31.4
Wasting	5.0	6.6	6.7	5.2	6.0	6.3
Overweight for age	0.6	0.7	0.4	0.5	0.4	1.0
Six to ten years old						
Underweight	34.2	32.5	30.5	28.3	30.2	32.9
Stunting	44.8	42.8	42.2	39.1	40.8	41.1
Overweight for age	0.1	0.2	0.6	0.4	neg	0.8

Source: FNRI-DOST, 2002.

There was a declining trend in the prevalence of underweight (weight-for-age) of children up to five years old, from 1989/90 through 2001, over a time span of 11 years. A reduction of 3.9 percentage points in the estimate of underweight, during the 11-year period, or an average of a 0.35 percentage point a year, indicates that the change in the national nutrition situation among children has been rather slow. A declining trend in the prevalence of stunting or chronic malnutrition in children up to five has likewise been reported with an average reduction of less than 1 percentage point a year. The picture of acute malnutrition (wasting) among these children has not improved through the 11-year period. The estimate in fact increased from 5.0 percent in 1989/90 to 6.7 percent in 1993, and showed very slight improvement in 2001 (6.3 percent). Among the school-age children, the trends were about the same as those of the preschool children.

A declining trend in the prevalence of underweight in children up to five years old was also recorded in Metro Manila for the period 1989/90 through 2001. The reduction of 8.3 percentage points in the prevalence of underweight for these children indicates that the improvement in the nutrition situation was faster in this urban region than at the national level. The picture of acute malnutrition did not improve. Among street children in Manila, the survey mentioned earlier noted that the prevalence of underweight-for-age in this group of high-risk children was 45.7 percent (Bacos *et al.*, 2002). The proportion who fell ill with infections (including respiratory and eye diseases) in the month prior to the survey period was 40 percent; 70 percent reported minor discomforts and pains (Bacos *et al.*, 2002).

As shown in Figures 3 and 4, the trends in underweight and wasting among children are clearly associated with the country's "boom-bust" pattern of growth.

TABLE 12
Trends in the nutritional status of preschool and school-age children, Metro Manila, the Philippines

	Prevalence (percentage)					
	1989/90	**1992**	**1993**	**1996**	**1998**	**2001**
Up to five years old						
Underweight	28.6	27.8	29.8	23.0	26.5	20.3
Stunting	27.9	28.8	30.0	22.8	25.7	20.0
Wasting	5.0	5.3	3.9	4.6	6.2	5.2
Overweight for age	1.7	1.4	0.6	1.2	0.7	2.5
Six to ten years old						
Underweight	33.0	33.0	31.6	26.6	*	*
Stunting	33.9	38.9	33.1	28.7	*	*
Overweight for age	0.4	0.7	2.2	1.3	*	*

* National estimates only.
Source: FNRI-DOST, 2002.

FIGURE 3
**Prevalence of wasting and GNP growth trends, 1989/90-2001
(children under five years of age)**

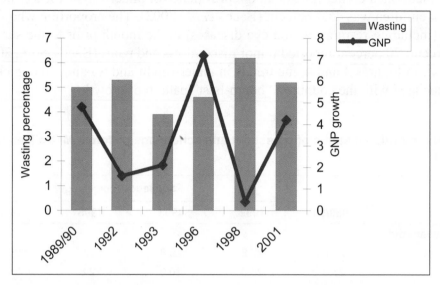

Source: FNRI-DOST, 2002; Templo, 2003.

FIGURE 4
**Prevalence of underweight and GNP growth trends, 1989/90-2001
(children under five years of age)**

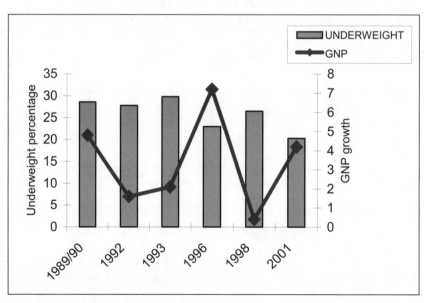

Source: FNRI-DOST, 2002; Templo, 2003.

With regard to overweight, the national prevalence among children up to five years old more than doubled during the 11-year period (i.e. from 0.4 to 1.0 percent). The same increased eightfold among school-age children (i.e. from 0.1 to 0.8 percent). Compared to estimates for Metro Manila, there were proportionately more overweight-for-age children up to five years old in the metropolis than in the Philippines as a whole during all the survey periods. The region of Central Luzon, which is the most accessible to Metro Manila, also reported statistics close to that of Metro Manila. Table 13 presents the nutritional status of these children in Metro Manila and other highly urbanized cities in various regions of the country.

TABLE 13
Nutritional status of children up to five years old in highly urbanized cities, the Philippines, 1998

	Prevalence (percentage)			
	Underweight	Stunting	Wasting	Overweight-for-age
Metro Manila	26.5	25.7	6.2	0.7
Iloilo	34.9	28.2	15.0	0.0
Bacolod	38.7	30.8	13.0	0.2
Cebu	34.5	41.2	4.6	0.2
Mandawe	36.5	39.3	2.5	0.3
Toledo	34.8	44.5	3.3	0.9
Zamboanga	33.3	29.7	5.3	0.6
Cagayan de Oro	32.5	29.7	11.4	0.0
Davao	27.6	36.2	4.3	0.0
Iligan	21.8	39.3	2.7	0.0
Baguio	18.7	32.9	1.1	0.2

Source: FNRI-DOST, 2002.

The higher prevalence of underweight and stunting in nearly all the other highly urbanized cities, compared to Metro Manila, and the higher prevalence of acute malnutrition in Iloilo, Bacolod and Cagayan de Oro reflect the stress from the rapid urbanization that these cities have experienced in recent years.

There were also increasing problems in terms of underweight among adolescents, both males and females, and overweight among females, but not males. The increasing overweight problem was also noted among adults of 20 years of age and over. In addition, 8.0 percent of adult males, vis-à-vis 40 percent of adult females, have a high waist-hip ratio (≥ 1.0 and ≥ 0.85, respectively).

Micronutrient malnutrition continues to be a significant public health problem in the country, although prevalence rates are lower in Metro Manila than the national average. Between 1993 and 1998, there were no major improvements with regard to the magnitude of the problem. As of 1998, vitamin A deficiency (VAD) prevalence stood at 38 percent among preschool children and 31 percent among pregnant women. Iron deficiency anaemia affected a third of the population, including ≥ 50 percent of infants and pregnant women, and a third of children aged six to 12 were iodine deficient (FNRI-DOST, 2002).

TABLE 14
Trends in the nutritional status of adolescents, adults and pregnant and lactating women, the Philippines and Metro Manila

Age group and nutritional status	Prevalence (percentage)			
	Philippines		Metro Manila	
	1993	1998	1993	1998
Adolescents (11-19 years old)				
Underweight, Male	21.6	23.0	*	*
Female	9.5	16.4	*	*
Male and female	15.8	19.8	*	*
Overweight, Male	2.6	1.2	*	*
Female	2.2	4.7	*	*
Male and female	2.4	2.9	*	*
Adults (20 years and over)				
Underweight, Male	11.5	11.1	*	*
Female	16.1	15.4	*	*
Male and female	16.6	13.2	*	*
Overweight, Male	14.4	17.0	*	*
Female	18.6	23.3	*	*
Male and female	16.6	20.2	*	*
Lactating women				
Underweight	10.9	13.4	11.9	19.5
Overweight	15.8	13.6	16.9	31.5
Pregnant women				
Nutritionally at risk	21.2	14.7	28.2	9.4

* National estimates only.
Source: National Nutrition Surveys, 1993 and 1998.

TRENDS IN HEALTH STATUS IN THE URBAN ENVIRONMENT
Infectious diseases
HIV/AIDS

From 1984, when the first AIDS case in the country was identified, until December 2001, 1 611 HIV Ab seropositive cases were recorded in the HIV/AIDS Registry; more males (61 percent) than females have been affected and 28 percent were OFWs. Various epidemiologists, however, estimate the actual number of HIV cases as between a low of 5 000 and a high of 13 000. Using the high estimate, this translates to a national prevalence of 0.02 percent of the total population.

Described as a "nascent epidemic", the number of HIV/AIDS cases has been increasing, albeit at a slow pace. Between 1984-92 and 1993-99, the annual confirmed cases ranged from fewer than 100 cases to more than 100 but less than 200 cases. Confirmed cases were reported from highly urban areas all over the Philippines. Higher prevalence rates (>1 percent) have been noted among registered female workers, homosexuals and drug addicts who use infected needles.

Tuberculosis

The Philippines continues to have one of the highest rates of tuberculosis in the world. It is common throughout all regions of the country, and all levels of society. According to the World Health Organization 1997 Annual Report, 22 million, or one out of four, Filipinos are infected with tuberculosis and 270 000 develop the disease each year. Each day 68 people die of tuberculosis (Reyes, 2003). Families living in slum areas are particularly susceptible to the disease as a result of crowded living conditions and poor hygiene practices.

Non-communicable diseases

While the leading causes of morbidity are communicable diseases (including diarrhoea, pneumonia, bronchitis, influenza, tuberculosis, malaria and chickenpox), deaths mainly result from non-communicable diseases and this trend has been increasing. The mortality rate from diseases of the heart and the vascular system (ranking first and second among the leading causes of mortality) were 73.2 and 56.2 per 100 000 population, respectively, in 1995. Cancer moved from fifth to fourth leading cause of death from 1975-90 to 1995, and deaths associated with diabetes mellitus have also been increasing.

The 1998 National Nutrition Survey revealed the data given in Table 15 on cholesterol, triglycerides, fasting blood glucose, hypertension, strokes and angina in adults aged 20 and over.

TABLE 15
Frequency distribution of total cholesterol, LDL-cholesterol, HDL-cholesterol, triglycerides and fasting blood glucose levels, and prevalence of hypertension, strokes and angina, the Philippines, 1998

	Result in mg (%)	Prevalence (%)
Total cholesterol	< 200	84
	200-239	12
	≥ 240	4
LDL-cholesterol	< 130	76
	130-159	16
	160-189	6
	≥ 190	2
HDL-cholesterol	< 35	65
	35-59	32
	≥ 60	3
Triglycerides	< 150	81
	150-199	10
	200-399	8
	≥ 400	1
Fasting blood glucose	< 110	94
	110-125	2
	≥ 126	4
Hypertension	-	27
Strokes	-	6
Angina	-	18

Source: Sy *et al.*, 2003.

Particular health problems in slums

The increasing congestion in metropolitan areas has taken its toll on the quantity and quality of urban services and infrastructure, mass transportation and general health conditions among the population. For example, the existing sewers in Metro Manila service more than the capacity they were constructed to serve. The waste generation rate in the city is 0.5-0.6 kg per capita/day, or approximately 6 000 tonnes of refuse each day. The government's waste collection agencies are able to collect and dispose of about 4 200 tonnes a day of this refuse, while the rest remains uncollected, dumped on street corners or vacant lots or thrown into storm drains and waterways.

Most of the urban poor live in high-risk areas such as along riverbanks and highly sensitive coastal areas, canals, railroad tracks, utility corridors and watersheds. These are the communities that are poorly serviced or not serviced at all.

PROGRAMMES THAT HAVE TRIED TO ADDRESS FOOD AND NUTRITION ISSUES

To improve the nutritional status of Filipinos, the country has drawn up a Philippine Plan of Action for Nutrition for 1999-2004, with the following targets.

1. Reduce the prevalence of protein energy malnutrition among preschool children and schoolchildren by 20 percent.
2. Reduce the prevalence of chronic energy deficiency among adults by 20 percent.
3. Reduce the prevalence of iron deficiency anaemia by 20 percent.
4. Reduce the prevalence of low to deficient serum retinol among children of six months to six years to values not higher than the 15 percent World Health Organization (WHO) cut-off for public health problems.
5. Reduce iodine deficiency indicated by the urinary iodine excretion level among school-age children to values not lower than the 100 µg/L WHO cut-off for public health problems.
6. Reduce the prevalence of overweight among preschool children, schoolchildren and adults by 20 percent.

National Nutrition Council Programmes

The National Nutrition Council has identified the following "impact programmes".

Home, school and community food production

The Philippines' Department of Agriculture implements the "Kabuhayan sa Gulayan" (livelihood through vegetable gardens) in Metro Manila and other cities to support urban agriculture and to address the issue of urban food security. Critical to the success of the programme is the identification and enactment of local ordinances to permit the use of public vacant lots for this purpose, as well as the provision of technical support, including cultivation technologies for urban areas.

Nutrition education

The programme includes the promotion of the nutritional guidelines for Filipinos through the school curricula, counselling activities and public campaigns.

Micronutrient supplementation

A policy of universal (i.e. for all children from one to five years old), twice-yearly dosing of vitamin A supplements has been adopted in the Philippines since 1993. High-dose (200 000 IU) vitamin A (VA) capsules are distributed to these children in health or micronutrient distribution centres on designated days.

Despite a high (80-90 percent) coverage in the VA supplementation programme, VA deficiency (serum retinol [SR]<20 mcg/dL) among children of one to five in the Philippines rose from 35 percent in 1993 to 38 percent in 1998. Analysis of the Philippines' 1998 National Nutrition Survey data, which had one-time SR measurements from 11 640 children of one to five, collected over an eight-month period, one month to more than six months after VA distribution, revealed that the impact of VA capsules on SR may be limited to the groups with the highest deficiency and up to four months or less after dose administration. This implies the need to shift from a policy of universal dosing to a targeted, more frequent (i.e. three times yearly) VA dosing scheme (Pedro *et al.*, 2003).

Meanwhile, iron supplementation, targeting pregnant and lactating women and children of six to 24 months old, as well as anaemic and underweight preschool and school-age children, adolescents and older persons, has also been beset with supply as well as compliance problems.

Food fortification

Two laws, Republic Act 8172 (an Act Promoting Salt Iodization Nationwide) and Republic Act 8976 (the Food Fortification Law), were enacted in 1995 and 1998, respectively, in support of food fortification. However, the salt iodization law, which requires that all salt for human consumption be iodized, has fallen short of target because of weaknesses in monitoring by concerned regulatory agencies. Efforts are now being made towards the strengthening of policies and infrastructures for the monitoring and regulation of salt in the market, as well as in preparation for the full implementation of the Food Fortification Law, which focuses on the staples – rice, sugar, cooking oil and flour.

In order to promote accessibility for both urban and rural poor households, fortified foods, particularly iodized salt and fortified staples (when these become available), are to be sold in "rolling stores" at government-subsidized prices.

Food assistance

The programme includes centre- or school-based regular supplementary feeding during calamities or civil disturbances, and feeding programmes such as school breakfasts and milk feeding, as well as price discount schemes for rice and other staples through the "rolling stores".

The major issue concerning this approach, as with other programmes, has always been sustainability.

Bibliography

Asian Development Bank (ADB). 2002. *Key indicators of developing Asia and Pacific countries 2002: population and human resource trends and challenges.* Pasig City, the Philippines (www.adb.org/statistics).

Bacos, F.F., Ramirez, M.A.R., Dorado, J.B., Velasco, R.E. & Barba, C.V.C. 2002. *The nutritional status of streetchildren in Manila – why some are nutritionally well-off or worst-off.* Terminal Report. Neys-Van Hogstraten Foundation. (unpublished paper)

Banaag, C.G. 1997. *Resiliency: stories found in Philippine streets.* Manila, AUSAID, National Project on Street Children, and the United Nations Children's Fund (UNICEF).

De Guzman, M.P.E., Agustin, C.P., Recto, M.R.C., Lana, R.D. & Diaz, J.H. 1987. Street foods in the Philippines. *JNDAP,* 1(4): 117-121.

Duante, C., Velandria, F., Orense, C. & Tangco, J. 2001. Correlates of hypertension and android obesity among Filipino adults. *Philippine J. Nutr.,* 48(1-2): 81-102.

Duque, F. 2003. *The national health insurance in the face of the demographic crisis.* A paper presented at the 25th Annual Meeting of the National Academy of Science and Technology, Manila. July.

Florentino, R.F. & Mondala, A.U. 1998. Streetfoods and junkfoods: facts, fads and fallacies. *Philippine J. Nutr.,* 45 (1-4): 19-30.

Florentino, R.F., Pedro, M.R.A. & Molano, W.L. 1996. The changing dietary intake and food consumption patterns in the Philippines. In *Changing dietary intake and food consumption in Asia and the Pacific.* Tokyo, Asian Productivity Organization.

Florentino, R.F., Villavieja, G.M. & Laña, R.D. 2002. Dietary and physical activity patterns of 8- to 10-year-old schoolchildren in Manila, Philippines. UNU Press. *Food and Nutr. Bull.,* 23(3): 267- 273.

FNRI-DOST (Food and Nutrition Research Institute, Department of Science and Technology). 2001. *The Philippine nutrition facts and figures.* Taguig, the Philippines.

FNRI-DOST (Food and Nutrition Research Institute, Department of Science and Technology). 2002. *The Philippine nutrition facts and figures.* Supplement 1. Taguig, the Philippines.

Lamberte, E.E. 2000. *Today's Metro Manila Streetchildren.* Manila, De La Salle University.

Molano, W., Yap, A., Barba, C. & Nueva-Espana, M. 2003. *An analysis of the nutritional status of rural households in the Philippines.* Philippines Food and Nutrition Research Institute. (unpublished paper)

National Statistics Office (NSO). 2000. *Census of Population and Housing.* Manila.

National Statistics Office (NSO). 2003. *2001 Survey on Children.* Presented during the Fourth National Health Research Forum, Manila, 6-7 August.

Ofreneo, R.P. 1997. *Globalization: from history to herstory.* Paper presented at the Roundtable Discussion on Globalization: from History to Herstory, sponsored by the National Centennial Commission – Women's Sector, University of the Philippines, 30 September.

Pedro, M.R.A., Cheong, R.L., Madriaga, J.R. & Barba, C.V.C. 2003. The Philippines' Vitamin A Supplementation Programme: Indicative Impact, Policy and Programme Implications. Paper presented at the satellite meeting on Programmes in Public Nutrition – Successful Micronutrient Programmes, 17th International Congress of Nutrition, Vienna, 23-25 August 2001 and XXI International Vitamin A Consultative Group, Morocco, 3-5 February 2003.

Philippine Institute of Development Studies (PIDS). 2003. National Statistical Coordination Board (dirp.pids.gov.ph).

Population Commission. 2002. *APPC Country Report,* p. 27-32 (www.popcom.gov.ph).

Reyes, C.M. 2003. *Country development programming framework for the Philippines: assessment of the social sector.* (unpublished paper)

Sy, R.G., Dans, A.L., Eduardo, F.B., Amarillo, M.L. & Velandria, F.V. 2003. The prevalence of dyslipidemia, diabetes, hypertension, strokes and angina pectoris in the Philippines. *Philippine J. Internal Medicine,* 41: 1-6.

Templo, O.M. 2003. *Country development programming framework for the Philippines: Philippine development context and challenges.* (unpublished paper)

Tiglau, T., Baltazar, J. & Baquilod, M. 2001. *Baseline Behavioural Risk Factor Survey.* Paper presented during the National Statistics Month. National Institute of Health 2001 Forum, the Philippines.

UNICEF. 1988. *The situation of streetchildren in ten cities.* Manila. United Nations Children's Fund.

Impact of globalization on food consumption, health and nutrition in urban areas: a case study of Brazil

Ana Lydia Sawaya, Paula Andrea Martins and Vinicíus Jose Baccin Martins[1]

URBANIZATION, DEMOGRAPHIC CHANGE AND HEALTH

Brazil's population in 2001 was estimated at 172 million, 80 percent of whom live in urban areas (United Nations Population Division [UNPD], 2001). Population growth in Brazil has slowed down significantly. In the last decades, population concentration has increased in the southeast, the country's most developed region in economic activity and creation of jobs. São Paulo is the largest city with approximately 17.9 million inhabitants, followed by Rio de Janeiro with over 10 million (UNPD, 2001). There are an additional 18 cities in Brazil with populations exceeding 750 000 (UNPD, 2001). The proportional population distribution by region practically did not change in the period analysed. More than half the population lives in the south and southeast (57.4 percent in 2000). Just under one-third lives in the northeast (28.1 percent in 2000). The north and centre-west – regions in which the economic frontiers are expanding – had a slight population increase (from 13.2 percent in 1991, to 14.5 percent in 2000) (OPAS, 2002). Urban concentration is more pronounced in the southeast, south and centre-west regions. The north and northeast, which are less developed, present the lowest urban concentrations (OPAS, 2002).

TABLE 1
Urbanization rate (percentage) in Brazil and major regions, 1991, 1996 and 2000

Regions	1991	1996	2000
Brazil	**75.6**	**78.4**	**81.3**
North	59.0	62.4	69.9
Northeast	60.7	65.2	69.1
Southeast	88.0	89.3	91.0
South	74.1	77.2	80.9
Centre-west	**81.3**	**84.4**	**86.7**

Source: IBGE demographic census (1991 and 2000) and population count (1996) (OPAS, 2002).

[1] Ana Lydia Sawaya, Ph.D.*
Paula Andrea Martins, M.Sc.
Vinicíus Jose Baccin Martins, B.Sc.
*Disciplina de Neurofisiologia e Fisiologia Endócrina
Departamento de Fisiologia Universidade Federal de São Paulo
R. Botucatu 862, Vila Clementino
04023-060 São Paulo, Brazil
Tel.: 55-11-5083-2108, Fax.: 55-11-5539-5365, E-mail: anafisi@ecb.epm.br

Shifts in demographic structure

The population distribution by age groups shows that 44.5 percent of the people were under 20 years of age in 1960 (Figure 1). There has been a marked increase in the population over 60 years of age: in 1970, older people represented 5 percent of the entire Brazilian population, and in the year 2000 they represented 12 percent. These changes are a result of a variety of factors, which are discussed below. They include declining fertility and infant mortality rates and a shifting proportion of mortality from younger to older age categories.

FIGURE 1
Population occupying the Brazilian territory, 1960 to 1990

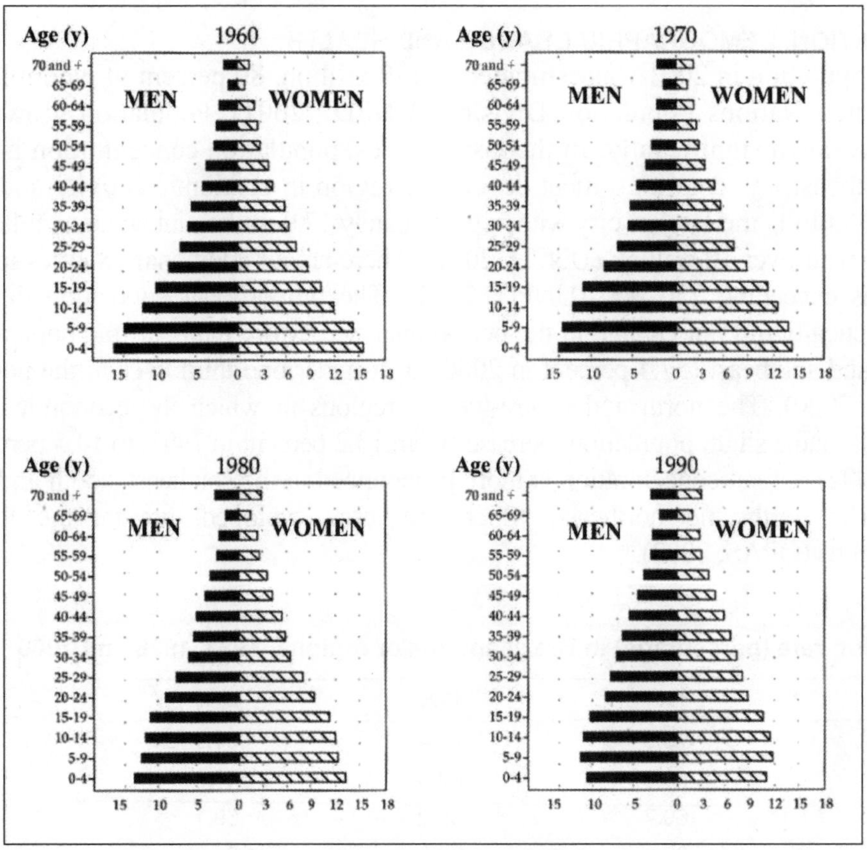

Reproduced by permission of Savier Editoria de Livros Médicos Ltda. Originally published in "A desnutrição dos pobres e dos ricos: dados sobre a alimentação no Brasil". Oliveira, J.E.D. de, Cunha, S.F. de C., Marchini, J.S, Sarvier Editora de Livros Médicos Ltda., São Paulo, 1996.

Total fertility rate decreasing

The total fertility rate is represented by the average number of live births that women have had by the end of their reproductive period. This rate has been progressively falling in Brazil (in 1991 it was 2.73; in 1996, 2.40; in 1999, 2.30). Rates below 2.1 are suggestive of fertility that is insufficient to ensure population replacement. The decreasing rate is associated with several factors such as growing urbanization; reduction of the infant mortality rate; improvement in educational levels; wider use of contraceptives; greater participation of women in the workforce; and job instability (OPAS, 2002). The only age group that has shown an increase in specific fertility rate is the adolescent group (15 to 19 years of age), especially in the northern region (OPAS, 2002).

Life expectancy increasing

Life expectancy at birth has been rising across all regions for both sexes and is currently 68.3 years – 64.5 for males and 72.3 for females (IBGE population projections for Brazil and its major regions, 1991-2020) (OPAS, 2002). The southern regions have the highest life expectancy, while the northeast has the lowest, but the latter region presents the highest average in number of years gained since the beginning of the period analysed.

Ageing structure of mortality

Brazil's infant mortality rate (IMR) is 49.7/1 000 live births, down from 69 in 1980-1990. The northeast region has the highest IMR (88) while the south has the lowest (26.7) (OPAS, 2002). There has been a consistent downward trend in IMRs across all regions of Brazil, reflecting improvements in living conditions, declining fertility and the effects of public interventions in the areas of health, sanitation and education, among other aspects.

The proportional death rate by age has decreased among the young and increased for the population over 60 years of age.

TABLE 2
Proportional death rate (percentage) per age group (in years),[1] 1990 and 1998

		Age group					
		<1	1-4	5-9	10-19	20-59	60 +
Brazil	1990	11.9	2.2	0.9	2.9	32.4	49.7
	1998	7.8	1.4	0.6	2.8	33.2	54.2

[1] Starting at ten years of age.
Source: OPAS, 2002.

Social inequality

There has been an increase in social inequality in the nation since 1960, with the northeast defined as the poorest region, and the south and part of the southeast as the wealthiest regions (Campos *et al.*, 2003).

Figure 2 shows these social inequality indexes – the higher the index, the better the social situation.

FIGURE 2
The evolution of the Social Inequality Index, 1960, 1980 and 2000

Reproduced by permission of Cortez Editoria. Originally published in *Atlas da exclusão social no Brazil, volume 2: dinâmica e manifestação territorial.* Campos, A., Pochmann, M., Amorim, R. & Silva, R., eds. Cortez Editora, São Paulo, 2003.

GROWTH IN GOODS, SERVICES AND COMMUNICATIONS

Increased access to consumer goods, water and sanitation facilities and communications can be used as a gauge to monitor changes in society.

In recent years there has been a very discrete increase in the consumer goods found in homes (Figure 3). Nearly all homes have a stove and most have radio and television. Ownership of a refrigerator has increased the most, although only 20 percent of homes have a freezer.

FIGURE 3
Homes with consumer goods, 1997-2001

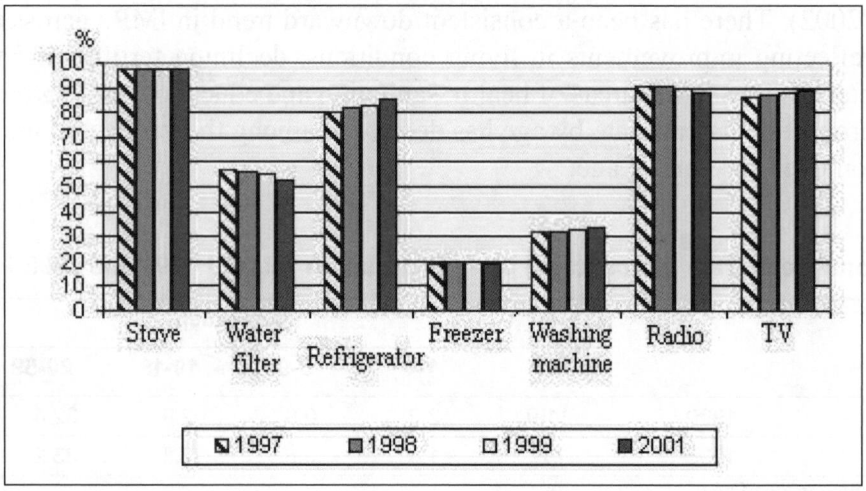

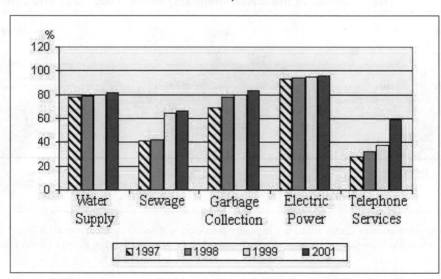

Source: IBGE, 2001.

Figure 4 illustrates the evolution over the past five years in access to basic utilities. Access to electricity and a clean water supply is above 80 percent. Access to sewage and telephones has increased the most. However, access to services is not evenly distributed throughout the country. For example, in 1999 in the northern, northeastern and centre-west regions, only 50 percent of the inhabitants had the advantage of sewage services (OPAS, 2002).

FIGURE 4
Access to utilities, 1997-2001

Source: IBGE, 2001.

Communications

Telephone

There has been a large increase in the number of homes with telephones. Land-line telephones were implemented in the country with internal services mainly provided by international corporations. The presence of national companies has traditionally been minor, gaining some relevance only after Telebrás established programmes to develop successful products. The sector's trade balance reflects the recent massive post-privatization investments, mainly in mobile phone businesses, where the telephone components are mostly imported (BNDES, 1999a).

Internet

The Internet in Brazil experienced an 84 percent growth leap between January 1998 and January 1999, as compared to the 46 percent worldwide rate. In addition, the Web in Brazil accounts for 50 percent of all Latin American traffic (BNDES, 1999b). Brazilian Internet traffic has increased significantly. An interesting indicator of this growth is the fact that, in late 1996, 90 percent of the traffic originating in the country went to internationally based sites, whereas that percentage has currently decreased to 60 percent, indicating greater interest in Brazilian sites, which consequently means more hits. The highest concentrations of traffic are in Rio de Janeiro and São Paulo. It is estimated that 60 percent of the national traffic total is from São Paulo, and 30 percent from Rio. The increased use of the Internet is explained by the greater availability of telephone lines and the overall reduction in Internet service provider subscriber fees, but it is also related to people's desire to be integrated with the Web (BNDES, 1999b).

Brazilian Internet users access the Web daily or almost daily. The majority of users reported accessing it either from home or work. Cyber cafés and other public Internet access points are not as commonly used (BNDES, 1999b).

Transportation

Road transport is the main transportation means in Brazil. Trucks carry 56 percent of all cargo within the country, while rail and fluvial transport account for 21 and 18 percent of the total, respectively. This predominance of road transport is explained by existing legislation, which hinders waterway transportation, by the lack of investments in rail and river links, and by the shortcomings of the public administration (Ministério dos Transportes, 2003). Both the national economy and the transportation systems before the mid-1950s were quite incipient. The gross domestic product (GDP) barely reached US$30 billion, and exports were practically limited to coffee. From that period on, there was accelerated development. The national motor industry was launched, the roster of export items was diversified, with the predominance of manufactured goods, and since then the GDP has increased 30-fold, which has also stimulated the expansion of the transportation grid. The national road network today covers 1 355 000 km, of which 140 000 km are paved (Ministério dos Transportes, 2003). The number of motor vehicles in the country has increased rapidly over the last decades (from 3 145 in 1991 to 19 310 in 2000), ahead of countries such as Mexico and China (ANFAVEA, 2003).

Air transport

Air travel in Brazil has paralleled the country's growth. Industrialization and progress, which caused a large number of the Brazilian population to migrate to the cities, and the need for interchange with other nations, made aeroplanes a necessity (Ministério dos Transportes, 2003). Each year new groups of passengers come on board, with the sector growing at an 8 percent annual rate in recent years, at twice the pace of the world average. The number of flying passengers per year went from 43 million in 1994 to more than 80 million in 2002. Tourism is expected to drive intense growth in air travel in the next few years (Ministério dos Transportes, 2003). Expensive fares, hard-to-reach airports, as well as the low incomes of most of the population are still some problems that make air travel in Brazil a means of transportation just for the elite (Ministério dos Transportes, 2003).

Other indicators of cultural and social change
A significant distortion in the distribution of cultural and entertainment assets and facilities can be seen. According to the Institute of Applied Economic Research, 73.2 percent of Brazilian municipalities do not even have a museum, and just 7.2 percent of towns have cinemas. With regard to public libraries and book stores, the situation is not very different, since only 10.9 percent have two or more libraries, and no more than 35.4 percent have book stores, facts which point to the geographic aspects of the existing cultural and economic inequalities (IBAM, 2001).

The banking sector has been modernizing rapidly. Banks have invested heavily in automating their activities, specifically in what is known as the frontline of banking (teller operations and ATMs). It is estimated that, between 1995 and 1998, the investments of Brazilian financial institutions in automation reached US$6.5 billion. In 1992 there were 4 900 ATMs in Brazil, a figure that in 2003 already exceeded 24 000 (BNDES, 2000a).

CHANGES IN DIETARY PATTERNS
The evolution of availability of nutrients (energy and types of foodstuffs) in urban areas
Metropolitan surveys of family budgets carried out in the 1960s, 1970s and 1980s collected information that permits the characterization of the evolution of the Brazilian diet. Over 30 years, important changes were detected, with obvious effects on the nutritional profile of the population. The observed changes include an increase in the consumption of products from animal sources, especially milk and dairy products, but also meat and eggs; a decline in the consumption of cereals, beans, roots and tubers; and a massive substitution of animal fats (lard, bacon and butter) by vegetable oils and margarine. Overall, the effects of these changes on the population's health were positive, improving the dietary protein, micronutrient and lipid composition of the diet (with an increase in the polyunsaturated and saturated fatty acids ratio and reduction of the cholesterol content). The negative aspect of these changes was an increase in the total lipid content of the diet observed in the southeast which, by 1988, had reached close to 30 percent, the highest recommended level (Oliveira, Cunha and Marchini, 1996).

For the period of 1974/75 to 1987/88, data regarding the food intake of the populations of the metropolitan areas show that there was a decrease in quantities and in the percentage of adequacy of calories. The decline in energy consumption ranged from 6 percent in the northeast to 26 percent in Brasilia (Sichieri *et al.*, 1997).

Direct information and measurements of food consumption for the period from 1990 to 1995 are rare and scattered. It is believed that the decrease in inflation and the rise in income among the lower socio-economic levels could have resulted in greater food consumption. The increase in agricultural output in the years 1993/94 and 1994/95 would speak in favour of a greater availability, but not necessarily of a greater consumption of food. Despite the overall increase, the production of rice and beans – the basis of the diet of a great majority of Brazilians – did not go up. With the increase in the population, albeit at a slower pace, it would seem that the poor are consuming fewer of these staples (Oliveira, Cunha and Marchini, 1996).

The National Metropolitan Surveys on Family Budgets were carried out between March 1987 and February 1988 (POF-1988) and again between October 1995 and September 1996 (POF-1996). The POF-1988 surveyed 13 611 homes and the POF-1996 assessed 16 014, covering 11 metropolitan areas. Both surveys arrived at a value for daily per capita domestic food availability, dividing the total quantity of food bought in the month by the number of residents and by the number of days in the month (Monteiro, Mondini and Costa, 2000).

The relative contribution of different food groups to dietary energy was calculated for two agglomerated metropolitan groups: the north-northeast and the more developed regions in the southeast, south and centre-west, referred to in Table 3 as centre-south. According to the POF-1996, families with incomes below two minimum monthly salaries represented 18.6 percent of the total number of families in the metropolitan areas of the northern and northeastern regions combined and only 5.8 percent of the total of metropolitan families living in the centre-south. On the other hand, family incomes above 30 minimum monthly salaries were found in 6.6 percent of the metropolitan families living in the north and northeast, and in 12.8 percent of the metropolitan families of the centre-south (Monteiro, Mondini and Costa, 2000).

The values of the daily per capita availability of energy declined from 1 919 kcals in 1988 to 1 711 kcals in 1996. The values for the northern and northeastern metropolitan areas were 1 704 kcals and 1 706 kcals, and 1 965 kcals and 1 712 kcals for the metropolitan areas of the centre-south (Monteiro, Mondini and Costa, 2000). For both regions, the most dramatic change was an increased percentage of dietary energy from meat and sausages. In the latter metropolitan areas, between 1988 and 1996, the proportion of expenses on meals away from home grew from 24.4 to 26.1 percent, while it declined from 25.6 percent to 21.7 percent in the metropolitan areas of the north and northeast (Monteiro, Mondini and Costa, 2000).

TABLE 3
Percentage of dietary energy supplied by different food groups in metropolitan areas of Brazil in 1988 and 1996

Food groups	North-northeast		Centre-south		Brazil	
	1988	1996	1988	1996	1988	1996
Cereals	30.6	32.9	35.0	35.3	34.4	34.8
Beans	7.4	7.3	5.6	5.3	5.8	5.7
Vegetables	0.5	0.5	0.6	0.5	0.6	0.5
Roots and tubers	12.1	8.9	3.2	2.7	4.6	4.0
Meat and sausages	12.5	14.1	10.5	13.0	10.8	13.2
Milk and dairy products	5.7	6.0	8.4	8.9	8.0	8.2
Sugar and soft drinks	13.5	13.9	13.2	13.5	13.2	13.7
Vegetable oils and fats	10.0	10.0	15.2	12.9	14.4	12.4
Fruit and fruit juices	3.3	2.4	3.2	3.2	3.2	3.0
Nuts	0.3	0.2	0.1	0.1	0.2	0.1
Eggs	1.5	1.3	1.5	1.0	1.5	1.0
Lard, bacon and butter	0.7	0.6	0.9	0.7	0.9	0.7
Alcohol	0.4	0.5	0.5	0.6	0.5	0.6
Seasoning and spices	0.2	0.3	0.4	0.4	0.4	0.4
Other preparations	1.2	1.0	1.7	1.8	1.6	1.6
TOTAL	**100.0**	**100.0**	**100.0**	**100.0**	**100.0**	**100.0**

Source: Monteiro, Mondini and Costa, 2000.

The importance of meals away from home and the growth of fast food chains

The fast-paced life in the large Brazilian cities has made the food service sector very promising, maintained by loyal clients, who by necessity have meals in restaurants every day. Currently, one out of every four meals is eaten away from home. This includes meals in bars, restaurants and bakeries; by delivery; in hospitals, aeroplanes, trains and fast food chains. It represents a market of R$3.5 billion. The figure is still low, when compared to European patterns, in which 70 percent of meals are eaten away from home. It does, however, represent a significant change, if compared to the beginning of the 1990s and it is already moving towards the North American pattern, in which the ratio is of one meal away from home for each two in the household. The food industry is growing at a pace of nearly 13 percent per year, representing 20 percent of the revenues of the food sector in the country. Products such as industrialized mayonnaise, ready-made dressings and canned oils, for restaurants and coffee bars, have been growing at 10 percent per year. Growth in this area has also been accelerated by the successive economic crises of the past years because, for fear of losing their jobs, employees put in longer hours at work, a pattern conducive to more meals away from home.

Fast food chains now have greater revenues than bars and a little under those of Brazilian bakeries. According to estimates, the fast food sector has revenues of R$2.7 billion per year in the country. McDonald's, the largest fast food chain in the country, opened in Brazil in 1979 and today owns 570 restaurants, 640 kiosks and 17 coffee stands. The total number of McDonald's restaurants grew 379 percent between 1993 and 2002. The most significant evolution occurred among the franchised outlets. From 1998 to 2002, the number of workers leapt from 22 000 to 36 000 (Jornal da Tarde, 2002).

The food retail sector in Brazil

A dramatic increase of 19.6 percent in the number of supermarkets and hypermarkets was observed between 1998 and 1999. During the same period, the number of traditional retail shops (mainly "mom-and-pop" produce and grocery stores) grew by only 1.8 percent. The poor performance of the traditional outlets has been associated with their conversion to self-service shops (BNDES, 2000b). The food retail sector in Brazil is undergoing an accelerated process of consolidation. The five largest chains went from a 23 percent share of gross revenues in 1994 to 40 percent by October 1999 (BNDES, 2000b).

THE IMPACT OF GLOBALIZATION ON LIFESTYLES
Types of occupation and sedentary work: more than half of all jobs are now in the service sector

Labour force distribution by economic sector has changed radically over time. Brazil has kept abreast of global changes in employment migration, first from agriculture to industrial activities, and then on to services. Service job openings have been considerably higher than new positions in the manufacturing industry since the 1960s, and have gone ahead of employment in agriculture since the 1980s. Today the service sector employs more people (33 million) than agriculture (11 million) and industry (10 million) combined (IPEA, 2002).

Types of leisure activities (television hours per day)

Data from the last National Home Sampling Survey, carried out in 2001, show that television ownership has permeated all layers of society, from the upper and middle classes to less privileged areas. In the poorest urban areas such as Natal, in the state of Maranhão, the number of television sets was close to 86 percent. Television is today the main source of entertainment, even for lower-income families, who spend five to eight hours a day in front of the television. It is watched mostly for entertainment. News and information come second (A Tribuna do Norte, 2002).

Crime

In the steps of the process of globalization of values and loss of cultural and religious traditions, there has been an increase in the mortality rate due to external causes in Brazil, a fact that is generally associated with the growth of social differences. Accidental deaths, mainly traffic fatalities, predominated mortality rates by the end of the 1970s. In the 1980s, however, those causes were overtaken by deaths caused by homicides (Figure 5). It is noted that the mortality rates from this specific cause increased considerably between 1979 and 1998. This increase becomes even more marked when the figures for males are analysed separately (IPEA, 2000).

FIGURE 5
Male mortality rates (per 100 000 inhabitants) resulting from external causes, Brazil, 1977/98

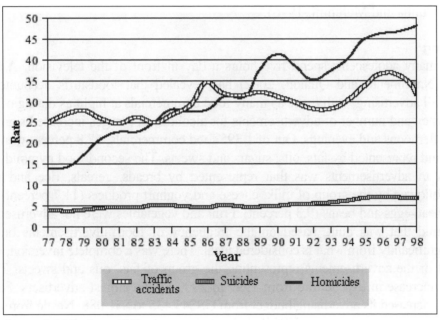

Source: de Mello Jorge, 2000.

Tobacco

Between 1970 and 1980, cigarette smoking increased by 132 percent. There were 25 million smokers in the second half of the 1970s but, by 1987, Brazilian capitals had close to 33 million smokers, which means a 32 percent increase in ten years. Approximately 32.6 percent of the adult population smokes regularly, with the habit distributed among 11.2 million women and 16.7 million men. Most smokers acquire the habit between the ages of 15 and 19, and the majority of smokers are found among people who are 20 to 49 years old. The percentage of smokers among females is higher than among males in the younger age groups, which suggests that the former are starting earlier and smoke more intensely. The proportion of smokers across all age groups is higher in rural areas than in urban centres. It is estimated that there are nearly 200 000 deaths per year in Brazil as a result of smoking.

Alcohol

Alcoholic beverages are easily available throughout Brazil, making alcoholism fairly prevalent. Pinga or cachaça, the most popular type of low-cost hard liquor in Brazil, is distilled from fermented sugarcane. It contains a high percentage of alcohol (around 40 percent) and this makes it a significant source of calories for a large part of the population (Oliveira, Cunha and Marchini, 1996).

It was estimated in 1980 that 41 million Brazilians regularly consumed alcoholic beverages, four million of whom drank often or a lot. In São Paulo, the prevalence of alcoholism represented 12 percent of the general population. In Rio de Janeiro, the prevalence of alcohol intake included 51 percent of the population, and 3 percent were regarded as alcoholics. There was a 22.6 percent prevalence of alcoholism among the low-income urban population of Salvador, Bahia. Studies show that poverty, unemployment and alcoholism are linked (Oliveira, Cunha and Marchini, 1996).

Epidemiological studies on alcoholism have shown that the male/female ratio ranges from 8:1 to 14:1. The prevalence of alcoholism is higher among individuals aged between 30 and 49, although there is evidence that addiction already sets in at 20 years of age (Oliveira, Cunha and Marchini, 1996).

Advertising

In Brazil, many adolescents spend five hours a day in front of the television. A 2002 study (Almeida, Nascimento and Quaioti, 2002) has revealed that foodstuffs accounted for 27.5 percent of all advertising, with twice as many food commercials at night as during other periods. The frequency and number of advertisements for alcoholic beverages increased significantly on Saturday afternoons and evenings. Out of 1 395 food commercials, 57.8 percent were within the food pyramid represented by fats, oils, sugars and sweets. The second food pyramid group most often seen in advertisements was that represented by breads, cereals, rice and pasta (21.2 percent), followed by the group of milk, cheese and yoghurt products (11.7 percent) and by the group of meat, eggs and beans (9.3 percent). Fruit and vegetables were not advertised at all. The food pyramid that was built, based on the frequency of food advertisements on television, differed significantly from what is considered ideal. There was a complete inversion, with almost 60 percent of the advertisements representing the group of fats, oils and sweets. There was a significant increase in expenditure from 1999 to 2000 by the largest advertisers. For example, Coca-Cola increased its advertising budget from US$43 435 to $51 088; Nestlè from US$42 231 to $45 804; and McDonald's from US$19 485 to $23 500 (Grupo de Mídia de São Paulo, 2003).

Changes in jobs occupied by women

Employment for females in Brazil has grown more rapidly than for males. It is estimated that women occupied 70 percent of the 1 158 000 new job positions created in São Paulo between 1989 and 2001. The level of female employment rose 32.9 percent, whereas the increase for men did not exceed 8.7 percent during that period. The participation of women among employed workers went from 38.4 to 43.2 percent. Above all, the restructuring of the job market has lead to a reduction in formal sector jobs and growth in self-employment. There has been an overall reduction in the number of registered salaried employees in the private sector, with opposing trends between the sexes: 358 000 men were fired and 43 000 women were hired, resulting in an overall reduction in the salaried employment rate, which fell from 72.1 to 63 percent (SEADE, 2002). Entrepreneurial activity rose 102.9 percent among women and 21.1 percent among men. Despite the difference in percentages, the absolute numbers were similar. Table 4 shows the growth in female employment in several professional sectors. However, despite this increase, there was a reduction of 19.5 percent in average income among women, a lesser decrease, therefore, than the 31.5 percent fall observed among average wages received by males. Yet, in terms of monetary values, the difference in income levels between women (R$677) and men (R$1 058) persisted in 2001, but the gap diminished (SEADE, 2002).

TABLE 4
Typically female jobs account for the largest portion of the rise in employment in São Paulo

Large occupation groups	1989	2000	Variation
			(percentage)
TOTAL	2 693 632	3 054 635	13.4
Cleaning service workers and others	423 370	602 867	42.4
Back office and administrative workers	799 562	946 630	18.4
Teachers, communication professionals and lawyers	369 591	503 731	36.3
Retail and wholesale workers	191 204	323 763	69.3
Directors and managers	21 805	59 079	170.9
Technical and scientific occupations	116 346	152 162	30.8
Agriculture and farm workers	45 000	43 813	-2.6
Industry workers	587 337	414 142	-29.5
Unknown or ill-defined occupations	139 417	8 448	-93.9

Source: Ministry of Labour and Employment – MTE/Annual Social Information Report – Rais (SAEDE, 2002).

Prevalence of breastfeeding

There has been a systematic increase in what is known as *full breastfeeding*, which includes: (i) exclusive breastfeeding; (ii) breastfeeding, in addition to the infant receiving water, tea and juice; and (iii) breastfeeding complemented by the intake of solids, semi-solids and liquids, including formula milk (OPAS, 2002). In 2000, only about half of Brazilian children were still being exclusively breastfed at 30 days of life. At four months, the proportion of children who were exclusively breastfed corresponded to 18 percent of the total, with that percentage falling to 8 percent at the end of the sixth month (OPAS, 2002).

NUTRITIONAL STATUS
Nutrition in children

In spite of the decrease in infant mortality and the improved nutritional conditions of children in general, malnutrition – particularly undernutrition – remains a serious concern in the poorest regions of the country and in pockets of poverty in large cities. There are regions with social and nutritional indicators that are equivalent to those in Africa, coexisting with regions where the situation is similar to that of the United States.

Three national studies, ENDEF (IBGE, 1974), PNSN (INAN, 1989) and PNDS (BENFAM, 1996), assessed the nutritional status of children under five years of age in Brazil, according to the criteria of weight-for-age, height-for-age, and weight-for-height.

Stunting is the main type of malnutrition in Brazil, although the prevalence of both stunting and underweight has dropped. Regional differences, however, increased, as the prevalence of malnutrition experienced its greatest drop in the richest regions of the country. Wasting has low prevalence in Brazil. The prevalence of malnutrition is greater in the rural population and the regions most affected are the north and northeast.

TABLE 5
Trends in undernutrition in children under five

	Stunting			Underweight			Wasting		
	1974-75	1989	1996	1974-75	1989	1996	1974-75	1989	1996
Brazil	32.0	15.4	10.5	18.4	7.0	5.7	5.0	2.0	2.3
North urban	38.9	23.0	16.2	24.5	10.7	7.7	6.4	3.1	1.2
Northeast	45.6	27.3	17.9	27.0	12.4	8.3	5.5	2.4	2.8
Southeast	22.0	8.1	-	13.4	4.2	-	5.2	1.9	-
South	25.1	8.7	5.1	11.7	2.3	2.0	3.6	1.4	0.9
Centre- west	25.5	8.2	8.2	13.3	4.0	3.0	3.9	2.0	2.9

Note: below two standard deviations (NCHS).
Source: WHO, 1997.

A reduction in the prevalence of malnutrition in Brazilian children is more related to improvements in the urban infrastructure than to the reduction of poverty in itself. Conditions that afforded gains in the reduction of malnutrition, particularly in the cities, are related to good practices in care, and access to basic health services, including family planning and water treatment and sanitation services. The reduction is also likely to be a result of the decrease in energy expenditure, as a consequence of the reduction in physical activity and of the lesser severity of infections, despite the increase in poverty and the probable reduction in food consumption. These data show that malnutrition was reduced by focused measures, such as better health care, and did not depend exclusively on the increase in income.

Nutritional status of adults

While undernutrition has also decreased among adults, obesity has increased, especially in the lower-income population of the richest region (southeast).

TABLE 6
Secular trend of the prevalence (percentage) of obesity in two regions of Brazil, according to per capita income quartiles

	Men			Women		
Region/income quartiles	1975	1989	1997	1975	1989	1997
Northeast						
1st quartile	0.7	0.8	1.7	3.0	5.2	8.0
2nd quartile	0.9	1.4	3.8	3.2	8.3	14.1
3rd quartile	1.1	3.0	4.1	4.5	7.8	13.3
4th quartile	2.8	5.2	8.4	7.6	9.9	14.6
Southeast						
1st quartile	1.6	2.9	3.8	6.6	11.6	15.0
2nd quartile	2.2	4.2	9.7	8.0	16.5	12.1
3rd quartile	3.3	7.8	9.6	10.3	14.8	13.2
4th quartile	5.3	8.1	9.5	9.1	13.2	8.2

Source: Monteiro, Conde and Popkin, 1999.

The socio-economic situation and nutritional status of families living in shantytowns

Brazil has the third highest rank for social inequality in the world and, as such, data that consider just the national average prevalence might mask the identification of the impact of globalization and of the existing differences between rich and poor. In view of this, the authors carried out several studies in populations living in shantytowns of the southeast (São Paulo) and northeast (Maceió). In São Paulo, the richest city in the country, the population of the shantytowns reaches 20 percent, or close to 2 million people (SEHAB, 1994), but it represents 50 percent of the total inhabitants of Maceió, capital of the second poorest state of the country.

Anthropometric and socio-economic censuses were carried out in 22 shantytowns of São Paulo in 1990-1991. Most adults were migrants (88 percent), of whom 70 percent had come from the northeast of the country. Many of the children were also migrants (26.5 percent), and 79 percent of them had also come from the northeast. Ninety percent of the population earned less than US$1/day. Data on illiteracy and level of schooling showed that 20 percent of the men and 23 percent of the women were illiterate and 11 percent of the men and 15 percent of the women had never gone to school. Illiteracy was also present in a high percentage of children older than ten (12 percent) (Sawaya *et al.*, 2003).

Most of the housing units were shacks made out of wood (74 percent) and had inadequate sanitary conditions (20 percent). An interesting observation was that the families, as far back as the beginning of the 1990s, were not very large (four to five persons). Despite the fact that living and income conditions were so precarious (average per capita income was US$0.54/day) and also despite the high prevalence of malnutrition – 44 percent of the families studied had at least one undernourished member – 15 percent of the families had at least one obese member (Sawaya *et al.*, 2003).

Multiple logistic regression analyses were carried out to identify the factors most associated with the presence of chronic malnutrition (short stature) in the family. In the complete model, the most important variable was the absence of floor tiles in at least one of the rooms of the dwelling, while living in wood shacks showed marginal statistical significance. After the elimination of the least significant variables, the most important factors for explaining the presence of malnutrition in the household were lack of tiled floors (b=0.739, OR=2.1, p=0.027) and absence of water taps (b=0.489, OR=1.6, p=0.042), both factors known to be strongly associated with parasitic infections and diarrhoea. The chance for a child or adolescent (up to 18 years) of suffering from short stature was twice higher when there was no floor covering in all rooms and increased by 60 percent when there was no treated water supplied to the household (Sawaya *et al.*, 2003).

Coexistence of malnutrition and obesity

The evaluation of the nutritional status of children, adolescents and adults showed the presence of both undernutrition and obesity. The study identified adolescent girls with short stature and obesity, with a prevalence of this group being almost twice higher than that of the group of obese girls with normal stature. Another finding that stood out was the simultaneous presence of malnutrition and obesity within the same family (13 percent of the families had at least one undernourished member and another obese) (Sawaya, 1997). These findings alone show the importance of classifying the nutritional status for programmes to prevent and treat malnutrition, and also that income is not a precise variable for poor populations living in urban areas.

Among adults, the prevalence of overweight and obesity was greater than that of undernourished individuals (Figure 6).

FIGURE 6
Nutritional status of adults living in 22 shantytowns in São Paulo

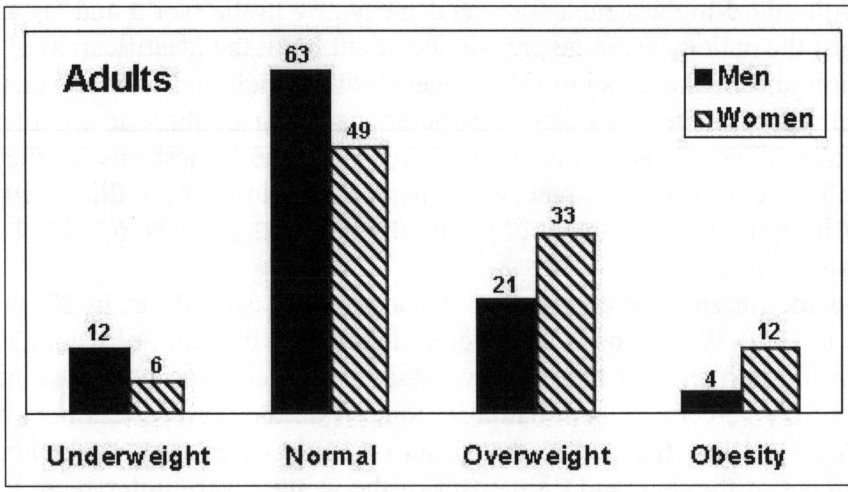

Note: underweight: BMI ≤ 20; normal: BMI >20 and < 25; overweight: BMI ≥ 25 and < 30; obesity: BMI ≥ 30.

The presence of some obese individuals and others malnourished in the same family, as well as that of adolescent girls with short stature (a consequence of undernutrition in childhood) and obesity, are facts that seem incompatible. If there is a high prevalence of undernutrition, there is clearly food insufficiency as a result of poverty and low incomes. How could there be obesity? The only plausible explanation could be changes in mechanisms by the human body to control energy expenditure. Studies performed by our group have shown reduced metabolic rates at rest in children with short stature (Grillo *et al.*, 2000), reduced fat oxidation (Hoffman *et al.*, 2000), higher susceptibility of weight/height gain when provided with diets richer in fat (Sawaya *et al.,* 1998), and increased blood pressure rates (Fernandes *et al.*, 2003), among other factors.

Undernutrition, obesity and food consumption
In addition to the studies undertaken in the shantytowns of São Paulo, our group also investigated an extremely poor population living in a shantytown in Maceió in 1999 (Florêncio *et al.*, 2001). Table 7 describes socio-economic and nutritional conditions even worse that those found in São Paulo. Almost the entire population lived in shacks made of plastic sheets, without any basic sanitation or supply of treated water. Most of the inhabitants were illiterate and unemployed, earning their living from odd jobs. The entire population was below the poverty line.

TABLE 7
Socio-economic conditions in the shantytown population of Maceió, Alagoas, 1999

Population	
Number of families	315
Number of people	1 247
Average number per shack	4
Income	
Monthly family income (US$)	40.32[1]
Per capita income (US$/day)	0.32[1]
Schooling (≥ seven years of age)	
Read	37.3%
Write	36.7%
Illiterate	63.3%
Occupation	
Unemployed	81.6%
Regularly employed	3.6%
Housing conditions	
Shacks made of plastic sheets	81.0%
Without floor covering	91.0%
Without refrigerator	80.6%
One-room dwellings	89.0%
Sanitary conditions	
Dwellings without water supply	97.0%
Dwellings without bathrooms	95.0%
Dwellings without treated water for drinking	78.0%

[1] Exchange rate as of 30 September 1999: US$1 = R$1.87.
Source: Florêncio *et al.*, 2001.

These conditions explain the high prevalence of moderate/severe undernutrition in children (21 percent, -2 Z score) and adults (19.5 percent, body mass index [BMI] <20 kg/m^2, calculated from Table 8). On the other hand, there is once again the coexistence, among adults, of undernutrition and overweight/obesity. Among women, the prevalences of undernutrition and obesity were higher than among men (Table 8).

TABLE 8
Nutritional classification, according to BMI, of adults living in a shantytown, Maceió, Alagoas

BMI	Sex		Total
	Males N (%)	Females N (%)	N (%)
Undernutrition (< 20 kg/m^2)	42 (16.9)	62 (22.1)	104 (19.5)
Normal (≥ 20 and <25 kg/m^2)	166 (66.1)	229 (45.9)	295 (55.5)
Overweight (≥ 25 and < 30 kg/m^2)	40 (15.9)	65 (23.1)	105 (19.7)
Obesity (>30 kg/m^2)	03 (1.2)	25 (8.9)	28 (5.3)
TOTAL	251 (47.2)	281 (52.8)	532 (100.0)

Source: Florêncio *et al.*, 2001.

When we analysed the food intake of adults, we found that they had a very monotonous diet, with little diversity and of poor quality (Table 9). Energy intake (adjusted for stature) was well below energy requirements, even for the obese individuals (Table 10). One of the findings that caught our attention was the fact that the short women, either obese or undernourished, had a similar energy intake (Florêncio *et al.*, 2003).

TABLE 9
Type of preparations consumed at main meals by men and women living in a shantytown, Maceió, Alagoas

Meal	No. of preparations reported	Preparations mentioned (by order of frequency)
Breakfast	13	Coffee w/ sugar, bread, corn porridge, fried egg, cream crackers, chicken, powdered milk, pumpkin, beef, sweet biscuit, fruit juice, salami and bologna sausage.
Snack	9	Bread w/ margarine, cream crackers, soft drink, fruit juice, sweet biscuit, coffee w/ sugar, sweets, bananas.
Lunch	12	Beans, rice, pasta, chicken, cassava flour, meat, fish, fried egg, fruit juice, coffee w/ sugar, jerked beef, beef liver.
Dinner	21	Coffee w/ sugar, porridge, rice, bread w/ margarine, beans, chicken, fried egg, meat, pasta, fish, cassava flour, jerked beef, milk, pumpkin, sweet biscuit, salami, sweet potatoes, sardines, yams.
Night snack	3	Coffee, cream crackers and milk.

Source: Florêncio *et al.*, 2003.

Food intake, therefore, does not seem to be the most important differential between obese and malnourished women. Even among those from the group of obese women without short stature, the fat ingestion was 27 percent of the energy intake. Which other factors would be involved? One factor that certainly could have contributed to obesity is the reduction of physical activity caused by the move from the countryside to the city. These findings also reveal how complex is the relation between consumption of foods and nutritional status. There are several mechanisms that the body might bring into play to save energy, in situations of nutritional deficiency.

TABLE 10
Adequacy of the energy intake, according to sex and anthropometrical characteristics, of an adult population living in a shantytown, Maceió, Alagoas

	Energy intake	Short			Non-short		
		U	N	O	U	N	O
Men	Intake, kJ	5 882	6 812	7 226	6 501	7 815	8 373
	Requirement adjusted for stature, kJ	8 987	8 987	8 987	8 987	8 987	8 987
	% adequacy	65	76	80	68	81	87
Women	Intake, kJ	4 527	5 029	4 686	5 560	5 497	6 556
	Requirement adjusted for stature, kJ	7 234	7 234	7 234	7 234	7 234	7 234
	% adequacy	62	69	65	73	72	86

Note: U = undernourished (BMI < 20); N = normal (BMI ≥ 20 and <25); O = overweight + obesity (BMI ≥ 25).
Source: Florêncio *et al.*, 2003.

THE EVOLUTION OF HEALTH PATTERNS
Child morbidity and mortality

The leading causes of death in children, diarrhoeal disease and acute respiratory infections, have progressively declined across most Brazilian regions. Mortality from diarrhoeal disease decreased over the decade of the 1990s from 9.3 to 6.8 percent. The highest mortality is in the northeast (11.9 percent) while in the southeast mortality from diarrhoeal disease is 3.3 percent. (Ministry of Health/Cenepi: SIM.) A persistent decline has been observed in the proportional mortality caused by acute respiratory infections (1991=10.5 percent; 1996=7.9 percent; 1998= 7.1 percent) (OPAS, 2002).

Adult morbidity and mortality

Close to 60 percent of the total deaths reported in the country in 1998 belonged to three groups: circulatory diseases (32.4 percent), external causes (14.9 percent) and neoplasias (14.0 percent), with slight variations in comparison with the values of 1991. During the years analysed, circulatory diseases were the most significant in all regions.

AIDS

There is a tendency towards a reduction of mortality through AIDS in all regions of the country, as a result of the adoption of therapy with anti-retroviral drugs and the implementation of a national policy of free distribution of these medicines. The AIDS mortality rate per 100 000 inhabitants fell from 9.6 in 1996 to 6.7 in 1998. Male AIDS mortality is two or three times greater than that of females, at 9.6 for males compared to 3.8 for females (OPAS, 2002).

The incidence of HIV/AIDS infection has stabilized in most regions. There is evidence however, that the incidence has been growing in the heterosexual segment, especially among women and newborns in the south and in socially less privileged population groups (OPAS, 2002).

Diabetes

Across the whole of Brazil, the mortality rate for diabetes is increasing. In 1998, the average rate of prevalence of diabetes mellitus in large Brazilian cities was 7.6 percent, varying from 5.2 percent in Brasília to 9.7 percent in São Paulo. The prevalence was approximately the same for men (7.5 percent) and women (7.7 percent). As might be expected, the rates rose with age: 30-39 years (2.7 percent), 40-49 years (5.5 percent), 50-59 years (12.7 percent) and 60-69 years (17.4 percent). Moreover, 46.5 percent of the diabetics did not have knowledge of their condition and 22.3 percent of those who were aware of being diabetic did not undergo any type of treatment (OPAS, 2002).

Cardiopathies and high blood pressure

From 1991 to 1998, there was an increase in the mortality rate through circulatory diseases in all regions of the country, except for the southeast, where a discrete reduction of ischemic heart and cerebral-vascular diseases was observed. For all of Brazil, the mortality rate per 100 000 persons for ischemic heart disease increased from 44.6 to 46.8 in 1991 and 1998 respectively, while the mortality rate for cerebral vascular disease was 51.6 for both periods. Mortality from all circulatory diseases is higher in males than in females. In 1998 the mortality rate for all circulatory diseases was 169.7 for males and 147.1 for females (OPAS, 2002).

Neoplasias

Between 1991 and 1998, the mortality rate through malignant neoplasias increased in all regions of Brazil. In 1998 malignant lung, stomach and prostate tumours predominated among males. In women, the breast, uterine cervix, lung and colon were the most frequent sites (OPAS, 2002).

The most frequent malignant neoplasia in Brazil is the non-melanoma skin neoplasia, with higher rates in the southeast, south and centre-west. Among males, most frequent were those of the prostate, stomach and lung (including the trachea and the bronchium), the latter two showing values well above those observed for women. Malignant breast neoplasia has the highest incidence among females (OPAS, 2002).

PROGRAMMES THAT ADDRESS FOOD AND NUTRITION
Pastoral da Criança (children's pastoral)

The programme with the widest national coverage (3 480 municipalities in 27 states) and local grassroots presence is the Pastoral da Criança, a non-governmental organization (NGO) linked to the Catholic Church, which operates with volunteer teams (134 344 active community leaders have visited 1 621 251 children). In recent years, its activities have expanded and been provided with better structures, as a result of partnerships with the federal government and universities. The main merits and the importance of this programme are centred on its wide outreach and in the mobilization of civil society that it promotes (REBIDIA, 2003).

Fome Zero (zero hunger)

The administration of President Lula launched in 2003 the Programa Fome Zero, which has been receiving sharp criticism in Brazil, because of its focus on aid and assistance (based on the distribution of food aid cards), its huge operational costs and relative inefficiency in regard to fighting the mechanisms that generate poverty and social exclusion in the country. Its outreach is still small (36 903 families) (MESA, 2003).

Centro de Recuperação e Educação Nutricional (CREN) (Centre for Nutritional Recovery and Education)

CREN was launched in 1994, as a university extension project. The objective of the project was to help fight malnutrition through research and development of methodologies suited to the Brazilian situation. The methodology developed includes the following.

- Active search through anthropometric surveys performed at the community level.
- Multiprofessional and interdisciplinary teamwork, with the participation of professionals from the fields of paediatrics, nutrition, social services, psychology, pedagogy and nursing.
- Treatment through home visits, outpatient clinics and day hospitals for the most severe cases.
- Identification and reinforcement of the social network of family and assessment.
- Nutritional education and psychological assistance.
- Offering courses to university-level (undergraduates and graduates) health care professionals, as well as health care workers and community health agents, focusing on practical activities in the communities; analysis of the information collected; follow-up of children's growth; nutritional education; and including a clear knowledge of the mechanisms that generate social exclusion.

A group of networks already exists in Brazil that uses the CREN methodology, in São Paulo, Campinas, Belo Horizonte, Salvador, Maceió, Rio de Janeiro, Pedras de Fogo, Itabuna and Fortaleza.

From the managerial point of view, CREN proposes the establishment of NGOs, with funding both from the state and the private sector, and a strong educational focus. The objective of this structure is to overcome the obstacles that have resulted in the failure of previous Brazilian governmental initiatives in the last decades, such as the discontinuity of social programmes; waste of financial resources; administrative and operational inefficiency; excessive managerial centralization; and lack of knowledge of the causes most often associated with poverty and social exclusion. In addition, there has been excessive political use of programmes.

The CREN team has published several studies on the subject, both in Brazil and abroad, in addition to running two Web sites (www.desnutricao.org.br) and (www.cren.org.br).

An outline of our proposal to fight malnutrition in Brazil, which has recently been presented to the Brazilian Federal Government, is presented as Figure 7.

CONCLUSION

Brazil has a wide geographic area but low population density – its growth has decreased considerably in the last decade. In economic terms, the country has grown just a little over 1 percent per year, and it presents one of the worst levels of social inequality, which has worsened even further during the past 40 years. The divide between rich and poor is structural, based mainly on educational differences and slave trade tradition. Given these characteristics, it is difficult to draw up a unified picture of the impact of globalization, based on national averages. The best description is a coexistence of characteristics typical of poor countries, especially in the north and northeast, with great technological advances, and the extreme momentum in the growth of the indicators of globalization, in the south and southeast. There are also certain specific characteristics, such as the great urban concentration (82 percent) of the population, and the concentration of the poor in shantytowns, already with the presence of factors that are typical of globalization, such as scant physical activity and consumption of industrialized foods. In addition, in recent years, the incidence of violence and drug addiction has grown systematically.

The most suitable programmes to fight poverty and social injustice, as well as to improve health and nutritional conditions, require direct and sustained contacts in and with poor communities (which are characterized by significant degrees of isolation and exclusion). Greater inclusion in the communities, with a robust educational component and attention to the improvement of living conditions, as well as level of education and job availability, are actions that can mobilize and bring together government, society and universities.

FIGURE 7
Framework proposed by CREN to fight malnutrition in Brazil

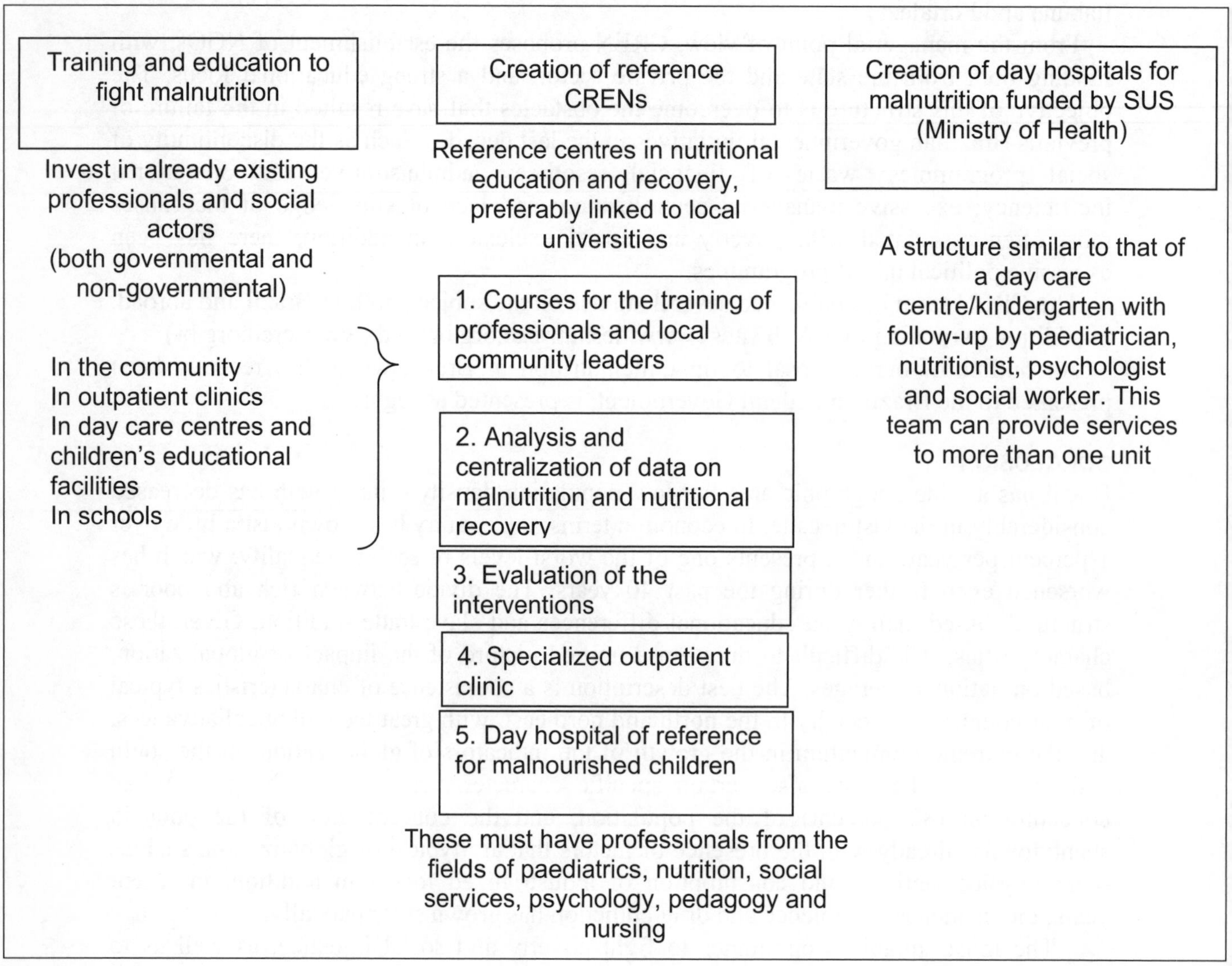

Training and education to fight malnutrition	Creation of reference CRENs	Creation of day hospitals for malnutrition funded by SUS (Ministry of Health)

Training and education to fight malnutrition

Invest in already existing professionals and social actors
(both governmental and non-governmental)

In the community
In outpatient clinics
In day care centres and children's educational facilities
In schools

Creation of reference CRENs

Reference centres in nutritional education and recovery, preferably linked to local universities

1. Courses for the training of professionals and local community leaders

2. Analysis and centralization of data on malnutrition and nutritional recovery

3. Evaluation of the interventions

4. Specialized outpatient clinic

5. Day hospital of reference for malnourished children

These must have professionals from the fields of paediatrics, nutrition, social services, psychology, pedagogy and nursing

Creation of day hospitals for malnutrition funded by SUS (Ministry of Health)

A structure similar to that of a day care centre/kindergarten with follow-up by paediatrician, nutritionist, psychologist and social worker. This team can provide services to more than one unit

Bibliography

A Tribuna do Norte. 2002. *Televisão é o principal lazer de carentes.* 19 September 2002 (www.tribunadonorte.com.br/anteriores/020917/natal/natal4.html). Accessed September 2003.

Almeida, S.S., Nascimento, P.C.B.D & Quaioti, T.C.B. 2002. Amount and quality of food advertisements on Brazilian television. *Rev. Saúde Pública*, 3: 353-5.

ANFAVEA. 2003. *Anuário Estatístico da Indústria Automobilística Brasileira.* Associação Nacional dos Fabricantes de Veículos Automotores (www.anfavea.com.br). Accessed September 2003.

BENFAM. 1996. Sociedade Civil Bem-Estar Familiar no Brasil. 1997. PNDS - Pesquisa Nacional sobre Demografia e Saúde, 1996. Rio de Janeiro, Brazil. Ed. Rio de Janeiro.

BNDES. 1999a. *Complexo eletrônico: diagnóstico e perspectivas.* Banco Nacional de Desenvolvimento Econômico e Social (BNDES) Setorial, Rio de Janeiro, No. 10, p. 269-284 (www.bndes.gov.br). Accessed September 2003.

BNDES. 1999b. *A internet e os provedores de acesso.* Banco Nacional de Desenvolvimento Econômico e Social (BNDES) Setorial, Rio de Janeiro, Brazil. No. 10, p. 115-172 (www.bndes.gov.br). Accessed September 2003.

BNDES. 2000a. *Os mercados de automação bancária e comercial.* Banco Nacional de Desenvolvimento Econômico e Social (BNDES) Setorial, Rio de Janeiro, Brazil. No. 11, p. 47-70 (www.bndes.gov.br). Accessed September 2003.

BNDES. 2000b. *Aspectos atuais do varejo de alimentos no mundo e no Brasil.* Banco Nacional de Desenvolvimento Econômico e Social (BNDES) Setorial, Rio de Janeiro, Brazil. No. 11, p. 101-122 (www.bndes.gov.br). Accessed September 2003.

Campos, A., Pochmann, M., Amorim, R. & Silva, R., eds. 2003. *Atlas da exclusão social no Brazil, volume 2: dinâmica e manifestação territorial.* São Paulo, Brazil. Cortez Editora.

de Mello Jorge, M. Helena. 2000. Acidentes e violências no Brasil: Breve análise de suas fontes de dados. *In* IPEA. *Forum de debates - Criminalidade, Violência e Segurança Pública no Brasil: Uma Discussão sobre as Bases de Dados e Questões Metodológicas Acidentes e violências no Brasil: breve análise de suas fontes de dados.* Instituto de Pesquisas Econômicas Aplicadas (www.ipea.gov.br). Accessed September 2003.

Fernandes, M.T., Sesso, R., Martins, P.A. & Sawaya, A.L. 2003. Increased blood pressure in adolescents of low socio-economic status with short stature. *Pediatric Nephrology*, 18: 435-439.

Florêncio, T.M., Ferreira, H.S., Cavalcante, J.C., Luciano, S.M. & Sawaya, A.L. 2003. Food consumed does not account for the higher prevalence of obesity among stunted adults in a very low income population in the Northeast of Brazil (Maceio, Alagoas). *Eur. J. Clin. Nutr.*, 11:1437-46.

Florêncio, T.M., Ferreira, H.S., De França, A.P., Cavalcante, J.C. & Sawaya, A.L. 2001. Obesity and undernutrition in a very low-income population in the city of Maceiò, northeastern Brazil. *Br. J. Nutr.*, 86: 277-285.

Grillo, L.P., De Carvalho, L.R., Silva, A.C., Verreschi, I.T.N. & Sawaya, A.L. 2000. Influência das condições socioeconômicas nas alterações nutricionais e na taxa de metabolismo de repouso em crianças escolares moradoras em favelas no município de São Paulo. *Rev. Assoc. Med. Bras.*, 46: 7-14.

Grupo de mídia São Paulo. *Mídia Dados 2* (www.gm.org.br). Accessed September 2003.

Hoffman, D.J., Sawaya, A.L., Verreschi, I., Tucker, K. & Roberts, S.B. 2000.Why are nutritionally stunted children at increased risk of obesity? Studies of metabolic rate and fat oxidation in shantytown children from São Paulo, Brazil. *Am. J. Clin. Nutr.*, 72: 702-707.

IBAM. 2001. Equipamentos culturais e de lazer existentes nos municípios. Instituto Brasileiro de Administração Municipal Série Estudos Especiais No. 31 Rio de Janeiro, Brazil. (www9.cultura.gov.br/relats/sav95_02.pdf). Accessed September 2003.

IBGE. 1974. *ENDEF – Estudo Nacional Despesa Familiares, 1974.* Instituto Brasileiro de Geografia e Estatística. (www.ibge.gov.br). Accessed September 2003.

IBGE. 2001. *National Home Sampling Survey.* Instituto Brasileiro de Geografia e Estatística (www.ibge.gov.br). Accessed September 2003.

INAN. 1989. *PNSN - Pesquisa Nacional sobre Saúde e Nutrição. Resultados Preliminares 1989.* Instituto Nacional de Alimentação e Nutrição. Brasília.

IPEA. 2000. Forum de debates - Criminalidade, Violência e Segurança Pública no Brasil: Uma Discussão sobre as Bases de Dados e Questões Metodológicas. Acidentes e violências no Brasil: breve análise de suas fontes de dados. Instituto de Pesquisas Econômicas Aplicadas (www.ipea.gov.br). Accessed September 2003.

IPEA. 2002. *Empregos no Brasil. Volume I: Sessão Informativa sobre Política 2002. Relatório conjunto* Banco Mundial/IPEA. Instituto de Pesquisas Econômicas Aplicadas (www.ipea.gov.br). Accessed September 2003.

Jornal da Tarde. 2002 *Comer fora é um mercado de R$3,5* bi. 22 September.

MESA. 2003. *Programa Fome Zero*. Ministério Extraordinário de Segurança Alimentar e Combate à Fome. (www.fomezero.gov.br/html/pfz_1070.htm). Accessed September 2003.

Ministério da Saúde. (www.saude.gov.br). Accessed September 2003.

Ministério dos Transportes. 2003. (www.transportes.gov.br). Accessed September 2003.

Monteiro, C.A., Conde, W.L. & Popkin, B.M. 1999. Secular trends in obesity by social class: northeast and southeast of Brazil, 1975-1989-1997. *Arq. Bras. Endocrinol. Metab.*, 3: 1-14.

Monteiro, C.A., Mondini, L. & Costa, R.B. 2000. Secular changes in dietary patterns in the metropolitan areas of Brazil (1988-1996). *Rev. Saúde Pública*, 34: 251-8.

Oliveira, J.E.D. de, Cunha, S.F. de C., Marchini, J.S. 1996. *A desnutrição dos pobres e dos ricos: dados sobre a alimentação no Brasil*. São Paulo, Brazil. Ed. Sarvier.

OPAS. 2002. *Indicadores básicos para a saúde no Brasil: conceitos e aplicações*. Organização Pan-Americana da Saúde (www.opas.org.br). Accessed September 2003.

REBIDIA. 2003. *Pastoral da criança*. Rede Brasileira de Informação e Documentação Sobre Infância e Adolescência (www.rebidia.org.br/pastoral/index1.html). Accessed September 2003.

Sawaya, A.L., Martins, P., Hoffman D. & Roberts, S.B. 2003. The link between childhood undernutrition and risk of chronic diseases in adulthood: a case study of Brazil. *Nutr. Rev.*, 5: 168-75.

Sawaya, A.L. 1997. Transição: desnutrição energético-protéica e obesidade. *In* A.L.Sawaya, ed. *Desnutrição Urbana no Brasil em um Período de Transição*. São Paulo, Cortez Editora.

Sawaya, A.L., Grillo, L.P., Verreschi, I., Silva, A.C. & Roberts, S.B. 1998. Mild stunting is associated with higher susceptibility to the effects of high fat diets: studies in a shantytown population in São Paulo, *Br. J. Nutr.*, 128: 415-420.

SEADE (Fundação Sistema Estadual de Análise de Dados.) 2002. *Ocupação Feminina e Flexibilização das Relações de Trabalho na RMSP – 1989-2001*. Mulher e Trabalho. São Paulo, 2002. No. 8 (www.seade.gov.br). Accessed September 2003.

SEHAB (Secretaria da Habitação). 1994. São Paulo. Favelas na cidade de São Paulo. São Paulo *apud*. *Transição: desnutrição energético-protéica e obesidade*. São Paulo, Cortez Editora.

Sichieri, R., Coitinho, D.C., Pereira, R.A., De Marins, V.M.R. & Moura, A.S. 1997. Variações temporais do estado nutricional e do consumo alimentar no Brasil. *Rev. Saúde Coletiva*, 7: 31-50.

UNPD. 2001. *World urbanization prospects: the 2001 revision*. United Nations Secretariat, Department of Economic and Social Affairs, Population Division. ESA/WP/.173

WHO. 1997. *Global database on child growth and malnutrition.* World Health Organization (www.who.int/nutgrowthdb). Accessed September 2003.

Nutrition transition in Chile: a case study

Fernando Vio and Cecilia Albala[1]

INTRODUCTION

Latin American countries have seen important demographic, epidemiological and nutritional changes in the last decades. The demographic transition has occurred through a sustained decrease in fecundity, an increase in life expectancy and changes in the age structure of the population. These demographic changes have modified the epidemiological profile of the population. Specifically, the prevalence of non-communicable chronic diseases has been increasing. Nutritional changes similar to those in more industrialized countries have resulted in an increase in the prevalence of obesity. The consumption of diets with a high caloric density and sedentary lifestyles are closely related to the increase in the frequency of nutrition-related diseases, diabetes, hypertension, cardiovascular diseases and some types of cancer (WHO/FAO, 2003).

The prevention and management of these problems in Latin America are great challenges, considering the levels of poverty and inequality of the region, the financial restrictions of the public sector and a historical institutional weakness.

DEMOGRAPHIC INDICATORS IN LATIN AMERICA

The main demographic indicators of selected Latin American countries and Canada are described in Table 1. According to the Pan American Health Organization and the World Health Organization methodology (PAHO/WHO, 2001), countries are classified in three categories: very low child and very low adult mortality rate; low child and low adult mortality rate; and high child and high adult mortality rate. In another publication (Albala, Vio and Uauy, 2003) and according to the last available report of WHO (2002), Chile was classified in the second category (low child and low adult mortality rate). However, considering the Chilean data of the 2002 national population census (National Institute of Statistics, 2002), Chile belongs to the first category, which confirms the rapid transition changes that occurred in the last decades in the country (Vio and Albala, 2000; Albala *et al.*, 2001a).

---

[1] Dr Fernando Vio
    Dra Cecilia Albala
    Institute of Nutrition and Food Technology (INTA)
    University of Chile
    E-mail: fvio@inta.cl

TABLE 1
Demographic indicators of selected Latin American countries and Canada, 2001

Countries/ mortality stratum	% pop. <15	% pop. ≥60	% annual population growth	Total fertility rate	Crude death rate	Infant mortality rate	Life expectancy at birth
Very low child and very low adult mortality rate							
Canada	18.4	17.2	1.0	1.6	7.5	5.3	79.3
Cuba	20.3	14.3	0.3	1.6	7.2	7.2	76.4
Chile	25.7	11.4	1.2	2.1	5.2	8.9	76.3
Low child and low adult mortality rate							
Brazil	27.9	8.0	1.4	2.2	7.2	31.8	68.7
Costa Rica	32.3	7.5	2.7	2.7	4.2	10.2	76.1
Mexico	32.2	7.2	1.4	2.5	5.1	14.5	73.0
High child and high adult mortality rate							
Bolivia	39.1	6.2	2.2	3.9	8.2	67.0	63.5
Ecuador	32.9	7.1	1.7	2.8	5.8	30.0	70.5
Guatemala	43.0	5.3	2.6	4.4	6.8	49.0	65.6
Haiti	39.4	5.5	1.6	4.0	11.7	80.3	54.8
Nicaragua	42.1	4.7	2.7	3.9	5.4	45.2	69.3
Peru	32.4	7.5	1.6	2.6	6.2	43.0	69.8

Source: PAHO/WHO, 2001.

DEMOGRAPHIC, SOCIO-ECONOMIC, EPIDEMIOLOGICAL AND NUTRITION CHANGES IN CHILE

In the last decades Chile has undergone important changes which are described in the following Tables. From the demographic point of view, population changes are significant, with a decrease of the population under 15 years of age from 39.2 percent in 1970 to 25.7 percent in 2002. On the other hand, the population over 65 years of age increased from 5 to 7.2 percent in the same period. The total fertility and birth rate suffered an important decrease in the period, with a fall in the percentage of annual population growth from 1.8 to 1.3 percent. The infant mortality rate also decreased dramatically from 82.2 in 1970 to 8.9 in 2002. As a consequence, life expectancy has increased from 60.5 years in men and 66.8 years in women in 1970 to 73.2 and 79.5 in 2002, respectively.

Chile was a very urbanized country before the 1970s, with more than 75 percent of the population living in urban settlements. However, the urbanization process continued in the last decades to reach 86.7 percent of the population living in cities (National Institute of Statistics, 2002). This process has positive effects: increasing access to drinking-water and dwellings with sewers, increased literacy rates (Table 3) and better access to housing and health services. On the other hand, the urbanization process produces an increase in risk factors for chronic diseases, such as changes to diets with more fat, sugar and salt; an increasing sedentary lifestyle; more access to tobacco, alcohol and drugs; and also increasing environmental and psychosocial problems.

TABLE 2
Chilean demographic indicators

Indicators/years	1970	1982	1992	2002
% population <15	39.2	32.2	29.4	25.7
% population ≥65	5.0	5.8	6.6	7.2
Crude death rate	8.7	6.1	5.4	5.2
Infant mortality rate	82.2	23.6	14.3	8.9
Total fertility rate	3.4	2.8	2.6	2.1
Birth rate	26.4	23.8	21.6	17.1
% annual population growth	1.8	1.8	1.6	1.3
Life expectancy at birth				
male	60.5	67.8	68.7	73.2
female	66.8	74.8	75.8	79.5

Source: National Institute of Statistics, 2002.

TABLE 3
Trends in socio-economic indicators, Chile 1970-2002

Indicators/years	1970	1982	1992	2002
% urban population	75.1	82.2	83.5	86.7
GNP per capita*	2 230	2 148	3 020	4 900
Literacy rate	89.0	91.8	94.3	96.0
Access to drinking-water (% population)	58.0	87.0	95.2	99.7
% urban dwellings with sewers	35.0	62	84.4	94.1
Health expenditure per capita/ US$	52	76	116	369

Source: National Institute of Statistics, 2002.

TABLE 4
Proportion of causes of death from total causes, 1970-2000

Groups of causes	1970*	1982†	1992†	2000
Cardiovascular diseases (390-459)† (A80-88)* (I00-I99)[#]	22.3	27.6	29.0	27.9
Malignant tumours (140-208)† (A45-59)* (C00-D48)[#]	12.0	16.8	20.0	24.2
Injuries (800-999)† (AN138-150+AE138-149)* (V00-Y98)[#]	19.0	12.1	12.0	9.8
Respiratory (460-519)† (A89-96)* (J00-J99)[#]	17.4	8.5	11.1	10.5
Digestive (520-579)† (A97-104)* (K00-K93)[#]	6.9	8.6	6.3	7.2
Ill defined (780-799)† A137* (R00-R99)[#]	4.5	8.8	5.6	3.9
Infectious and parasitic (1-139)† A1-44* (A00-B99)[#]	10.9	3.8	2.9	2.6
Perinatal causes (760-779)† A131-135* (P00-P96)[#]	5.0	3.5	1.9	1.2
All others	2.0	10.3	11.2	12.7
Total	100	100	100	100

* ICD-VIII
† ICD-IX
# ICD-X
Source: National Institute of Statistics, 2000.

Demographic changes and increasing risk factors for chronic diseases have meant significant changes in the epidemiological profile of the population since the 1970s, which are described in Table 4. Cardiovascular diseases and tumours increased from 34.3 percent in 1970 to 52.1 percent in 2000. On the other hand, infectious diseases and perinatal causes decreased from 15.9 to 3.8 percent in the same period. Injuries and respiratory causes have also been reduced. These rapid changes occurred in a short time compared with other epidemiological transition situations (Frenk, Bobadilla and Lozano, 1991).

Despite the increase in the proportion of the total causes of death for cardiovascular diseases, and as a consequence of the decreased crude death rate (Table 2), the trend in the rates of cerebral-vascular disease and ischemic heart disease was also reduced from 1970 to 2000. However, the death rates for other diet-related diseases such as diabetes, breast cancer, prostate cancer and gall bladder cancer increased. In the last two cases, rates were almost three times the initial rate (Table 5).

TABLE 5
Mortality[1] by diet-related diseases in Chile, 1970-2000

Causes	1970	1980	1990	2000
Cerebrovascular disease	118.7	106.7	85.4	68.5
Ischemic heart disease	107.8	86.9	81.3	70.5
Diabetes	15.0	15.9	13.6	23
Breast cancer[2]	13.5	14.6	16.2	18.5
Prostate cancer	9.5	19.5	10.8	24.1
Gall bladder cancer	6.6	-	14.1	16.9

[1] Rates ≥15 years of age per 100 000.
[2] Females.
Source: National Institute of Statistics, 2000.

With the urbanization process, diets changed dramatically at the end of the 1980s and at the beginning of the 1990s. From 1982 to 1986 there was a huge economic crisis in Chile with a fall of 14 percent of the gross domestic product (GDP) in 1982 and 2 percent in 1983, with high unemployment and an increase in poverty (Tokman, 1985). In this period there was malnutrition in Chile but, after a few years, at the end of the 1980s, economic growth began. For the poor, more than 50 percent of incomes went on food expenditure, but unfortunately to buy food with a high proportion of fat, sugar and salt. On the contrary, consumption of cereals, legumes and other fibre-rich foods, such as vegetables and fruit, remained stable or declined (Table 6) (Crovetto, 2002).

Unbalanced and excessive food intake is associated with other lifestyle changes related to the increasing urbanization process in Chile, such as sedentary activities, stress, alcohol intake and smoking. In general, all these risk factors for non-communicable diseases are worst in low socio-economic levels (Table 7).

TABLE 6
Trends in food availability (by food group) in Chile, 1980, 1990 and 2000[1]

	1980	1990	2000	% change
Kcals/ per capita/day	2664	2519	2870	+ 7.8
% as fat per capita	20.4	22.0	26.6	+ 30.4
Vegetable fat g/per capita/day	30.9	27.5	39.4	+ 27.8
Animal fat g/per capita/day	29.6	33.9	45.4	+ 53.6
Cereals and pulses kg/per capita/year	159.1	143.4	142.6	-10.4
Vegetables and fruit kg/per capita/year	170.5	144.6	168.4	-1.2

[1]Average figures for 1979-1980, 1989-1990, 1999-2000.
Source: FAOSTAT data, 2003.

TABLE 7
Prevalence of risk factors for chronic diseases by socio-economic level (SEL), 25-64 years, Valparaiso, Chile, 1997

Risk factor	Socio-economic stratum			p value
	High	Medium	Low	
HDL cholesterol ≤ 35 mg%	13.8%	16.1%	12.6%	0.20
Total cholesterol ≥200 mg%	49.0%	47.1%	45.7%	0.68
Hypertension ≥140/90 mm hg	9.3%	9.8%	14.2%	0.00
Sedentarism (in leisure time)	78.9	83.1	89.4	0.00
Overweight BMI ≥ 25kg/m^2	56.4	61.0	65.3	0.00
Smoking habit (current)	39.8	39.5	42.9	0.22

Source: Jadue *et al.*, 1999.

The epidemiological and nutritional transition of Chile's native populations over the past 20 years is a clear example of the situation described above. We have examined over the past five years the effect of changes of socio-economic and cultural conditions on obesity prevalence and type-2 diabetes (TTD), in the Mapuche and Aymara groups. Our current data from rural communities show a threefold increase in the prevalence of diabetes, 3.5 percent in contrast to the 1 percent reported in 1985. Moreover, as the Mapuche migrated to urban zones of the major metropolis, Santiago, the prevalence of TTD rose to 9.8 percent. This population, believed to be genetically protected from TTD, in fact shows increased susceptibility to diabetes relative to the general population. This is clearly the effect of changing dietary patterns and physical inactivity in the urban setting (Pérez-Bravo *et al.*, 2001). The early report of a low prevalence of diabetes in the presence of high rates of obesity in Aymara and Mapuche Indians was not upheld by our recent studies, suggesting that the apparent protection of aboriginal people to nutrition-related chronic disease is dependent on diet and physical activity patterns (Uauy, Albala and Kain, 2001).

Most aboriginal populations today have changed their diet and physical activity patterns, following the model of industrialized societies. They now derive their diets completely or in large part from refined grains and high-sugar, high-fat foods (with elevated trans- and saturated fatty acid content) that are low in fibre. There is a decreased consumption of legumes and other plant-based foods. Life in urban and progressively even more in rural areas is predominantly sedentary and physically inactive. In these circumstances it is not surprising that obesity, insulin resistance and type-2 diabetes have reached epidemic proportions.

The combination of the change in diets and a sedentary lifestyle triggers increasing adiposity. The progressive increase in overweight and obesity is more prevalent in low socio-economic groups who have improved their incomes and bought not only high-fat/high-carbohydrate energy-dense food but also more televisions, increasing the number of hours spent in front of the television to an average of two to three hours on weekdays and three to four hours at the weekend. Data obtained in Santiago demonstrate that, besides inactivity, television viewing stimulates a child's preference for certain television commercials and increases the consumption of snacks in front of the television and other food purchased by children at school (Olivares *et al.*, 1999).

All these factors have increased the prevalence of obesity in preschool children (Figure 1), in first-grade children (six years old) (Figure 2), in pregnant women (Figure 3) (Albala *et al.*, 2001b) and in younger and older adults measured by different surveys in the country (Figures 4 and 5) (Vio, Albala and Crovetto, 2000; Ministry of Health, 2003).

FIGURE 1
**Prevalence of obesity in children two to five years old
(country and preschool), Chile 1996-2001**

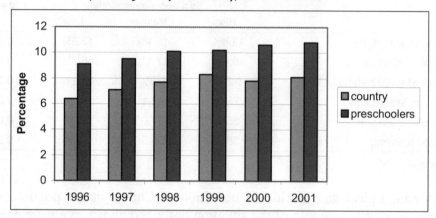

Sources: Ministry of Health (2003) and Junta Nacional de Jardines Infantiles (National board for Day care centres statistics).

FIGURE 2
**Trends in prevalence of obesity[1] in first-grade schoolchildren,
Chile 1987-2000**

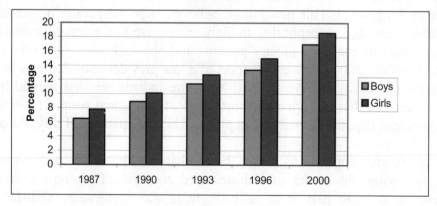

Source: Ministry of Education, 1987-2000.
[1] Weight/height>2 SD.

FIGURE 3
Prevalence of obesity and underweight in pregnant women,[1] Chile 1987-2002

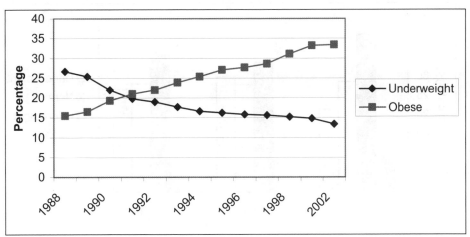

Source: Ministry of Health, Chile, 2003.
[1] Ministry of Health reference for pregnant women.

FIGURE 4
Obesity prevalence in adults, Santiago 1988-1992, Valparaiso 1997

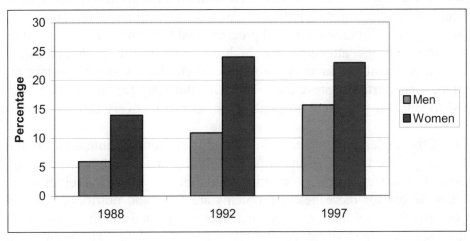

Source: Santiago Metropolitan Region Surveys 1988 and 1992 (Dra X. Berríos); Jadue *et al.,* 1999.

In all cases, the increasing obesity is impressive and constitutes the first nutrition problem in the country and one of the most important public health issues. Unfortunately, a situation similar to that in Chile is being observed in other Latin American countries (PAHO, 2000; Kain, Vio and Albala, 2003).

FIGURE 5
Nutritional state in the elderly, Chile 2002

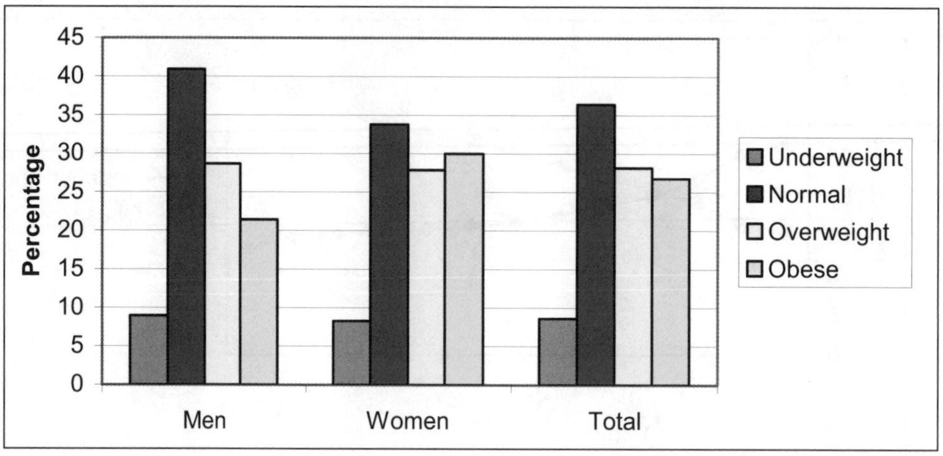

Source: Ministry of Health, 2003.

PROGRAMMES TO ADDRESS FOOD AND NUTRITION ISSUES

In the past, Chile was able to decrease malnutrition in a relatively short time with the implementation of adequate policies related to primary prevention (National Complementary Food Programme for all pregnant and lactating women and for all children under six years of age attending the high-coverage health programmes); secondary prevention for pregnant and lactating mothers and children who were at risk or had mild malnutrition; and tertiary prevention or rehabilitation for moderately or severely malnourished children who were hospitalized in special recovery centres (Vio and Albala, 2000).

As part of the epidemiological and nutritional transition in Chile, in 1998 the Ministry of Health changed the traditional maternal and child policies with new priorities based on cardiovascular diseases, cancer, injuries and mental health problems. The main conditioning factors for these health problems are food and nutrition, physical activity, tobacco and psychosocial and environmental factors. To address these factors, a strategic plan with goals for the period 2000-2010 was established, based on an intersector organization integrated by 28 governmental organizations and the National Board for Health Promotion (VIDA CHILE), which was decentralized to 12 regions and 308 counties. Strategies were developed for each one of the conditioning factors, which were implemented at the local level in preschool and school facilities, workplaces and municipalities. The main accomplishments of this policy have been a decentralized management model for health promotion with projects and programmes working throughout the country, goals to be fulfilled and a baseline founded on a national survey carried out in November 2000. At present, the challenge needs an integrated effort to change the behaviour of the population regarding food, physical activity, tobacco consumption and stress. This is difficult in the current environment, which promotes increasing the intake of fast food and soft drinks, a greater use of cars and electrical appliances, minimal physical activity, and an increased consumption of tobacco and other addictive substances.

The accomplishments in the food and nutrition aspects are in part a result of the elaboration of dietary guidelines in 1995-1997 by a group of experts following the methodology established by FAO with seven messages for the population (Ministry of Health, 1997); the reformulation of the food and nutrition programmes (National

Complementary Food Programme at the Ministry of Health and School Food Programme and Preschool Food Programmes at the Ministry of Education); and Food Sanitary Regulations for the industry to produce more healthy and safe food (Vio and Albala, 2000).

But the main advances in the food and nutrition area are related to education at the preschool and basic school level. In 2001 and 2002 an FAO project (food and nutrition education at the basic schools) was carried out in ten primary schools in four regions of the country to elaborate a methodology and materials to introduce food and nutrition contents in the basic education curricula (FAO, 2001). This project has been successful in producing the methodology and materials and is now in the phase of training schoolteachers throughout Chile in utilizing the methodology and materials in the 11 000 basic primary schools in the country. There is another ongoing project to integrate food and nutrition education with physical activity for preschool children and there is a campaign to educate consumers at the supermarkets with materials to induce the purchasing of more healthy food.

To cope with the high sedentary aspect of the Chilean population, physical activity guidelines were developed in 2001-2002 with six messages (Salinas, Vio and Bahamondes, 2003). Additionally, there is a specific policy to improve the number and intensity of physical activity hours at day care centres and primary schools in the whole country as well as to introduce physical activity in primary health care facilities through an agreement between the Ministry of Health and the National Institute of Sports.

CONCLUSION

Demographic, epidemiological and nutrition changes were so rapid in Chile that maternal and child policies were not changed successfully until the end of the 1990s. However, in 1998 a strong health promotion policy was implemented to cope with the increasing obesity in the population and the high levels of sedentarism. This policy has been successful in creating a state policy backed with funding, regulations and high coverage in the country but it is still insufficient for the magnitude of the problem.

Bibliography

Albala, C., Vio, F., Kain, J. & Uauy, R. 2001a. Nutrition transition in Chile: determinants and consequences. *Public Health Nutr.,* 5: 1-7.

Albala, C., Vio, F., Kain, J. & Uauy, R. 2001b. Nutrition transition in Latin America: the case of Chile. *Nutr. Review,* 56 : 170-176.

Albala, C., Vio, F. & Uauy, R. 2003. The global burden of nutritional disease: the case of Latin America. *In* M.J.G. Farthing & D. Mahalanabis, eds. *The control of food and fluid intake in health and disease.* Nestlé Nutrition Workshop Series. Pediatric Program. Vol. 51. Nestec Ltd, Vevey/Lippincott, Williams & Wilkins, Philadelphia, United States.

Crovetto, M. 2002. Changes in food structure and food consumption in Gran Santiago households 1988-1997. *Rev. Chil. Nutr.,* 29: 24-32.

FAO. 2001. Technical Cooperation Project. Educación en alimentación y nutrición en escuelas básicas. TCP/CHI/0065, 2001-2003. University of Chile, Ministry of Education, INTA.

FAO. 2003. *FAO food balance sheets, 1979, 1980, 1989, 1990, 1999 and 2000* (www.fao.org). Accessed January 2003.

Frenk, J., Bobadilla, J.L. & Lozano, R. 1991. *The epidemiologic transition: the Latin American experience.* Seminar on Causes and Prevention of Adult Mortality in Developing Countries, Santiago, Chile. International Union for the Scientific Study of Population (IUSSP).

Jadue, L., Vega, J., Escobar, M.C., Delgado, I., Garrido, C., Lastra, P., Espejo, F. & Peruga, A. 1999. Risk factors for chronic non-communicable diseases: methods and results of CARMEN program basal survey. *Rev. Med. Chile,* 127: 1004-1013.

Kain, J., Vio, F. & Albala, C. 2003. Obesity trends and determinant factors in Latin America. *Cad. Saude Pública, Rio de Janeiro*; 19: (suppl.1): S77- S86.

Larenas, G., Arias, G., Espinoza, O. *et al.* 1985. Prevalence of diabetes mellitus in an indigenous community (Mapuche) in IX Region. *Chile Rev. Med.,* 113: 1121.

Ministry of Health. 1997. *Guías de alimentación para la población chilena.* C. Castillo, R. Uauy & E. Atalah, eds. Santiago de Chile, Ed. Diario La Nación.

Ministry of Health. 2003. Departamento de Estadísticas e Información de Salud (www.minsal.cl). Accessed September 2003.

National Institute of Statistics. 2000. *Demographic Annual Reports 1970, 1982, 1992 and 2000.* Chile, INE.

National Institute of Statistics. 2002. *Census 1970, 1982, 1992 and 2002.* Chile, INE.

Olivares, S., Albala, C., García, F. & Jofré, I. 1999. Television publicity and food preferences of school-age children of the Metropolitan Region. *Rev. Med. Chile,* 127: 791-799.

PAHO. 2000. *Obesity and poverty. A new public health challenge.* M. Peña & J. Bacallao, eds. Scientific Publication No. 576. Washington, DC.

PAHO/WHO. 2001. *Special Program for Health Analysis.* Regional Core Health Data Initiative. Technical Health Information System. Washington, DC, PAHO (www.paho.org). Accessed September 2003.

Pérez-Bravo, F., Carrasco, E., Santos, J.L., Calvillan, M., Larenas, G. & Alba, C. 2001. Prevalence of type 2 diabetes and obesity in a rural Mapuche population from Chile. *Nutrition,* 17: 236-38.

Salinas, J., Vio, F. & Bahamondes, C., eds. 2003. *Guías de vida activa para la población chilena.* Santiago de Chile, Ed. Andros Impresores.

Tokman, V. 1985. Wages and employment in international recessions: recent Latin American experience. *In* K.S. Kim & D.F. Ruccio, eds. *Debt and development in Latin America.* Notre Dame, Canada, University of Notre Dame Press.

Uauy, R., Albala, C. & Kain, J. 2001. Obesity trends in Latin America: transiting from under- to overweight. *J. Nutr.,* 131: 893-898.

Vio, F. & Albala, C. 2000. Nutrition policy in the Chilean transition. *Public Health Nutr.* 3: 49-55.

Vio, F., Albala, C. & Crovetto, M. 2000. Health promotion in the context of the epidemiological transition in Chile. *Rev. Chil. Nutr.,* 27: 21-29.

WHO. 2002. *The world health report 2002: reducing risks, promoting healthy life.* Geneva, World Health Organization.

WHO/FAO. 2003. *Diet, nutrition and the prevention of chronic diseases.* Report of a Joint WHO/FAO Expert Consultation. WHO Technical Report Series No. 916. Geneva, World Health Organization.

Impact of globalization on food consumption, health and nutrition in urban areas of Colombia

Luis F. Fajardo[1]

INTRODUCTION: TRENDS AND CHANGE

Colombia's population, estimated at 44 million, occupies an area of just over 1 million km^2. About a quarter of the population lives in rural areas. Natural resources are plentiful, and include agricultural land, water for irrigation, energy resources (oil, natural gas and coal), and minerals such as nickel, gold and emeralds. Colombia has a significant advantage in terms of its location: it is close to North America with coasts on both the Pacific and Atlantic Oceans. Mountainous terrain, however, makes internal transportation costly and slows physical and social integration. A wealth of physical resources, a literate and dependable workforce, a robust private sector, competent macroeconomic management and political stability are major factors that have explained Colombia's good record of economic development and social improvements over the last 30 years. Nevertheless, the growth of the illegal drug industry, the presence of active insurgent groups and the pressure of external shocks have had an increasingly negative impact on the overall economic performance of the country.

Trends in urbanization and demographic pyramid

In the twentieth century Colombia experienced formidable growth in its population and in the second half of the century it also experienced an intensive process of internal migration from rural to urban areas. In 1938, 70 percent of the population lived in rural areas; Table 1 shows the evolution of the percentage of the population living in urban areas up until the present estimate of 75 percent (DANE, 2003a). The rural population increased from 6 million in 1938 to 10 million in 1990 whereas the urban population increased from 2.7 million in 1938 to 22.9 million in 1990. The growth of individual cities has also been important. In 1985, 32 percent of the population resided in eight main cities. According to UN population projections, by 2005 the population of Bogotá will reach 7.5 million, while that of Cali and Medellín will be 2.5 and 5.2 million respectively (United Nations Population Division, 2002).

---

[1] Luis F. Fajardo, MD, M.Sc.
Universidad Javeriana
Bogotá
Colombia
E-mail: lfajardo@javeriana.edu.co

TABLE 1
**Percentage distribution of the population
by urban and rural location**

Year	Urban	Rural
1938	30	70
1951	43	57
1964	52	48
1973	61	39
1985	65	35
1993	75	25
2000	75	25

Source: DANE, 2003a.

Equally important have been changes in demographic factors. The total fertility rate for the period 1997-2000 was 2.6 children per female, indicating a decline from earlier years. Previous fertility rates were 6.8, 3.2 and 3.0 in 1965, 1984-1986 and 1993-1995, respectively. In urban communities fertility rates decreased from 2.7 in 1985 to 2.3 in 2000 (Ojeda, Ordóñez and Ochoa, 2000). The achievements in this field are thought to be the results of family planning programmes, and the increased role of women in the labour force. As a result of the decrease in fertility rate the period 1995 to 2000 is estimated to have a rate of natural growth of 18 percent and a projected growth rate of 17 percent (DANE, 2003a). The crude birth rate and crude mortality have also decreased and were estimated at 24 and 5.9 percent between 1990 and 1995 (DANE, 2003a). Life expectancy has increased from 61.6 in 1970-75 to an estimated 72.2 in the period 2000-2005 (UNDP, 2003).

The population pyramid has evolved from a wider base pyramid to a narrower one as a result of the changes described previously (Figures 1a and 1b). Two important factors characterize the evolution of the family in the second half of the twentieth century, and they are highly relevant to food security and nutrition. The first factor is a preponderance of urban zones as the preferred place of residence, leaving no place for subsistence agriculture or the production of food by the family unit and favouring lifestyles considered urban. The second factor is a constant decrease in the fertility rate which translates into fewer children per family.

FIGURE 1a
Population pyramid, 1951

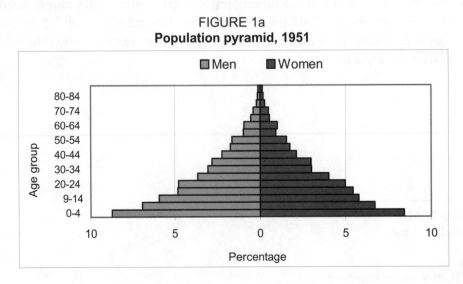

FIGURE 1b
Population pyramid, 1993

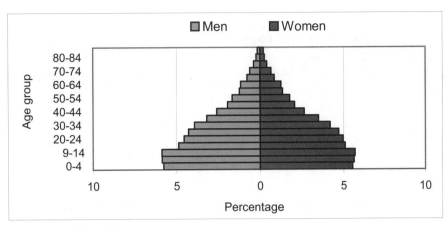

Source: DANE, 2003a.

Indicators of globalization

"Globalization is viewed as a reduction in barriers to the cross-border movement of goods, services and capital with accelerated integration of world markets and increased flow of commodities, technologies, information, financial capital, modes of distribution and marketing and, to an extent, migration of peoples and labour. A common feature of this process of globalization is a convergence, though at differing speeds, of many institutional, legal, economic, social and cultural practices and processes across different countries" (Shetty, 2003). This view of globalization expresses many of our own opinions on the subject, and some detail of how the process evolves will set the scenario for the discussion in this paper related to food and nutrition.

In 1990, a new government took office and immediately undertook the initiative of economic reform, market liberalization and democratization of the political system. Reforms were carried out by issuing new laws, constitutional changes and administrative decisions that soon resulted in a new set of rules for the economy. These changes marked a break with the traditional way of doing things and with old government institutions. The new government abandoned the old interventionist model preached by the Economic Commission for Latin America and the Caribbean (ECLAC) and created a new economic model characterized by economic opening, competition and greater opportunities for the citizens. During this process the National Department of Planning and the Ministry of Treasury shared objectives to design and implement neutral incentives between sectors and regions to help the government preserve a stable macroeconomic environment and provide incentives for technological change and increased competitiveness. Agriculture was included in the general strategy of institutional reforms. For this specific case, trade liberalization translated into elimination of traditional government intervention of control to imports, and guaranteed prices for main crops.

Communications, transportation and infrastructure

As illustrated in Table 2, telephone lines and other indicators of goods and services related to a better flow of communication and transportation flourished in the 1990s. Car ownership, evaluated as new cars per capita, also experienced a major increase in the period, although in the 1970s the number of cars increased fourfold (Dirección General de Transporte Terrestre Automotor, 2000). However, roads did not improve, with the percentage of paved roads remaining stagnant at 12 percent.

TABLE 2
Technology and infrastructure

	1997	2000	2001
Land lines and mobile telephones (per 1 000 people)	166.2	223.3	246.8
Personal computers (per 1 000 people)	30.3	35.4	42.1
Internet users	208 000	878 000	1.2 million
New cars per 1 000 people	4.74	1.6	1.7
Roads (km)	109 800	112 988	112 988
Paved roads (percentage of total)	12	12	12

Source: Dirección General de Transporte Terrestre Automotor, 2000.

ROLE OF GLOBALIZATION AND URBANIZATION ON DIETARY CHANGE AND LIFESTYLES
Evolution of the urban food supply
From the previous pages it is clear that Colombia has experienced both urbanization and many other features that characterize globalization, particularly since 1990. The paper will now focus on changes in the food supply and the impact of these changes on nutritional status. Changes in production and availability of food items that account for most of the calories available to the population, changes in ways foods are marketed, changes in food prices and changes in food preferences will be reviewed.

Changes in food production
The crop production index is used as a measure of agricultural production relative to a base period (1989-91). It includes all edible crops, but not fodder. Figure 2 shows a steady increase from the 1960s until 1990, when the index reaches a plateau. For the past ten years levels of crop production have remained stable.

From 1970 to 1990, the government assigned a central role for agriculture in the recovery of the country's economy and consolidation of development, trying to offer plentiful foods at low cost. The government wanted to modernize the agricultural sector and implemented incentives for private inversion in the sector, such as restructuring the prices for agricultural inputs, increasing prices to farmers and subordination of the import policies to protect national production. By 1988 the production policy was explicitly directed towards the achievement of food self-sufficiency (sovereignty), and food stocks to regulate the market forces. The plan was centred in a few food items important in the diet. These interventions of the government coupled with research and technology transfers (seeds, irrigation, credits, etc.) were associated with the sustained growth in productivity seen prior to globalization.

FIGURE 2
Crop production index[1] – World Development Indicators (WDI)

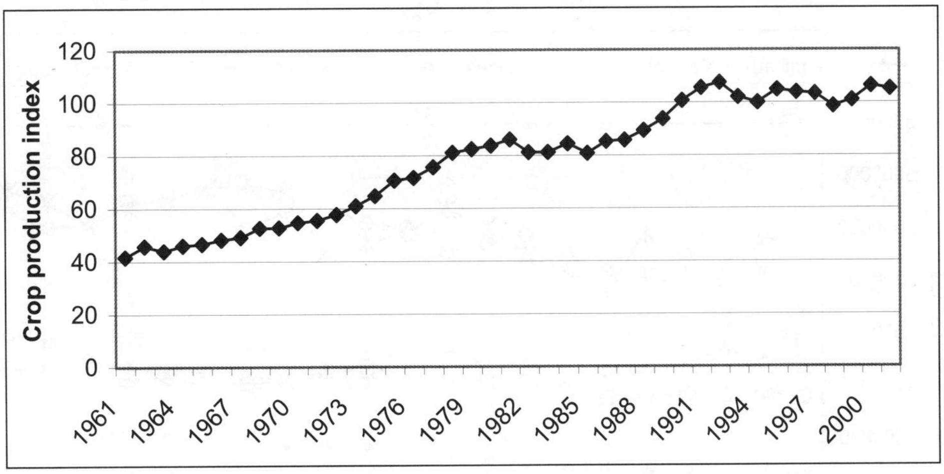

[1]The crop production index shows agricultural production for each year relative to the base period 1989-91. It includes all crops except fodder crops. The base period 1989-91 = 100: Food and Agriculture Organization of the United Nations, *Production Yearbook* and data files.
Source: World Bank, 2003.

Vegetable products
Staple food production
The main energy sources in the Colombian diet are potatoes, rice, plantains, pulses, sugar, oil and wheat (Figure 3). Most of these products are produced nationally, with the exception of wheat which is mainly imported. Before the 1990s there was a trend towards an increase in production of potatoes, plantains, sugar and vegetable oils. The production of pulses was low and has remained the same over the past 20 years. After 1990, there were no further gains in production of potatoes (growth for the decade 1.2 percent) or plantains, but refined sugar production increased by 3.6 percent[2] (Ministerio de Agricultura y Desarrollo Rural, 2003).

Although rice production initially decreased, it soon recovered and experienced substantial growth from 1990 to 2002. The production of vegetable oils has also maintained steady growth since 1990. Wheat production in the country has always been limited, although the population consumes 33 percent of dietary energy supply (DES) from wheat. In the 1970s imports more than doubled the maximum yearly production ever reached. Since 1990 wheat imports increased from 600 000 to nearly 1 200 000 tonnes in 1999.

---

[2] FAOSTAT (FAO, 2003) figures for 2001 production are 1 165 211 tonnes, while government figures for the same year are 2 241 59 tonnes.

FIGURE 3
Yearly production of basic foods (tonnes)

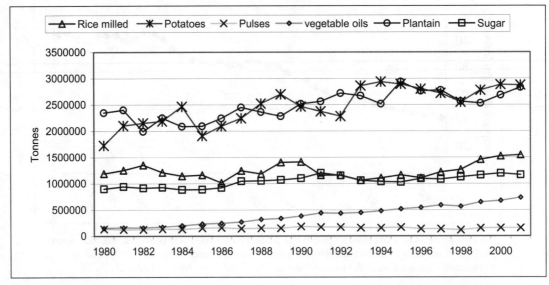

Source: FAO, 2003.

Panela is registered by FAOSTAT (FAO, 2003) as a special item and not centrifuged sugar. It is a commodity of social importance in the rural zone where it is estimated that 12 percent of the economically active population, some 350 000 rural people, work in activities related to panela. Culturally panela consumption has been linked to the rural way of life; hence, given the rural to urban migration and globalization, one might assume that its production would have declined, but in fact it has increased by 31 percent since 1990.

Livestock: beef, poultry, pork, milk and eggs

Beef, poultry, pork, milk and eggs constitute an important part of the modern Colombian diet, both in terms of nutritional value and as a share in the household food budget.

During the globalization period heads of cattle increased by 2.6 million animals, while the number of chickens went from 21 million to more than 110 million birds. Other authors estimate the production to be as much as 375 million birds (Kalmanovitz and López, 2003). Modernization of the poultry and pork industries is one of the more successful examples of decreases in trade barriers, resulting in improved availability of animal feed, which in turn made it possible to increase total production and availability for human consumption. Production of chicken meat increased from 172 973 tonnes in 1982 to 348 507 tonnes in 1990 and to 539 760 tonnes in 2001, a 54.8 percent increase during this period. Egg production also increased by 36 percent. From 1991 to 2001, per capita availability of eggs increased from 7.4 to 10.1 kg (Ministerio de Agricultura y Desarrollo Rural, 2002).

FIGURE 4
Livestock production, 1980-2000

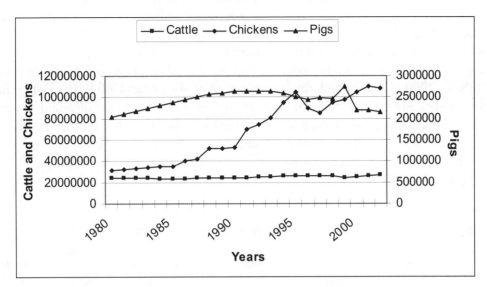

Source: FAO, 2003.

FIGURE 5
Production of cow milk, whole

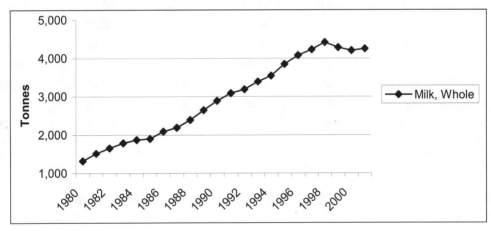

Source: FAO, 2003.

Within the category of animal source foods, milk, cheese and other milk products represent those with highest production and consumption volumes. Prior to 1990, the production of whole milk was growing at 8.2 percent, after which it slowed to 3.6 percent. The production of liquid milk increased from 2 million tonnes in 1980 to 5.8 million tonnes in 2001.

Production of key foods during the past ten years has been mixed. In general the rate of growth for production decreased, although the actual amount in tonnes was as high as in the previous decade. Wheat production almost halted and was replaced by ever increasing imports. Gains in poultry production provide a good example of increases resulting from changes in trade barriers and liberalization. The production of vegetable oils has also continued to grow.

Current role of imported foods and role of traditional foods

Globalization means liberalization of trade, therefore a massive importation of foods might have been expected. This is not the case for key food items such as potatoes, sugar, plantains, beef and liquid milk, where the percentage of imports in relation to production was minimal since the lifting of trade restrictions in 1990 (Table 3).

However, in terms of available energy, imported foods represented nearly 40 percent of total DES in 2000. Cereals and fats represent over 43 percent of DES. Dependency on imported energy sources is concentrated around wheat, vegetable oils and products for animal feed. Rice and powder milk are imported in relation to the gap in supply by local production. Domestic production of milk and cheese has steadily increased from 1993 to the present. Imports of these commodities peaked during 1996-1998 and have since declined (DANE, 2003b).

TABLE 3
Imported food as a percentage of availability (import [production + imports] 100)

Year	Potatoes	Plantains	Rice	Sugar	Wheat	Oil/margarine
1990	0.00	0.00			87.55	8.52
1991	0.01	0.00	0.02		87.25	10.65
1992	0.02	0.00	5.06		91.99	30.66
1993	0.13	0.00	3.17		89.85	44.44
1994	0.20	0.00	17.31		88.98	43.76
1995	0.43	0.78	8.08		93.04	40.16
1996	0.31	0.76	10.87		93.83	52.83
1997	1.02	0.37	12.25		95.32	52.68
1998	1.60	0.34	18.96	0.19	96.60	50.39
1999	0.91	0.07	2.58	0.48	96.35	45.43
2000	2.49	0.40	3.70	0.52	96.24	54.23
2001	1.28	2.11	9.18	2.49	97.84	57.31

Source: FAO, 2003.

The diversity of food items available, locally produced and imported

In terms of diversity of food items available, it is without doubt that globalization and urbanization have made it possible to expand the choice of foods. Large supermarkets linked to worldwide operations have made a variety of new foods available. For example, 12 different varieties of salami and sliced turkey cold cuts are available on supermarket shelves in Bogotá. However, the percentage of households actually shopping in the supermarkets and buying these new products is remarkably low, especially in the lower-income stratum.

We have no data yet on the quantitative effect on food habits from this avalanche of new products. Supermarkets in Colombia contain many of the same products to be found in any supermarket in a developed country. It is even possible to shop for food via the Internet.

From traditional open markets (*plazas de mercado*) to traditional neighbourhood stores, supermarkets and large transnational supermarkets

Marketing and purchase of foods are changing dramatically in larger cities. In the first half of the twentieth century food was bought at the *plazas de mercado*, open markets which were typically open once a week. As cities grew, *tiendas*, small family enterprises, emerged on nearly every corner of the townships. Self-service markets and larger supermarkets were introduced in the 1970s and 1980s. In the 1990s the large national and transnational chains appeared on the supply side. Currently, there is a growing concern by the government to begin comprehensive planning for food supply in large cities, taking into account the physical aspects of food access and supply as well as the operational infrastructure.

Corabastos is the name of the largest wholesale market in Bogotá. It handles 6 700 tonnes of food daily, in an area of 420 000 m^2. There are 137 000 m^2 of storage area, 33 warehouses, nine banks, several automatic cash dispensers, cafés, bakeries, one public notary and cold storage facilities. The market is only 30 years old, but has become the largest wholesale centre in Colombia. It supplies food to 7 million people in Bogotá and the surroundings areas and is one of the places where prices are set for both farmers and consumers.

The importance of changes in the way foods are marketed can be assessed by comparing sales by different types of retail facilities. Sales of large supermarkets represent nearly 41 percent of sales in Colombia. (In Spain, sales by big stores represent 35 percent). By contrast, in Colombia 46.4 percent of the value of sales correspond to traditional stores, while this is only 10 percent in Spain.

TABLE 4
Percentage of total sales by size of facility in Colombia and Spain, 1998

	Colombia	Spain
Large supermarkets	20.5	34.8
1 000-2 499 m^2	20.8	14.5
400-999 m^2	8.3	17.8
100-399 m^2	4	22.9
Traditional stores	46.4	10

Source: España, 1999.

Although supermarket sales represented 20.5 percent of total sales, it was found that fewer than 7 percent of households purchase food in large supermarkets (Table 5). Traditional stores and small self-service markets continue to be the preferred places to shop for food. In other words, this aspect of globalization of the food system seems only to have reached the wealthy population with sufficient purchasing power.

TABLE 5
Percentage distribution of households buying foods by type of selling facility, 1999

City	Traditional stores	Small self-service markets	Large supermarkets	Cooperatives and similar
Bogotá	16.1	32.5	6.5	38.6
Medellín	46.6	30.5	0.6	9.1
Cali	31.9	42.1	1.8	3.7
Barranquilla	38.6	34.1	0.9	4.9

Source: España, 2000.

But not only small traditional stores and self-service markets survive. The open market – *plaza de mercado* – is still used by more than half of households to obtain their vegetables, meat and other perishable fresh foods. A study by España (2000) showed a correlation between city size and purchase of food in the open market. In smaller cities, 50-75 percent of the population bought produce in the open market, while in Bogotá, the largest city, only 30 percent of the population shopped there. Despite the presence of big transnational market chains, people continue to use the traditional stores and markets to buy essential foods. The role of these new actors in price formation and food habits needs to be further studied.

Importance of street foods and emergence of fast food chains

Eating outside the home is one of the major changes observed during the last decade. Factors such as distances within larger cities, women entering the workforce and government programmes giving food assistance to both preschool and school-age children, reinforce the pattern of eating at least some meals away from home. Decisions about what family members eat are now are in the hands of restaurants, fast food chains and catering services. The choice of foods on offer should be balanced by nutritional guidelines, although managerial and economic realities should also be considered.

With increasing numbers of people living in cities, city boundaries can either expand, or the fixed areas become more densely populated. In Bogotá and other Colombian cities both have happened. Bogotá and Medellín are the only cities with some sort of rapid transit system. For many workers, the time it would take to get home and back for a meal would be longer than the allocated work break. Equally important is the increasing amount of money needed for transport, reflecting the need to travel longer distances, and thus decreasing the money available to buy food.

While some workers and students bring food from home for their midday meals, this practice does not seem to be very extensive, but we do not have reliable data. Many children receive at least one meal in day care centres or school. With the vision to guarantee the rights of children, and alleviate the social effects of mothers leaving home to enter the workforce, the government has implemented one of the most successful child-feeding programmes. Both national and local branches of the government have implemented programmes to provide care and meals for children. In 2003 the Instituto Colombiano de Bienestar Familiar (ICBF) (Colombian Institute for Family Well-being) is expected to give assistance to over 2 500 000 children.

Over the past 20 years expenditure on food has decreased from 48.9 to 29.5 percent of the household budget. Expenditure on housing has remained relatively constant at 28-29 percent, while expenditure on transportation and communications, education and health has increased (DANE, no date). Table 6 shows food expenditure by location and household income level. The largest city in Colombia is Bogotá, followed by Cali, Medellín and Barranquilla with over one million residents, while Pereira has fewer than 500 000. Trends in lower consumption of cereals and increased expenditure on food eaten outside the home are relatively consistent with larger city size.

TABLE 6
Food expenditure by income levels, 1995-1999, percentage of food budget for each item

	National	Bogotá	Barranquilla	Cali	Medellín	Pereira
Low income						
Cereals	12.60	11.52	14.77	13.12	12.56	14.70
Tubers	7.76	8.14	6.20	6.51	7.36	7.51
Greens	7.54	7.70	6.50	7.93	8.14	7.42
Fruit	3.60	3.74	2.50	4.59	2.65	2.28
Meat	20.93	18.57	19.59	22.56	24.35	26.70
Fish	1.90	1.44	3.78	2.25	0.85	1.49
Milk products	16.50	16.92	17.65	13.85	19.85	16.96
Other	12.11	10.12	12.95	12.70	14.68	14.11
Food eaten outside the home	17.05	21.84	16.08	16.55	9.57	8.82
Middle income						
Cereals	10.50	9.50	11.98	11.60	10.51	11.61
Tubers	5.38	4.81	5.53	5.21	5.37	4.84
Greens	6.01	5.43	5.88	6.48	6.67	6.79
Fruit	4.50	4.54	2.84	5.40	3.92	4.73
Meat	20.99	18.14	22.11	22.56	24.83	25.69
Fish	2.16	1.84	4.24	2.38	1.25	1.68
Milk products	15.21	15.23	15.55	13.28	17.75	16.63
Other	11.11	9.47	11.60	11.26	14.09	12.43
Food eaten outside the home	24.13	31.03	20.28	21.85	15.62	15.60
High income						
Cereals	8.69	7.51	10.38	8.48	10.79	8.03
Tubers	3.34	2.67	3.82	3.27	3.61	3.26
Greens	4.96	3.72	6.75	5.88	5.99	5.24
Fruit	5.35	4.50	5.59	7.00	5.10	6.70
Meat	18.35	13.71	21.09	21.52	22.00	21.69
Fish	2.23	1.98	2.92	2.96	1.07	1.34
Milk products	13.52	12.71	15.67	12.73	15.65	13.32
Other	10.36	9.13	11.12	10.12	15.09	8.48
Food eaten outside the home	33.18	44.08	22.66	28.08	20.71	31.94

Source: DANE, no date.

From the data available, it is evident that there has been a major change in purchasing practices related to food, particularly the amount of money allocated to buying food to be consumed outside the home. We are beginning to assimilate the effects of these changes in the nutritional well-being of the population, in terms of habits, lifestyles, obesity and other specific nutritional disorders.

From home-prepared meals to mass services
Fast food chains, restaurants and catering services have replaced the dedication of mothers and families in the selection and preparation of foods. Practically in all socio-economic strata establishments can be found selling chicken, pizzas and hamburgers as a means to attract customers or encourage them to form new habits. Some facilities are quite unsanitary and have

poor food handling practices. New kinds of restaurants now exist to offer midday meals at low cost. They are located throughout the city and reflect the need of workers for a place to buy an inexpensive meal with a homely feel rather than a restaurant-type of meal.

Globalization and increased urbanization have been associated with important changes in the way foods are selected, bought and prepared. Nearly 30 percent of food budgets are devoted to buying food prepared outside the home. Instead of the housewife figure in charge of food selection and distribution, this role has been replaced by specialized organizations of food services and restaurants. Many informal family enterprises have used the sale of food as a way to increase their income; however, they have little or no technical expertise in safe food preparation for large numbers of people and economic considerations often outweigh those of nutrition and health.

PREVALENCE OF MALNUTRITION IN URBAN AREAS
The prevalence of malnutrition in women of child-bearing age and children under five years of age decreased during the second half of the twentieth century. Malnutrition in children has also decreased, although there is no evidence of the influence of globalization in the process. However, urbanization is associated with less malnutrition in children.

Trends in children under five years of age
Figures 6 and 7 show the trends in rates of chronic and acute malnutrition in urban and rural areas and in Bogotá compared to the national average. Chronic malnutrition remains most prevalent in rural areas, but the prevalence of chronic malnutrition in Bogotá is higher than the urban average. Acute malnutrition in Colombia has decreased dramatically in the past 15 years, most probably as a result of improvements in food supply, food distribution and health care services.

As might be expected, socio-economic differences do have an effect on the rate of malnutrition. In Bogotá the prevalence of acute malnutrition in children of low socio-economic status is five times greater than the total for Bogotá. The current prevalence of wasting in children of low socio-economic status living in Bogotá is similar to levels found in the 1970s.

FIGURE 6
Prevalence of chronic malnutrition in urban and rural areas, 1982-2000

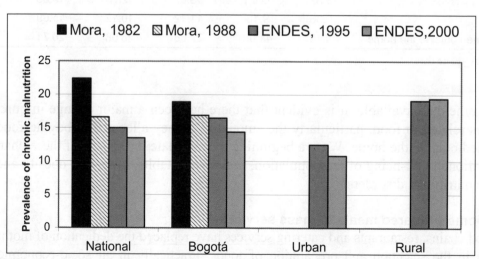

Source: FAO,2001. The Mora and ENDES surveys used two different cut-off measures to determine the prevalence of malnutrition. The Mora studies used percentile cut-off of <3 while the ENDES studies use <-2Z scores.

FIGURE 7
Prevalence of acute malnutrition in urban and rural areas, 1982-2000

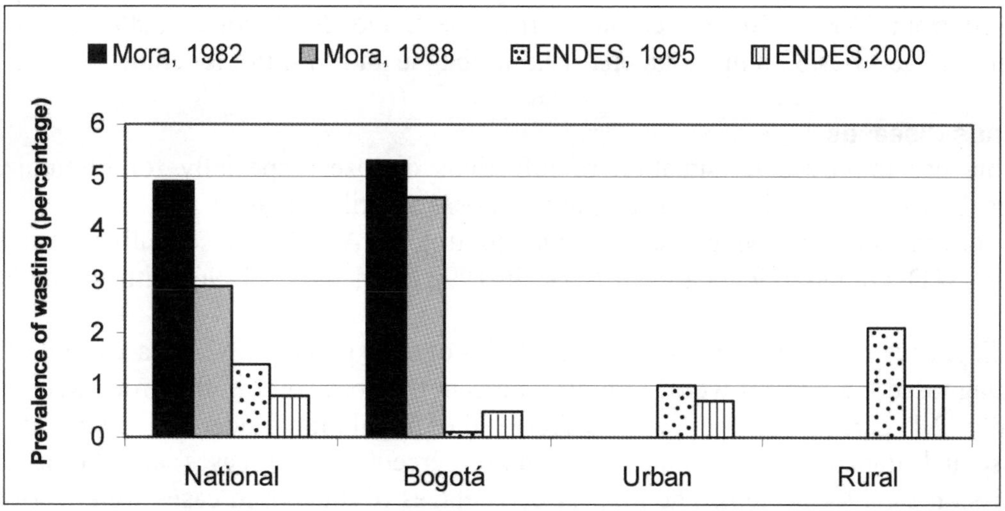

Source. FAO, 2001 The Mora and ENDES surveys used two different cut-off measures to determine the prevalence of malnutrition. The Mora studies used percentile cut-off of <3 while the ENDES studies use <-2Z scores.

TABLE 7
Prevalence of malnutrition in children of low socio-economic status

	1997	1998	1999	2000	2001	2002
Chronic malnutrition	15.5	14.9	15.1	16.1	14.7	15.3
Acute malnutrition	5.1	5.5	5.2	5.2	5.7	6.2

Source. Secretaría Distrital de Salud de Bogotá, 2003.

Trends in women of child-bearing age

Transition from the epidemiological point of view has been associated with the presence of both malnutrition and obesity. Unfortunately there are no national data on obesity among adults. However, data on women of child-bearing age show that overweight does exist. Table 8 shows data from the 1995 and 2000 national surveys, which found an overweight prevalence of over 40 percent in women of child-bearing age (BMI above 25). Women with no formal education or only primary school and women with a higher education had a similar prevalence of overweight.

TABLE 8
Nutritional status of women of child-bearing age

Sample	Mean BMI		Chronic energy deficiency (BMI <18.5)		Overweight (BMI >25)	
	1995	2000	1995	2000	1995	2000
National	24.5	24.7	3.8	3.2	40.3	40.7
Urban	24.5	24.7	3.8	3.2		40.8
Rural	24.5	24.6	3.9	3.1		40.5
Bogotá	24.4	24.7	1.5	1.7		39.1

Source. FAO, 2001.

TRENDS IN HEALTH STATUS IN THE URBAN ENVIRONMENT
Trends in health status

Since 1990, the health of the population in Bogotá has improved. The infant mortality rate decreased from 26.8 to 20 (Secretaría Distrital de Salud de Bogotá, 2000a) and infant mortality in 2000 was 33.8 in Cartagena, 19.5 in Ibagué and 17.4 in Medellín.

Infectious diseases

Colombia has improved its situation of infectious diseases especially for immunizable diseases. However, malaria, dengue and tuberculosis are still prevalent.

The programme for the prevention and control of AIDS and sexually transmitted diseases (STDs) reported 933 cases of AIDS in 1992 and 1 042 in 1996, with a cumulative total of 7 776 diagnosed cases and a cumulative mortality of 41.5 percent (3 226 cases). Of all the cases diagnosed, 85 percent were men; 40.5 percent of those were in the group aged 25 to 34. Only 2.1 percent of the cases affected the population under 15 years of age. Heterosexual transmission accounted for 44.0 percent of the cases and homosexual transmission for 27.4 percent. The highest percentages of diagnosed cases were in Bogotá (46.4 percent) and the district of Antioquia (15 percent). In 2002 the number of new cases was 933 (Pan American Health Organization, 2002).

Chronic non-communicable diseases (NCDs)

Cardiovascular diseases are the leading cause of death in women, the second leading cause in men, and the primary cause of death in the group aged 45 to 64. In 1994, 44 percent of deaths attributed to this cause were a result of ischemic heart disease – 93 percent of them were persons aged 45 and older, and 56 percent were men. Cerebrovascular diseases represented 28 percent of deaths from cardiovascular conditions, 91 percent of which occurred in the over-45 age group and 54 percent in women.

Arterial hypertension is the most important risk factor for cardiovascular diseases. According to the 1987 national health study, the prevalence of arterial hypertension in Colombia was 11.6 percent in the population over 15 years of age. However, a study conducted in 1995 among the population of Quibdó revealed a prevalence of 35 percent in all persons over the age of 18 and a prevalence of 39 percent in the Colombian population of African ancestry – percentages significantly higher than those observed in the rest of the population (21 percent). The prevalence rates varied by age, from 10 percent in young persons to 50 percent in those aged 49 and over. No differences were noted according to sex. Only 16 percent of the persons surveyed said that they participated in some form of exercise in their free time. Somatometry showed that 50 percent were at least 10 percent overweight. A comparison between BMI means showed that hypertensive individuals were more obese than those who were not hypertensive (P<0.0001) (Pan American Health Organization, 2002). Diabetes incidence has also increased by 30 percent (Table 9).

TABLE 9
Incidence of diabetes and hypertension in Bogotá, 1987-1998

	Cases		Rate per 10 000	
Year	Diabetes	HTN[1]	Diabetes	HTN[1]
1987	392	693	0.92	1.63
1988	433	699	0.9	1.45
1989	490	826	1.02	1.72
1990	525	813	1.06	1.65
1991	517	854	1.01	1.67
1992	582	873	1.11	1.67
1993	600	934	1.1	1.72
1994	635	938	1.14	1.69
1995	700	899	1.23	1.58
1996	620	946	1.07	1.63
1997	823	833	1.39	1.49
1998	829	781	1.37	1.29

HTN = hypertension.
Source: Secretaría Distrital de Salud de Bogotá, 2000a.

The rate of incidence of type-2 diabetes in Bogotá increased, reaching a level 30 percent higher than previously, perhaps reflecting the changes in increasing sedentary behaviour, coupled with changing dietary habits (Table 9). Colombia represents a typical transition country, with continuing problems from infectious diseases such as malaria and tuberculosis, and increasing prevalence of NCDs such as cardiovascular diseases and diabetes.

PROGRAMMES TO ADDRESS FOOD AND NUTRITION ISSUES
There are two types of programme being carried out by the government in order to address the effects emerging in the globalization/urbanization period.

As mentioned before, food assistance is given to nearly 2 500 000 children, both at school and in special day care centres. The focus is on children belonging to families of the lower socio-economic strata. Equally, pregnant and lactating women of the same socio-economic strata receive some food assistance.

On the other hand, the government is also starting to implement programmes aimed at creating healthier lifestyles – promoting nutritional guides, schools and regular exercise. Most of these programmes are new or are functioning at the pilot level.

Bibliography

Departamento Administrativo Nacional de Estadística (DANE). 1967. *XIII Censo Nacional de Población y II de Vivienda. 1964. Resumen Nacional. Manual de Empadronador.* Bogotá, DANE.

Departamento Administrativo Nacional de Estadística (DANE). 1980. *XIV Censo Nacional de Población y III de Vivienda. 1973. Resumen Nacional.* Bogotá, DANE.

Departamento Administrativo Nacional de Estadística (DANE). 1986. *XV Censo Nacional de Población y IV de Vivienda. 1985. Características Económicas. Vol. IV. Metodología. Vol. II.* Bogotá, DANE.

Departamento Administrativo Nacional de Estadística (DANE). 1996. *XVI Censo Nacional de Población y V de Vivienda. 1993. Resumen Nacional. Manual de Empadronador.* Bogotá, DANE.

Departamento Administrativo Nacional de Estadística (DANE). 2003a. *Población Total Censada en 1993, 1985, 1973 y 1964 por Sexo, según Grupos de Edad. Total Nacional* (www.dane.gov.co).

Departamento Administrativo Nacional de Estadística (DANE). 2003b. *Encuesta Anual Manufacturera 2001.* CIIU Rev. 3 A.C (www.dane.gov.co).

Departamento Administrativo Nacional de Estadística (DANE). 2003c. *Colombia: indicadores demográficos. 1985-2015* (www.dane.gov.co).

Departamento Administrativo Nacional de Estadística (DANE). *Encuesta Nacional de Ingresos y Gastos 1994-1995. Gasto Total Mensual Por Artículo, Total Nacional y Por Ciudad, Según Deciles de Ingreso de Hogares.*

Dirección General de Transporte Terrestre Automotor. Subdirección Operativa de Transporte Automotor Grupo de Estudios de Carga. 2000. Parque Automotor de Transporte de Carga en Colombia. Bogotá (www.mintransporte.gov.co/Servicios/Biblioteca/documentos/PDF/Analisis_Parque_Automotor.pdf).

España, R. 1999. *El presente y futuro del comercio.* Federación Nacional de Comerciantes Fenalco Congreso "Góndola". Bogotá (fenalco.com.co/fenalco/frames.asp).

España, R. 2000. *El cambiante entorno del retail en Colombia.* Federación Nacional de Comerciantes Fenalco Congreso "Góndola". Bogotá (fenalco.com.co/fenalco/frames.asp).

FAO. 2001. *Nutrition country profile, Colombia* (www.fao.org/es/ESN/nutrition/col-s.stm).

FAO. 2003. FAOSTAT (www.fao.org).

Kalmanovitz, S. & López, E. 2003. *La agricultura en Colombia entre 1950 y 2001* (banrep.org/junta/trabajo4-kalmanovitz.htm).

Martínez, H., Acevedo, X. 2003. Características y estructura de la cadena agroindustrial de la panela en Colombia. Ministerio de Agricultura y Desarrollo Rural (www.agrocadenas.gov.co/home.htm).

Ministerio de Agricultura y Desarrollo Rural. 2002. *Anuario Estadístico del Sector Agropecuario 2001.*

Ministerio de Agricultura y Desarrollo Rural. 2003. Producción Agrícola por Cultivos (www.agrocadenas.gov.co/home.htm).

Ministerio de Protección Social. 2002. *Indicadores de salud vigilancia epidemiológica* – Ministerio de Salud. 2002 (www.minproteccionsocial.gov.co/MseContent/newsdetail).

Ojeda, G., Ordóñez, M. & Ochoa, L.H. 2000. *Salud sexual y reproductiva. Colombia: resultados de la Encuesta de Demografía y Salud.*

Pan American Health Organization. 2002. *Country profile.* PAHO (www.paho.org/English/DD/AIS/cp_170.htm).

Secretaría Distrital de Salud de Bogotá. 2000a. *Diagnóstico Distrital de Salud.*

Secretaría Distrital de Salud de Bogotá. 2000b. *Registros de defunción, área de análisis y políticas en salud pública.*

Secretaría Distrital de Salud de Bogotá. 2003. *Programa de Vigilancia Nutricional.* Bogotá, 31 June.

Shetty, P. 2003. *Impact of globalization on food and agriculture from the farm to the plate.* Presented at Impacts of Globalization on Agricultural Production and Marketing with Focus on Food Quality, 22-24 January, Tokyo.

United Nations Development Programme (UNDP). 2003. *Human Development Report 2003* (www.undp.org/hdr2003/).

United Nations Population Division. 2002. *World Urbanization Prospects: the 2001 Revision.*

World Bank. 2003. World Development Indicators (WDI) database.

FAO TECHNICAL PAPERS

FAO FOOD AND NUTRITION PAPERS

Availability: November 2004

Ar – Arabic   Multil – Multilingual
C   – Chinese   *   Out of print
E   – English   **   In preparation
F   – French
P   – Portuguese
S   – Spanish

The FAO Technical Papers are available through the authorized FAO Sales Agents or directly from Sales and Marketing Group, FAO, Viale delle Terme di Caracalla, 00100 Rome, Italy.